NEWNES INTERNATIONAL MONOGRAPHS ON
MATERIALS SCIENCE AND TECHNOLOGY

THE TECHNOLOGY OF FERROUS ALLOYS
FOR AMBIENT AND LOW-TEMPERATURE USE

NEWNES INTERNATIONAL MONOGRAPHS ON
MATERIALS SCIENCE AND TECHNOLOGY

Advisory Editor
N. L. Parr, C.Eng., M.I.Mech.E., F.I.M.

This new and timely series of monographs provides information on the various aspects of materials science and technology in relation to the needs of engineering design and construction. Allied volumes survey separate areas and give the latest information on processes, structures and properties in order that materials may be employed to maximum benefit. The series is equally suited to the needs of students for use as reading in connection with university or technical college studies. Titles include:

The Technology of Ferrous Alloys for Ambient and Low-Temperature Use, by T. F. Pearson, M.Sc., F.I.M., Research Manager, Consett Iron Co. Ltd.

The Technology and Properties of Ferrous Alloys for High-Temperature Use, by M. G. Gemmill, B.Sc., F.I.M., Generation Design Department, Central Electricity Generating Board.

The Technology of Heavy Non-Ferrous Metals and Alloys, by J. H. Cairns, M.Sc.Tech., Ph.D., A.I.M., and P. T. Gilbert, B.Sc., Ph.D., F.R.I.C., F.I.M., M.Inst.Mar.Eng., both of Yorkshire Imperial Metals Ltd., Leeds.

Mechanical Testing of Materials, by A. J. Fenner, B.Sc.(Eng.), A.M.I.Mech.E., Principal Scientific Officer, National Engineering Laboratory, East Kilbride, Glasgow.

Powder Metallurgy; Practice and Applications, by R. L. Sands, A.I.M. and C. R. Shakespeare, A.I.M., A.C.T.(Birm.)., both of the B.S.A. Group Research Centre, Birmingham.

The Magnetic Properties of Materials, by John E. Thompson, B.Sc.(Hons), Ph.D., F.Inst.P., C.Eng., M.I.E.E., University of Wales Institute of Science and Technology.

Other titles in preparation

The Technology of
FERROUS ALLOYS FOR
AMBIENT AND
LOW-TEMPERATURE USE

by

T. F. Pearson
M.Sc., F.I.M.

NEWNES BOOKS

First published 1968

Published for
NEWNES BOOKS
by
The Hamlyn Publishing Group Ltd.
Hamlyn House, 42 The Centre, Feltham, Middlesex

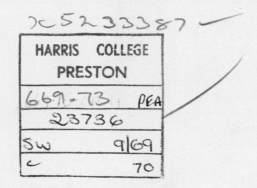
Printed in Great Britain by Butler & Tanner Ltd., Frome and London

CONTENTS

PART III. FORMS OF FERROUS PRODUCTS AND THEIR
CHARACTERISTICS IN RELATION TO TOUGHNESS

PLATES

xi

PREFACE

It is symptomatic of the complexity of modern engineering technology that the birth of an idea and its translation into an accomplishment poses many problems apart from those involved in the idea itself. An obvious illustration of this is the suitability or otherwise of available materials of construction to achieve an end in view. While to the layman the term 'steel' obviously implies by tradition and usage, the ubiquitous mild steel, the evolution and development of different varieties to meet specific requirements of the designer and engineer has proceeded at such a pace over the last ten to fifteen years that ferrous materials for construction are no longer classifiable as such but must be subdivided and related more specifically to the service conditions they are intended to fulfil.

A backward glance to the early days of bulk steelmaking, which commenced in 1856 with the successful evolution of the Bessemer process in this country, indicates that the engineer made use of the one material available for most constructions. His sense of adventure in its application sometimes led to disasters for which the underlying reason was not always known or found. Inevitably, there developed a realization of the material's limitations. This was succeeded in time by an increasing demand for material which would be better fitted for its intended purpose than existing material. Concurrently there was a parallel development in the science of metallurgy. So began the race between the demands made by the designer and the progress of the metallurgist in the provision of more suitable material to meet these demands.

The growth of the idea therefore of specific suitability for a purpose justifies the title of the book, which deals only with ambient and low temperature considerations as applied to ferrous alloys.

Having been engaged in the steel industry for many years and continuously endeavouring to meet the challenge for improved steels for specific applications—particularly for use at low temperatures—I have been biased towards the practical aspects. Hence, I have included as much practical data as possible—much of it obtained in my company's laboratories. For permission to publish this material therefore I am indebted to the Consett Iron Company Limited and to my colleagues there.

Further indebtedness exists to my many colleagues in the industry and particularly to fellow members of the Heavy Steels Technical Committee of

xiii

the British Iron and Steel Federation who have collectively, under the chairmanship of Dr L. Reeve of the Appleby-Frodingham Steel Co., played a very significant role in the development of improved British Standards for precisely those conditions defined by the title of this book. The free exchange of knowledge and details of individual developments and trials contributed significantly to the establishment for the first time in the world of a standard for notch ductile steels for shipbuilding and general engineering purposes.

I have endeavoured in the presentation to avoid the excessive use of references. In present times the advance of science and technology is so rapid as to render the novelty of today the commonplace of tomorrow. Discussion of the available literature leads to conclusions which are accepted or rejected in the light of general experience and thereby rapidly become common knowledge. Apart therefore from appropriate historical references that have a significance in respect of time, references are mainly confined to the past ten years.

To those workers quoted grateful acknowledgement is made. My sincere thanks are due to Mr G. N. J. Gilbert of the British Cast Iron Research Association and many others who have so freely supplied information. To Mr M. Z. de Lippa, a friend and colleague over many years, I owe much, for his discussion, criticism and proof reading which have enabled me to present this book.

T. F. P.

GENERAL INTRODUCTION AND SCOPE

In this book an attempt has been made to deal with a subject of rapidly growing importance—the mechanical behaviour of ferrous alloys at low temperatures. The use of high temperatures to extract metals from their ores and to enable them to be shaped gave a natural lead to the study of their resistance to elevated temperatures. There has been, over the past quarter of a century, however, the development of a new field. The engineer now makes increasing use of 'cold' for industrial purposes, for example, the separation of mixed gases and the liquefaction of these to facilitate their economical storage. It has been found in practice that this reversal of the application of metals from high temperature uses to low temperature conditions has resulted in new problems (e.g. the increased liability to brittle fracture) and the metallurgist has therefore been called upon to initiate studies in this field.

As in most fields of endeavour, there are two approaches—the so-called 'academic' and the 'practical', both equally important. To deal with reasonable adequacy, therefore, with the subject of this book implies some reference to both these approaches. Also, since we are dealing with 'technology' then references to the historical development are implied.

It has been considered advisable, therefore, to divide the text into four main parts.

In Part I consideration is given to the effects of low temperatures on the more common properties of ferrous alloys, and some attempt is made to introduce concepts of 'toughness' and 'brittleness'. These indeed form the underlying theme of the book. In chapter 2 the more academic aspects of the structure of metals are dealt with. These include the dislocation theory and types of dislocations. A study of the imperfections existing in metals renders possible certain concepts as to the origin and mechanism of failure. Since the behaviour of ferrous alloys with respect to brittleness or toughness may be markedly affected by various types of heat-treatment, chapter 3 deals with the characteristics which result from these. Brief reference is also made to the effects of irradiation.

In Part II—The Technology of Steels—the history of Bessemer mild steel is outlined. This indicates that the theme of this book—toughness and brittleness—dates back to the early days of steelmaking. The Bessemer process has been replaced in this country by the open-hearth process, and more recently signs are apparent that the newest 'oxygen' processes will in turn replace the open hearth. It has been thought appropriate therefore to consider briefly these other processes and mention those features of their products which have some bearing on toughness properties.

Part III deals with the products of the processes. Since steel produced by all large steelworks is hot-rolled at source the chief features of plates and sections form the basis of chapter 6. The problem of adequate toughness at low temperatures is most emphasized in these two products since they form the material for precisely those constructions (e.g. ships, tanks, and bridges) in which some of the most spectacular failures have taken place in recent years. For this reason also chapters 8 and 9 deal with the problem of hydrogen contamination and the significance of welding in relation to plates and sections. Both of these features can play an important part in the service behaviour of steel castings and forgings, which are discussed in chapter 7.

Part IV deals generally with the notch toughness characteristics of steels. The presentation is based on a consideration first of ordinary mild steel followed by the development of the 'improved' mild steels. This is followed by a discussion of the 'higher' tensile steels in which higher strengths with equal or better notch toughness characteristics are achieved. The presentation endeavours to follow the order of development.

Chapters 12 and 13 introduce the practical aspects of the production, by quenching and tempering, of the highest strength constructional steels so far achieved.

The 'cryogenic' steels may be considered apart from those mentioned previously and are therefore discussed separately in the context of extremely low temperatures, i.e. —100° to —196° C. Stainless steels and the more recent 9% nickel steel satisfy requirements and chapter 14 is devoted to these types.

In chapter 15 a review of various methods of testing for toughness at low temperatures is given. The list is by no means exhaustive. An attempt has been made to classify methods according to the major principle involved.

Finally, brief notes are added on the protection of steel against corrosion— a matter of considerable importance with respect to plates and sections—and methods of securing low temperatures for test purposes.

PART I

PHYSICAL AND METALLURGICAL PRINCIPLES

CHAPTER 1

THE SIGNIFICANCE OF AMBIENT AND LOW TEMPERATURES IN RELATION TO THE PROPERTIES OF FERROUS ALLOYS

Introduction

By far the largest proportion of steel consumed in the world is applied and used under temperature conditions described as ambient, which while definable as 'surrounding or encompassing', also implies a relatively small range of temperature more or less tolerable to the human individual. Railway lines, bridges, steel-framed buildings and ships exist under ambient temperature conditions which by reference to the extremes of climatic conditions over the world may be stated to be roughly $-40°$ C to $+40°$ C representing arctic and tropical conditions respectively.

Man has learned to extend this range in both directions, but not equally. While temperatures of $3000°$ C or more are achievable in special furnaces, low temperatures beyond $-273°$ C cannot be achieved. The absolute zero of $-273°$ C at which (by Charles' law) a gas should theoretically occupy no volume offers an insurmountable barrier.

In this book we are concerned therefore with the mechanical and metallurgical characteristics of ferrous alloys from approximately room temperature down to absolute zero. Elevated temperature properties are dealt with in a separate volume and we shall be interested only in elevated temperatures themselves by reason of their effects on the behaviour of ferrous materials when used in ambient and low-temperature service conditions.

It is not perhaps generally realized that the application of artificially produced low temperature environments is extending rapidly in modern industry as a means of achieving desired ends. The household refrigerator is a very modest example in this respect. More impressive are the large refrigerated ships involving enormous lengths of tubing carrying liquid refrigerants and maintaining temperatures down to $-50°$ C. Gas fractionating columns in the chemical industry commonly operate at $-100°$ C, and the growth of the use of industrial gases such as oxygen, nitrogen, carbon dioxide, hydrogen, propane and methane involves very large quantities of metal equipment for

Table 1. *Low-temperature properties of some common gases*

Name	Formula	Normal boiling point (°C)	Liquid density (lb/ft³)	Gas density at 20° C and 1 atm (lb/ft³)	Critical point at Tempera- ture (°C)	Critical point at Pressure lb/in² absolute
Acetylene	C_2H_2	−84·0	38·7	0·0680	36·3	906
Air	N_2-78%					
	O_2-21%	−194·4	54·57	0·0749	—	—
Ammonia	NH_3	−33·4	42·56	0·0445	132·4	1639
Argon	A	−185·9	87·4	0·1033	−122·0	706
Carbon dioxide	CO_2	−78·5	94·4	0·1144	31·1	1073
Carbon monoxide	CO	−191·4	50·6	0·0725	−139·0	509
Chlorine	Cl	−33·9	97·4	0·1853	145·0	1118
Ethane	C_2H_6	−88·7	33·8	0·0783	32·3	708
Ethylene	C_2H_4	−103·8	35·2	0·0729	9·9	742
'Freon 12'	CCl_2F_2	−29·8	—	0·3180	112·0	600
Helium	He	−268·9	7·80	0·0103	−267·9	33·2
Hydrogen	H_2	−252·8	4·43	0·0052	−239·9	188
Methane	CH_4	−161·5	26·3	0·0416	−82·5	673
Methyl chloride	CH_3Cl	−24·2	62·2	—	143·1	967
Nitrogen	N_2	−195·8	50·4	0·0725	−147·1	492
Oxygen	O_2	−182·9	71·2	0·0828	−118·8	730
Propane	C_3H_8	−42·0	36·2	0·1154	96·8	617
Propylene	C_3H_6	−47·7	37·5	0·1070	91·9	667

both manipulation and transport. Oil refining necessitates low temperatures for de-waxing, and the vessels involved may be very large, thick-walled constructions many tons in weight.

It is probably, however, the field involving the production of individual industrial gases which is likely, in the future, to demand the greatest tonnages of suitable materials for construction. The rate at which tonnage-oxygen plants (each capable of producing 100–300 tons per day of gaseous oxygen from the atmosphere by liquefaction—see Table 1) are being built indicates the importance of low-temperature properties of metals and alloys. Curiously, this enormous expansion has come about through the application of oxygen to the steelmaking process itself by the development of the L.D. and Kaldo processes. This rapid catalytic effect of the demands made by one industry upon another has been a powerful stimulus to progress within the past ten years. The new L.D. and Kaldo processes depend upon continuous supplies of tonnage oxygen. Its availability for this purpose has stimulated its application to other older processes such as the open-hearth furnace with a consequent significant increase in production rates.

Gases such as oxygen, hydrogen, nitrogen and carbon dioxide require the development of low temperatures in suitable equipment for their extraction. While they can be stored in the gaseous form at ambient temperatures and low pressures, it is obviously more economic to store them in the liquid (or in the case of CO_2, in the solid) condition since the volumes occupied are very much smaller. In the liquid or solid condition their transport can be effected in containers from which the gaseous form can be obtained by subsequent evaporation for final distribution and use. Lengthy expensive pipelines are thereby avoided. A common sight nowadays in many areas is the transport by road of liquid oxygen. The application of metals to the batch transport of gases at low temperatures is increasing rapidly. Recent discoveries of large quantities of methane in the Sahara and the relative ease with which the gas may be liquefied, have led to the construction of tankers for sea transport on similar lines to the oil tanker, and from which the liquid can be pumped and evaporated for distribution at great distances from the source.

Table 1 shows the physical properties of the commoner industrial gases and the temperatures involved.

The Effect of Temperatures on Metals and Alloys

A simple fact which is readily apparent is that most solids become softer the higher the temperatures to which they are raised. If the temperature is sufficiently high they may become liquid or they may decompose with the evolution of a gas. Paraffin wax is a simple example. Metals and alloys become softer on heating, similarly, and it is upon this characteristic that we depend for our ability to work and change their shapes. Steels are heated to a forging or rolling temperature which may be in the region 1150/1320° C. This softening, which implies a decrease in tensile strength, is in most cases accompanied by the persistence of a degree of toughness or resistance to fracture. Hence the metal retains coherence and does not disintegrate under the deforming forces. There are certain exceptions to this general rule, some materials depending on their composition and structure may betray hot shortness.

It is to be expected, therefore, that by reversing the direction of the temperature change from higher to lower, the resulting effect would be opposite, that is, an increase in hardness will occur, together with a decrease in the plasticity. Common observation again confirms this—rubber, which is plastic at room temperatures, becomes hard and brittle when frozen. Similarly, most ferrous alloys behave in this manner, and a fuller consideration of the effect of ambient and low temperatures in relation to certain physical and mechanical properties is given under specific headings.

Table 2. *Strength and ductility of some wrought and cast steels at low temperatures*

No.	Steel composition	Condition	Test temperature (°C)	Yield stress (tons/in²)	Ultimate strength (tons/in²)	Elongation % 2 in. g.l.	Reduction of area (%)
1	0·035 C- plain C-Mn	A.R.*	+ 20	—	20·4	28	73
		A.R.	− 20	13·7	24·0	42	75
		A.R.	− 50	18·8	26·5	43	74
		A.R.	− 70	19·3	27·6	37·5	72
		A.R.	−100	25·5	29·8	26·5	70
		A.R.	−120	29·8	34·3	17	68
2	0·35 C- plain C-Mn	Norm.†	+ 4	22·3	38·0	29	52
		Norm.	− 32	26·9	42·4	29	48
		Norm.	− 51	33·9	45·5	30	48
		Norm.	−123	63·9	64·3	5	5
3	Ni-Cr-Mo wrought steel C Cr Ni Mo 0·33 0·67 2·45 0·64	Oil Q.‡ 850° C Temper. 640° C	+ 21 − 20 − 68 − 96 −180	61·4 62·9 64·7 66·5 82·0	68·8 69·0 72·8 76·0 90·0	14 16 16 16 17	65 64 62 61 63
4	3% Ni wrought steel C Mn Ni Cr Si 0·13 0·47 3·04 0·23 0·16	Norm. 900° C	+ 20 − 78 −196	20·5 22·6 44·5	33·3 39·4 54·8	40§ 45 23	63 63 15
5	Low C 18% Cr 8% Ni— stainless steel C Si Mn Ni 0·09 0·72 0·23 8·2 Cr Mo 19·0 0·09	Water Q. 900°C	+ 20 − 78 −196	14·5 16·6 17·1	42·2 82·5 113·8	70§ 47 39	69 66 56
6	0·21 C 0·70 Mn— cast steel		+ 24 − 80	16·6 18·0	32·0 34·6	35 33	55 53
7	2½% Ni cast steel C Mn Ni 0·10 0·69 2·48		+ 24 − 80	22·7 23·4	30·5 32·9	37 38	66 65

* A.R. signifies the hot-rolled condition.   † Norm. signifies normalized.
‡ Water or Oil Q. signifies quenched.
§ Elongation percentage determined on 4 $\sqrt{\text{area}}$.

Tensile Strength, Yield Stress and Elongation

The ability of a uniform section to withstand an increased static loading without fracture, over that possible at room temperature, increases markedly as the temperature is lowered.

Table 2 illustrates this and incorporates values obtained by various workers. The effect on the room temperature value of the yield stress and percentage elongation is also apparent. From this table the increases shown in tensile strength, over equal falling temperature intervals, do not appear to possess any marked consistency for different steels. Out of three steels (nos. 4, 6 and 7) having a room temperature tensile strength in the range 30/33 tons/in², nos. 6 and 7 increase in strength by some 2/3 tons/in² only when cooled to −80° C. No. 4, however, increases by 6 tons/in² over practically the same temperature interval. It must be observed that there is a considerable difference in the two metallurgical states, nos. 6 and 7 being cast steels while no. 4 is a wrought normalized steel.

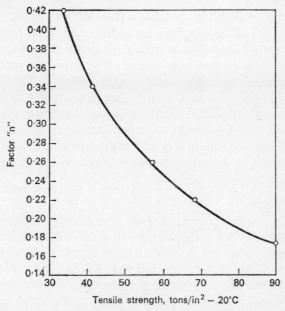

FIG. 1. Relationship between room temperature tensile strength of low-alloy steels and a factor *n*. (*Courtesy International Nickel Co. Ltd.*)

In spite of these inconsistencies it has been found that for both quenched and tempered low-alloy steels and those in the normalized or normalized and tempered condition, a broad generalization can be applied with respect to tensile property changes as the temperature is lowered. Statistical examination of results for wrought steels in the above metallurgical states reveals an empirical relationship between tensile strength and the absolute temperature thus:

$$M_{ST} = cT^{-n},$$

where M_{ST} is the tensile strength at temperature T measured in degrees absolute; c and n are constants and depend on M_{S20} which is the tensile strength at +20° C.

c can be found from

$$\log c = n \log 293 + \log M_{S20}.$$

Developing the first equation we get

$$\log M_{ST} = \log c - n \log T.$$

Substituting for $\log c$ we have

$$\log M_{ST} = n \log 293 + \log M_{S20} - n \log T,$$

or $$\log M_{ST} - \log M_{S20} = n(\log 293 - \log T),$$

from which an appropriate value for n can be determined from the empirical curve shown in Fig. 1. The expected tensile strength at $T°$ (absolute) can then be obtained.

Such empirical relationships provide a reasonable estimate. As in the case of similarly established relationships, for example, hardness v. tensile strength —or tensile strength based on empirical formulae involving composition, the results should be treated with caution. A practical determination of the required value under the proper conditions is preferable. Table 2 also shows that the yield stresses increase with falling temperature. Increasing yield stresses are usually associated with decreasing elongation values. In some cases, however, there is evidence of a persistent ductility—as indicated by maintained elongation values at lower temperatures. At very low temperatures these values fall rapidly as a general rule and brittleness (as the converse of ductility) becomes apparent.

Modulus of Elasticity

The elastic properties of ferrous alloys also undergo changes with falling temperature. We may define elasticity by the slope of the elastic portion of the stress/strain curve obtained in tensile testing. In this portion the strain produced is proportional to the stress applied (Hooke's law). From this slope the modulus of elasticity, or Young's modulus, is defined as that value in lb/in^2 which would double the original length of the unloaded specimen if the material behaved in a perfectly elastic manner up to the breaking stress.

For plain carbon and low-alloy steels at room temperature Young's modulus is approximately $28/30 \times 10^6$ lb/in^2. Within this range the precise value depends upon the treatment, i.e. the specimen may have been quenched and tempered, cold drawn or softened by annealing or normalizing. Keulegan and Houseman[1]* have determined values for the temperature coefficients of the modulus of elasticity for a number of steels in various conditions of heat treatment, including stainless and plain high carbon varieties. The coefficient which changes with temperature is expressed as:

$$e = \frac{1}{E} \times \frac{dE}{dT},$$

where E = modulus of elasticity and T = absolute temperature in $°$ K;
          e_0 = average value of the coefficient between $-50°$ and $+50°$ C.

* Figures within parentheses refer to references given at the ends of chapters.

The authors' values for the coefficients for each steel, expressed in terms of $-e_0 \times 10^5$, varied between $-20 \cdot 1$ and $-43 \cdot 2$, the majority being in the range $-20 \cdot 1$ to $-29 \cdot 0$. Low carbon stainless steels in the hard drawn condition gave values of $-37 \cdot 9$ to $-43 \cdot 2$. Since the coefficients are negative, then the modulus of elasticity increases as the temperature is lowered. For all the steels examined the ratio $e + 25° C/e - 25° C$ varied between $1 \cdot 04$ and $1 \cdot 19$.

Electrical and Thermal Conductivity

The electrical conductivity of all metals and alloys increases as the temperature is lowered, and it is generally true that the thermal conductivity also increases. A list of most of the metallic elements arranged in order of magnitude of their electrical conductivities also indicates approximately the order of their thermal conductivities. It is well known that the electrical resistance of many metals diminishes almost to zero when measured at temperatures near absolute zero. When near to $-273°$ C they become super conductors. The level of thermal conductivity of low carbon steels at $0°$ C is about $0 \cdot 16$–$0 \cdot 18$ cals/cm^2/sec/$°$ C. This level increases to $0 \cdot 22$/$0 \cdot 23$ at $-108°$ C. Some highly alloyed steels are poor conductors of both heat and electricity, for example, stainless steels. The thermal conductivity of 9% Ni steel is between $0 \cdot 046$ and $0 \cdot 077$ cals/cm^2/sec/$°$ C for a temperature range of $-153°$ C to $+527°$ C, a drop to almost one-third of the value for low carbon steels. Thermal conductivity is of obvious importance in the design of plant for low-temperature applications. Preservation of low temperatures in order to prevent loss by evaporation is essential and the thermal conductivity characteristics of the steels used influence the type or principle of insulation used to achieve this end.

Table 3. *Variation of coefficients of thermal expansion with temperature*

Metal or alloy	Temperature or range (° C)	Coefficient (10^{-6} in./in./$°$ C)
Pure iron	0 to -20	10·93
Pure iron carbon	-160 to -180	5·85
Plain carbon steels<1·0% C	-200	5·8 to 8·4
Grey cast iron—3·5% C approx.	$+16$ to -191	8·5
Invar—Fe + 36% Ni	$+38$ to 0	0·877
Invar—Fe + 36% Ni	-20 to -200	0·25
Invar—Fe + 36% Ni	-100	1·06

Thermal Expansion

All metals and alloys in the solid state possess lower coefficients of expansion at sub-ambient temperatures than at elevated temperatures. As in the case of temperatures above ambient where, due to phase changes, the coefficient of expansion varies over a range of temperature—this coefficient at sub-zero temperatures must be defined as the average value for a temperature range or as a definite value for a single temperature. Table 3 gives some representative values. It will be seen that the Fe–Ni alloys are anomalous, being characterized by a remarkably small coefficient of expansion. This constitutes the reason for their use for permanent dimensional standards and clock pendulums.

Toughness and Brittleness

The examples given, of the changes which take place in several physical properties of ferrous alloys as temperature decreases, show that designing for low-temperature service presents no insuperable difficulties since the changes which take place as temperature decreases are of the same order or less than those which take place for an equivalent increase in temperature above the ambient range. There can obviously be no disadvantage in a metal or alloy actually increasing in strength with a decrease in temperature since the reverse which tends to apply with increased temperature is a characteristic sufficiently well catered for in the design factors used. There is, however, a suggestion in Table 2 of an undesirable feature of low temperature strength properties because elongation values may diminish as temperatures are reduced. This is accompanied by a diminishing percentage reduction of area. Service conditions can arise in which the static strength as defined by yield stress and tensile strength, thermal or electrical conductivity and size contraction give no cause for anxiety; but unfortunately loss of ductility can be important due to the fact that stresses encountered are not likely to be static or constant. They may vary smoothly with time up or down as in heating up or cooling down a boiler, but they may also occur instantaneously as when a heavy load travelling at high speed crosses a bridge, or when a ship is momentarily subjected to an enormous bending moment if a large wave crest passes the centre of its length. The effect of shock loading must therefore be considered. Although such loading may be insufficient to cause a structure to flex uniformly as a whole within the elastic limit, it can cause failure (which may be catastrophic) by virtue of a lack of ductility or ability to deform locally. The use of the term shock therefore introduces the concept of toughness and brittleness.

Toughness is a term covering a composite response by a metal or alloy to the application of energy. It implies the ability to absorb energy without fracture, particularly under shock conditions. Because in total, toughness can be assessed by the area lying under a stress-strain curve up to the point of fracture, the term obviously involves both tensile strength and ductility. This definition is incomplete since the area can be the same if one property varies inversely as the other.

Brittleness, while being an obvious antonym, is not strictly translatable in the same terms. A hard white cast iron, while being extremely strong in the sense that a high energy level is required to fracture, cannot be described as tough when compared with a heat-treated high carbon steel. The white iron when it does fracture, displays no signs of deformation. It is said to break in a brittle manner and it is possible to fit the fractured pieces together to give the original shape. Brittleness implies, therefore, a tendency to fracture without deformation, and the ambient temperature range and particularly sub-zero temperatures exercise a marked effect on the tough/brittle characteristics of ferrous alloys. Their behaviour under these conditions forms the major theme of this book.

Generally, it is found that the commoner plain carbon and low-alloy steels, whether in the cast or wrought condition, and which at ambient or elevated temperatures may be tough, behave in an increasingly brittle manner as the temperature is lowered. If a suitable shock test is applied to specimens actually maintained at a series of different temperatures it is found, particularly if the applied stress is concentrated locally, for example, by the presence of a notch, that at the higher end of the temperature range the specimens behave in a ductile manner, that is, they may fracture, but in doing so they first deform plastically. This deformation is apparent and the fracture itself may be fine and silky in appearance. As the testing temperature is lowered, fractures begin to show mixed characteristics in that bright crystalline areas appear, and as these become more extensive the amount of deformation decreases.

Finally at some specific low temperature the silky ductile appearance of the fracture disappears and is wholly replaced by a crystalline appearance. This is the well-known 'cleavage' type of fracture. Apparent deformation here is negligible and the specimen has obviously broken in a completely brittle manner with a much smaller energy requirement than that necessary at the higher temperatures. This state can be described by a diagram shown in Fig. 2.

This tough/brittle transition diagram is not constant in shape for all ferrous alloys. There are considerable shifts, both with respect to energy levels required to cause complete fracture at any temperature and an arbitrary midpoint on the slope between the ductile or tough level and the brittle state. This arbitrary point may be fixed by noting that temperature at which, for example, there is present in the fracture equal areas of fibrous (or ductile) and crystalline (or brittle) surface. This temperature can then be called the ductile/brittle transition temperature.

It is obviously desirable that a ferrous alloy for use at low temperatures should possess a transition temperature below the lowest service temperature contemplated. This will then guarantee that no risk of brittleness in service will result.

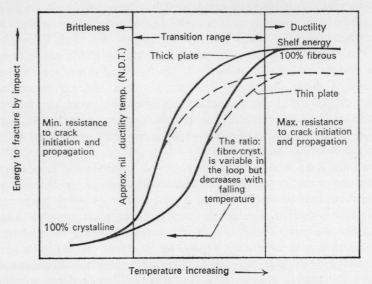

FIG. 2. Schematic transition curve. NOTE: The shelf energy is sometimes lower in thin plates than in thick plates of the same steel—the deleterious effect of inclusions being more severe in the former. The transition range, however (or arbitrary transition temperature), remains the same.

This characteristic change from a ductile to brittle state for plain carbon and low-alloy steels is not universal for all ferrous alloys. Marked exceptions exist in the stainless steels (18/8 varieties) and some of the iron-nickel alloys (9% Ni steel). No marked change to brittleness as indicated by the relatively steep slope shown in Fig. 2 actually occurs. For these materials the energy levels which are required to fracture in the ambient temperature range are practically maintained down to very low temperatures, $-160/-200°$ C. Below these temperatures the energy levels diminish gradually. These materials are considered in greater detail elsewhere.

To a lesser extent the maintenance of energy levels to fracture over a wide range of low temperatures occurs also in low-alloy steels fully heat-treated, that is, in the quenched and tempered condition. A metallurgical generalization is possible by stating that metals (other than iron) which possess a body centred cubic structure (b.c.c.) such as molybdenum, tungsten and chromium are all seriously embrittled as temperatures are lowered, whereas face centred cubic (f.c.c.) metals such as aluminium, copper, nickel and lead do not show this characteristic. If therefore we convert, at least partially, the body centred

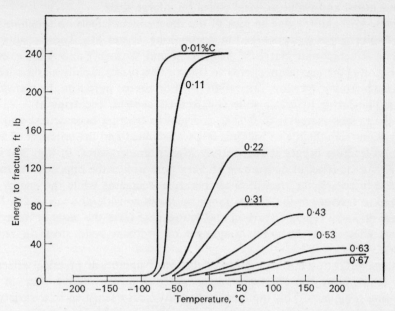

FIG. 3(*a*). Effect of carbon on energy transition curves for Fe–C alloys. (J. A. Rinebolt and W. J. Harris, *Trans. Am. Soc. Metals*, **43** (1951), 1197.)

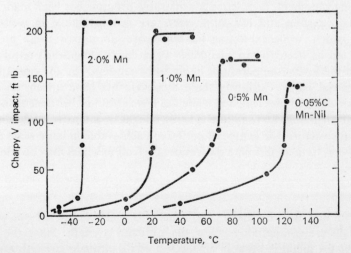

FIG. 3(*b*). Effect of manganese on energy transition curves for high-purity Fe–Mn alloys containing 0·05% C. (N. P. Allen, W. P. Rees, B. E. Hopkins and H. T. Tipler, *J. Iron Steel Inst.*, **174**, pt. 2 (1953), 108.)

cubic form of structure to the face centred cubic form by heat-treatment, then the transition temperature from the ductile state to the brittle state is appreciably lowered. Today, this is an important reason for the production of quenched and tempered steel plates on a large scale.

Figs. 3 (a) and (b) give an idea of the independent effects on toughness of the two principal elements used in steelmaking, C and Mn. These results are due to Rinebolt and Harris[2], Armstrong and Warner[3] and Allen et al.[4] In Fig. 3(a) the maximum energy to fracture decreases rapidly as the carbon increases from a very low value (0·01%). For almost pure iron the transition from the ductile to brittle state is extremely sudden, occurring at −73° C. As the carbon increases to 0·67%, energies to fracture become less and the transition from ductile to brittle is less well defined and the criterion of 50% fibrous fracture occurs at successively higher temperatures. In Fig. 3(b) it is seen that the effect of manganese on very pure iron is the opposite. As manganese increases, the transition temperature decreases while the energy required to fracture in the ductile range increases considerably up to 2% Mn. These opposite effects of carbon and manganese form the basis of improvements effected in the notch toughness of ordinary mild steels in recent years.

Some indication has been given of the most significant practical effect of low temperatures on an important property of ferrous alloys—that of decreasing toughness. This diminished ductility is also sensitive to a variety of metallurgical and environmental features and is probably the least consistent of all mechanical properties in an absolute sense. While this may seem a disconcerting statement, in practice considerable progress has been made in that both plain carbon and low-alloy steels are now available in well-defined classes, which, while exhibiting interclass overlapping of some properties such as tensile strength can adequately cater for the engineer's requirements down to the lowest temperatures likely to be required for any operations on an industrial scale. Curiously these achievements have arisen, to a large extent, through empiricism, and while the mechanism of brittleness and crack propagation giving rise to failure is being sought by intensive studies in terms of crystal structure, the degree of perfection achievable in large-scale practice must always limit an ultimate theoretical perfection which may be considered possible.

Fatigue

A metal may fracture under conditions of repeated cyclic stresses, which in magnitude are considerably below the ultimate strength. Since the fatigue strength of a metal is broadly a function of its ultimate strength and since this latter increases with decreasing temperature it follows that fatigue strength also increases. True brittle fracture arising from a concentrated stress in material at a low temperature is not necessarily associated with failure by fatigue.

It is easily imagined that the hull of a large vessel passing through a regular wave formation at sea will be exposed to a low cycle–high amplitude form of stressing, the equivalent of a fatigue test in which the applied energy is high. Failure might be expected to occur after a relatively small number of stress reversals. Since a hull must contain discontinuities then stress concentrations at these are high. One might expect that cracks would increase in seriousness with the age of the ship. Murray[5], however, states that cracks arising from low frequency–high amplitude fatigue stresses have, in practice, been relatively fewer than brittle fractures arising from other causes in newer ships, and while fatigue cracks do arise in both welded and riveted ships of all ages they do not appear to initiate brittle fractures but grow at a slow rate and are consequently repairable. Why weld defects and the presence of a notch brittle steel are more powerful than fatigue in promoting brittle fracture, is not yet solved. It appears that under conditions of low frequency–high amplitude stresses, the sensitivity to notches is not seriously increased. Experimental work has shown that under these conditions the fatigue strength is not suddenly reduced as the transition temperature range from the ductile to the brittle condition is crossed.

REFERENCES

1. G. H. Keulegan and M. R. Houseman. *Bur. Stand. J. Res.*, **10** (1933), 289.
2. J. A. Rinebolt and W. J. Harris. *Trans. Am. Soc. Metals*, **43** (1951), 1175; **44** (1952), 225.
3. T. N. Armstrong and W. L. Warner. *Symposium on Impact Testing*, A.S.T.M. 1955, Spec. publ. 176, p. 40.
4. N. P. Allen *et al.* *J. Iron Steel Inst.*, **174,** pt. 2 (1953), 108.
5. J. M. Murray. *Standards of Strength in Relation to Bulk Carriers*, No. 24, Lecture to Collegio Nazionale degli Ingeneri Navali e Meccanici 1963 May. Lloyd's Register of Shipping.

CHAPTER 2

ASPECTS OF THE METALLIC STRUCTURE AND THE INITIATION OF FRACTURE

The term *malleability* as applied to a metal or alloy indicates its ability to be deformed without rupture. The term may be applied when the deforming force operates while the metal is at either an elevated or an ambient temperature. Without this property we should not be able to hot or cold roll steel or to produce wires by cold drawing. The property is akin to that of ductility although the latter is generally associated with increase in length, as in wire drawing. The most malleable metal is gold since it can be beaten into 'leaf' which may have a thickness of only $\frac{1}{275,000}$ in. and is sufficiently thin to transmit the green component of white light. The property of malleability or ability to flow in a plastic manner may at first sight be associated principally with the intrinsically softer metals, for example, gold, silver, lead, aluminium, tin and copper since these are familiar to us as metallic 'foils'. Even much harder metals possess the property to some extent. It is known that traces of certain impurities in a pure metal may seriously affect the property adversely. One of the best examples is provided by traces of bismuth in copper. The bismuth forms brittle films round the crystal grains of copper and 0·005% is sufficient to destroy malleability.

The theoretical mechanism of plastic deformation as an indication of malleability can be presented on a rational basis if we assume that a metal is an isotropic and perfectly homogeneous medium. In chapter 4 an attempt is made to indicate that methods of manufacture exert influences on properties of steels. Because these properties show degrees of variability in the same material they indicate that the medium is in fact neither isotropic nor homogeneous. Hence the prediction of behaviour for instance under stress, from theoretical considerations, becomes unsafe and reliance on experimental data becomes a practical necessity. This experimental data indicates that various steels possess different degrees of malleability or toughness, some being quite brittle in the sense that they do not visibly deform plastically before fracture takes place. Consideration will therefore be given in this chapter to

PLATE 1

(a) 5 ft wide plate fracture—$\frac{1}{2}$ in. mild steel—stress 10 tons/in². Temp. —5° C. Notch cooled to —60° C to initiate fracture.

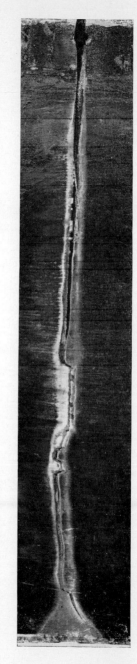

(b) 2 ft 8 in. wide plate fracture—shows 'thumbnail' arrests and restarts—stress 12 tons/in². Temp. —30° C. Notch cooled locally to —80° C to initiate fracture.

(c) Side view of (b) showing yielding at arrests—plate 3 in. thick.

PLATE 2

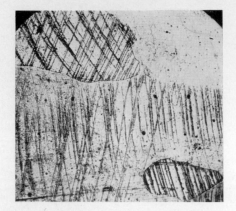

(*a*) Slip lines in
pure iron.

(*b*) Pure iron creep-tested for 250 hr, 1½ tons/in² at 500° C (plastic strain 3–4%).
Shows regular dislocation network typical of creep of pure metals. × 75,000.
Reduced by ⅓ on reproduction. (*Courtesy of Research Dept. Colvilles Ltd.*)

various aspects of metallic structures and mechanisms whereby failure can be initiated.

Surface Energy

If we consider a liquid-gas interface, the outstanding property of the liquid surface is that of surface tension—the liquid behaving as if covered by a tightened membrane. This has the effect of making the surface area as small as possible. If we consider a line l cm long on the liquid surface the tension on each side is equal and opposite in its pull. If this stretching force is f then the ratio $f:2l$ is the surface tension. Being defined therefore by length and force it is measured in dynes/cm.

In the case of solids, e.g. metals, we may consider the surface tension as surface energy. When a crack is produced in a metal, either from outside to inside or wholly internally, two new surfaces are produced. Work must be expended to produce the crack and the new surfaces. This work is stored in the surfaces. If the area of the new surfaces is A created by the work W then the ratio of $W:A$ is the specific surface energy. Since the dimensions involve energy and area the surface energy is expressed in ergs/cm^2.

Whereas in liquids the molecules are randomly arranged, the atoms in a metal exist as crystal lattices. Hence surface energy can be calculated from interatomic forces. The results are much greater than those for liquids for which they can be determined experimentally. The propagation of an initiated crack and the effect of low temperatures is considered subsequently.

Fracture of Brittle Materials

At first sight it appears easy to scale down the overall concept of a non-homogeneous mass of steel to microscopic dimensions. One can then postulate that the initiation of a failure in the form of a crack arises from a local concentration of stress at some micro weakness resulting from non-uniformity. This condition may be sufficient to initiate a parting of adjacent metal atoms thereby creating a void. This in turn gives rise to fresh concentrations of stress again sufficient to cause further rupture in the vicinity. Such a simple picture is not, however, entirely adequate. It is not possible, for example, to imagine how, in an ordinary tensile testpiece, the stress applied to the whole area of the piece can be concentrated sufficiently at one critical point so that it is of sufficient magnitude to overcome the cohesive force between two adjoining layers of atoms.

This cohesive force constitutes the theoretical strength of any solid and in all cases it is many times greater than the actual strength encountered in practice. It varies with the interatomic distances in the material. For pure iron the unit crystal is in the form of a body centred cube, the distance between

c

the atoms forming the corners being 2·8606 Å. The cohesive strength is given by

$$\sigma_c = \left(\frac{ES}{a}\right)^{\frac{1}{2}},$$ (1)

where E is the elastic modulus, S is surface energy, and a is the interatomic distance. An example may be quoted: if $S = 1200$ ergs/cm² for iron then $\sigma_c = 5 \times 10^6$ lb/in² (or 2230 tons/in²), which for soft iron is about 100 times greater than that encountered in practice.*

Results of calculations for different materials on the basis of the example above, show that strengths far beyond those normally encountered in practice are indicated. That these results are not absurd is shown by the fact that glass fibres of extremely small diameter and metal 'whiskers' do indeed possess, individually, rupture strengths which approach their theoretical strengths.

This fact introduces the first difficulty in attempting to explain the production of a crack in a solid, that is, the difference in strength between a macro-volume and a micro-volume within large and small masses. In 1920 Griffith[1] postulated the concept for brittle materials that micro-weaknesses which govern the concentration of an applied stress exist in the form of minute cracks, there being an absence of theoretically perfect uniformity in any plane.

If we consider an existing Griffith crack whose length is $2l$, then the total surface energy of the two surfaces is $4lS$, where $S =$ surface energy per unit area.

This energy is supplied by the elastic strain energy released by the formation of the crack. It follows that if the surface energy of the crack is less than the decrease in strain energy, then the crack will propagate.

Now the elastic strain energy may be expressed as

$$\sigma_S = \frac{\pi l^2 \sigma^2}{E},$$

where σ is the tensile stress normal to the crack and E is the elastic modulus.

When therefore the elastic strain energy just equals the total surface energy of the crack for both surfaces, we may equate thus,

$$\frac{2\pi l^2 \sigma^2}{E} = 4lS.$$

From which

$$\sigma = \left(\frac{2ES}{\pi l}\right)^{\frac{1}{2}}.$$ (2)

* The surface tension of *liquid* iron containing 3·5% C is approximately 1200 dynes/cm.

This is the Griffith equation which indicates that there is a critical length of crack (2l) for which the stress to propagate can equal and exceed the cohesive strength.

For a completely brittle material such as glass the critical length of crack can be calculated to be about 1 μ (0·001 mm), which, if the crack is assumed to be ellipsoidal in shape (i.e. it is postulated to exist as a flattened sphere), then gives a radius of curvature at the extreme edge, or end of the crack, which is of the order of the interatomic spacing.

Inglis[2], in an earlier consideration of a three-dimensional ellipsoidal crack, had calculated that the stress at the edge which had a radius of curvature r is

$$\sigma_{max} = 2\sigma\left(\frac{l}{r}\right)^{\frac{1}{2}}.$$

In this equation σ is a nominal stress present when there is no crack.

This expression can be equated to the cohesive strength equation thus

$$\sigma_c \text{ (or } \sigma_{max}) = 2\sigma\left(\frac{l}{r}\right)^{\frac{1}{2}} = \left(\frac{ES}{a}\right)^{\frac{1}{2}}.$$

Now if the radius r becomes equal to a the interatomic distance, then the crack will propagate.

From the above equation we can obtain the value of σ, or the stress necessary to propagate, that is,

$$\sigma = \left(\frac{ES}{4l}\right)^{\frac{1}{2}}. \tag{3}$$

Equations (2) and (3) are derived in different ways. They are similar in form and may be taken as equivalent within the accuracy of the estimations.

While this holds for a brittle material such as glass, the theory establishes a critical crack length of several millimetres for metallic zinc. In this case the theory breaks down because such a crack length can obviously be greater than a chosen thickness of specimen the testing of which experimentally would reveal no crack of such dimensions.

The foregoing picture of the fracture of a brittle material has been amplified by Weibull[3] who accepted the Griffith's flaws as existing in a random distribution and being of random severity. Any particular one or other of these flaws which was suitably orientated with respect to an applied stress and of a particular size would then increase in size, so initiating and causing visible fracture. He defined the mathematical probability of fracture on these assumptions in terms of size (volume) and certain constants for the particular material, one of which was an index of the relative number of assumed flaws per unit volume.

The distribution curve of the probability of fracture occurring on this basis was shown to be narrow if the number of flaws increases, that is there is less scatter in the actual results obtained. Similarly an increase in size or volume increased the chances of there being a flaw correctly orientated and favourable to initiation of fracture. The greater or less scatter of results encountered for any one material has been interpreted by Fisher and Hollomon[4] as shown in Fig. 4.

In Fig. 4 N is the assumed number of flaws, and if the number is large then little or no spread in the value of the stress required to fracture is encountered. If, however, N is relatively small (i.e. few flaws) then while the stress required to fracture increases in magnitude, on the average the values obtained show

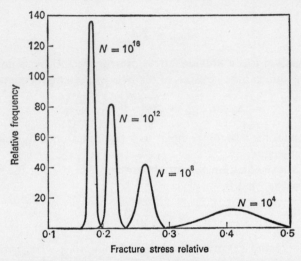

FIG. 4. Frequency distribution of stress to fracture as a function of the number N of cracks in a metal. (J. C. Fisher and J. H. Hollomon, *Trans. A.I.M.E.*, **171** (1947), 546.)

a much greater spread—a feature one would expect since the chances of a flaw favourable to the initiation of fracture are so much less.

Now it is found in practice that brittle materials do indeed fracture over a wide range of tensile stress under various conditions of temperature, size and other factors. Testing of hard brittle white irons which show practically no elongation will reveal a spread of results much greater in magnitude than those obtained for test specimens prepared from ductile mild steel. The results for the brittle material may be perhaps described as 'haphazard'. Considering such results on the basis of Fisher and Holloman's mathematical statistics leads to the conclusion that the odds for the existence of a crack of the critical dimensions required by Griffith's theory are accordingly reduced.

It is not likely, therefore, that a relatively simple concept of critical flaw size is completely adequate to explain why a known brittle material fractures and further consideration must be given to the degree of plastic deformation which a steel may undergo when subjected to stress at any chosen temperature. This necessity arises from the fact that in all cases of brittle fracture evidence is obtainable that failure is preceded by some degree of plastic deformation. Sometimes this evidence is visual such as occurs in breaking a hardened steel testpiece—when in spite of the fact that no measurable elongation is produced there are signs of a 'thin skin' surrounding the fracture which is obviously the result of some deformation and which in a more ductile material

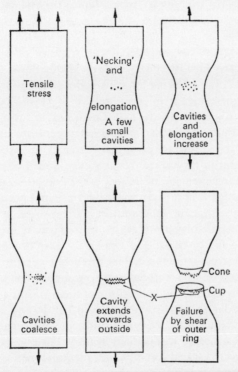

FIG. 5. Development of ductile 'cup' and 'cone' fracture.

grows in extent during deformation to give the familiar cup and cone fracture as in Fig. 5—with distinct evidence of 'necking'.

In other less obvious cases microscopic examination is necessary to discover the evidence of some plasticity.

This 'skin' appearance is the result of final rupture taking place from the development of a critical shear stress and a certain degree of shear strain as the crack extends towards the walls across the diameter or cross-section (see X in Fig. 5). The thinner is the skin then the larger the central flat area of the fracture and consequently the more brittle the material. Pellini[5] suggests that a completely brittle fracture can be defined arbitrarily as such if this skin is less than 0·01 in. thick. Similar effects can be seen in fractured Charpy test-pieces, even in those which show 100% crystallinity or cleavage—the skin being present to some slight degree at the base of the notch, indicating that some deformation has taken place just prior to the start of the brittle fracture. In Plate 1 a further example is shown of a brittle ship-plate fracture. Here the chevron markings in (*a*) point to the origin of fracture. It will be noted that there appears to be a thin skin indicative of some degree of ductility along each edge of the fracture in the example 1(*b*) and (*c*).

Plastic Deformation

The previous section has considered the fracture of a steel in a brittle manner, and the early Griffith theory of pre-existing flaws, one of which may be of a critical size, thus initiating fracture under stress, is not now considered adequate in view of evidence of some degree of plastic behaviour prior to fracture even in so-called brittle materials. Let us now consider plastic behaviour itself. Pure iron exists at room temperature as a body centred structure, that is, the atoms are arranged regularly in space to form a cubic lattice with an atom in the centre of each cube and it is possible to distort slightly such an arrangement of atoms by an applied stress whereby, if the stress is released, the atoms return to their original positions. This constitutes an example of elastic deformation. If, however, a certain stress is exceeded then plastic deformation results, in which state the atoms have been moved a little too far to be able to return to their original positions even when the applied stress is released. Under such a condition movement has resulted in slip along certain well-defined crystallographic planes. These slips are not individually visible, but collections of them within a crystal grain may become visible under the microscope as slip bands (see Plate 2(*a*)). In an adjacent grain the bands may occur at a different angle in any plane since the orientation of the structure within each grain varies one from the other.

In order to move whole planes of fundamental crystals by slip, however, implies that the cohesive forces between the atoms is being exceeded as mentioned earlier when considering theoretical strength. Experiments indicate that forces of such magnitude are not necessary to produce slip. An explanation of the discrepancy was suggested some thirty years ago. This explanation constitutes the dislocation theory. Essentially, certain imperfections are present in the arrangement of the atoms in each crystal grain, a polycrystalline mass being a collection of such grains. These imperfections are called dislocations and these are responsible for the weaknesses encountered in practice. Instead, therefore, of visualized discrete flaws nominated by Griffith we now have imperfections on a much smaller scale. They are present in crystals by accident, and arise during the change from liquid to solid. They can also

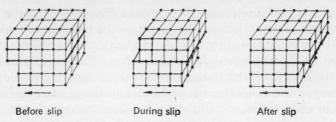

Before slip   During slip   After slip

Fig. 6. The application of high energy is causing a whole crystal plane to slip.

be caused by stressing. Fig. 6 illustrates diagrammatically the mechanism of slip of a whole plane of unit crystals and slip in the presence of a dislocation showing that the end effect may be the same in both cases. The exceptional strength of metallic whiskers previously referred to is known to be due to the perfection of their crystal make-up, and absence of dislocations. Plastic deformation in these takes place by the mechanism shown in Fig. 7. Under

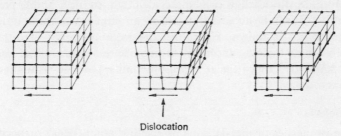

Dislocation

FIG. 7. Slip is occurring from the movement of a dislocation through the plane, requiring less energy but giving a similar result.

these 'near perfect' conditions elastic deformation under stress can reach 3–4% without becoming permanent plastic deformation. The average sample of steel, however, can become permanently deformed at only 0·2% strain or less. To strengthen a steel, therefore, the requirement is that dislocations should be immobilized in some way.

Dislocations

Von Laue in 1912 discovered the diffraction of X-rays by metallic crystals. From this work was established the fact that metals were composed of atoms arranged in specific geometric forms called lattices.

The concept of the dislocation was introduced and developed by Orowan, Taylor and Polanyi in 1930 as an aid to understanding the behaviour of atoms when a crystal is deformed under stress. It is pointed out that the dislocation theory cannot be used in a precise way but constitutes a concept for explaining behaviour. This does not imply that dislocations are theoretical only. The development of the electron microscope has made direct observation of them possible in many materials although not to so fine a degree as the displacement of single atoms. The resolving power of the best electron microscope would have to be improved by a factor of 10 in order to observe single lattice planes. What is achieved, however, is their detection in groups by increasing their effective sizes through the use of the field of strain existing in their vicinity. Because of these strained areas the metal in the vicinity of the dislocations etches differently and where a dislocation intersects the polished surface an etch pit may result which follows the form of the dislocation and renders it visible on an enlarged scale, thus placing it within the resolving power of an electron microscope.

If metals are prepared in the form of thin foil and reduced to about 1000 Å in thickness by electropolishing they are transparent to electrons and the intensity of the diffracted electron beam is altered by the strains already mentioned and which exist around the dislocations. Hence they can be photographed. In certain optically transparent chemical crystals, for example sodium chloride, dislocations can be revealed by forming a visible precipitate along them. This can be achieved by adding an impurity to the solution from which the crystal is grown. Plate 2(*b*) illustrates examples of dislocations made visible (note the magnification). It must be remembered that magnifications of 3000–4000 times linear represent limits possible with the normal optical microscope.

Lattice Defects

Certain properties of metals, such as melting point, density, specific heat, coefficient of thermal expansion and the elastic constants may be termed 'structure insensitive'. These properties can be explained satisfactorily by assuming that the atomic lattice is indeed perfect and without defects.

Certain other properties, however, particularly mechanical properties such as the yield stress, tensile strength, creep strength, electrical conductivity and semiconductor properties make it necessary to assume that lattice defects do indeed exist. These defects may be of three kinds: (*a*) point defect, (*b*) line defects, and (*c*) surface defects.

Point Defect

This is the simplest form of imperfection and as indicated by its designation it is confined to a local spot surrounded in the three dimensions by the normal structure. The conventional representation of the three types of this defect is illustrated in Fig. 8, where an atom different from those composing the regular lattice may replace the atom in the regular lattice, that is, an impurity as in (*c*). In (*a*) an extra atom has become located between the atoms composing the regular lattice. This is an interstitial atom, and the elements carbon, boron and nitrogen (characterized by very small atomic radii) are

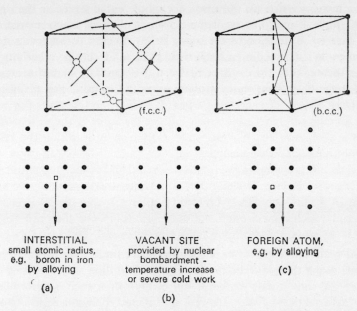

FIG. 8. Unit crystals of iron [f.c.c. and b.c.c.] and lattice faults (*a*, *b* and *c*).

able to locate themselves in this way between the atoms of the iron lattice. The element boron is particularly effective in hardening and strengthening by this mechanism. In (*b*) an atom of the regular lattice is missing, that is there is a vacancy. Vacancies can arise from the destruction of an atom (or atoms) by bombardment with high-energy nuclear particles, and this mechanism which is responsible for the detrimental effects of neutron irradiation is described in chapter 3. Vacancies can be caused in pure metals by heating to high temperatures, that is, near to the melting point of the metal. When nearing the liquid condition all atoms in the lattice are excited thermally, so that a change to the liquid condition results in a destruction of the lattice. All atoms are then random in position with respect to each other. By very rapid quenching from just below the melting point it is possible to retain some vacancies by preventing a more completely regular reformation of the lattice structure such as occurs during normal solidification. Vacancies can also be caused by cold work, that is, by deforming the material severely. Vacancies, if increased sufficiently in number in a lattice structure and if sufficiently localized, may actually form a discrete hole or void.

Line Defect

In the previous section the defect has been defined in relation to points within the three-dimensional lattice. Because the volume of the crystal grain within a metal consists (in the case of a simple cubic structure such as iron) of parallel planes of atoms, we can picture one plane of atoms moved slightly out of position in relation to the plane below. Such a defect forms a line in one plane and it is two dimensional within the solid, that is, it has length and breadth greater than the distance between two regularly spaced atoms in the lattice. It therefore constitutes a plane network in itself. Fig. 9 illustrates a line defect.

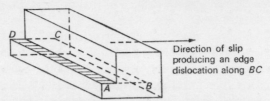

FIG. 9. Edge dislocation producing a line defect.

If one plane of atoms is, by a shearing force, moved up a whole number of atoms along the plane below (in Fig. 9 if the line *AD* advances equally over say 100 interatomic distances uniformly), then such a movement constitutes deformation by slip—along a slip plane. A crystal grain distorted in this way will show, when polished and etched, parallel lines due to the steps produced, that is, slip bands (see Plate 2 (*a*)).

In metals possessing a body centred cubic structure as in Fig. 10, slip is known to occur on the {110}, {112} and {123} planes. In the case of α-iron,

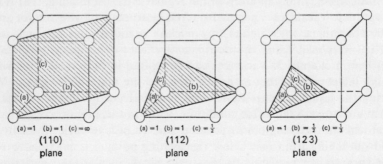

FIG. 10. Three planes (110), (112) and (123), along which slip occurs in the body-centred crystal lattice (e.g. α iron).

however, the fact that observed slip lines are often wavy and not perfectly straight suggests strongly that slip may not occur strictly on these planes preferentially and hence is not strictly crystallographic in its behaviour.

If slip does not take place to the extent of a distance equal to a whole number of interatomic distances over a plane, then an edge dislocation is produced as at *BC* in Fig. 9.

The Plane (Surface) Defect

Distinct from the line defect which is a two-dimensional net within the lattice and which moves to form lines, is the plane or surface defect. Grain boundaries within a metal and low-angle boundaries are examples of plane defects.

Normally, a metal or alloy is composed of crystal grains. These may be fine or coarse. A crystal grain may be defined as that volume within the metal in which the unit crystal lattices themselves are regularly arranged at some specific angle when referred to one particular reference line. The adjacent grain or grains, however, may not have this same angle of reference or orientation. Therefore at the boundary between two grains the lattices within each grain do not register. If registration of the lattices is achieved between two adjacent grains (which may be done by first distorting by cold work and then annealing at a suitable temperature) there is produced a single larger crystal grain and by this process it is possible to change the whole specimen into one single crystal grain.

Grain boundaries in a pure metallic polycrystalline aggregate are only a few atomic diameters wide and possess a relatively high surface energy because their formation has taken place during solidification as a region of random misfits. In the case of a slip plane where the misfit may be described as more regular and of a lesser degree the surface energy is very much less. It is easier, therefore, to produce slip by a given amount of deformation than it is to rupture a grain boundary. On the other hand, while the shear stress of a crystal depends on the interaction of dislocations with themselves and is greater than the stress required to produce a single dislocation, it is lower than that which can produce slip in a lattice free from imperfections. Grain boundaries in a metal exercise several effects, each of which may contribute towards either strengthening or weakening of the mass. The fact that they are regions of high energy implies that they influence reactions which can occur on heat-treatment in the solid state, for example, preferential precipitation of carbides can take place at the original grain boundaries; transformations from the α form to the γ form on heating up pure iron are initiated at the original grain boundaries. Similarly the breakdown of the γ structure by tempering begins at the grain boundaries. Their effect on strength can result in either a decrease or an increase depending on the changes occurring. If a metal is strained at a slow rate at elevated temperatures (as in stress-rupture testing) then deformation takes place preferentially at the grain boundaries and the final fracture is intergranular. Conversely, if the metal is deformed at a rapid rate (as in normal testing for tensile strength), then the presence of grain boundaries results in an increase in the rate of strain-hardening so that strength is effectively increased by their presence. If preferential precipitation of a brittle constituent takes place at the grain boundary either during solidification from the liquid state or as a result of heat-treatment, it is obvious that resistance to shock may be decreased seriously.

Grain boundaries are barriers to slip because they prevent a constant orientation of the lattices within the mass. For this reason they strengthen a metal because of a higher rate of strain-hardening when stressed. Their absence in a single crystal specimen allows slip to take place more easily. It is possible to visualize therefore why a fine grain material has certain improved mechanical properties compared with a coarse grain material of the same composition. Due to rapid strain-hardening in the early stages of stressing a fine-grain material possesses an enhanced yield stress, although the effect on the ultimate strength is less. The enhanced yield stress also assists in developing higher energy absorption values in an impact test since the material must yield before fracture can take place.

Low-angle Grain Boundaries

These are a second form of the plane type of defect and are perhaps more easily pictured than described (see Plate 3(a)). The defect is composed of a sub-network of grain boundaries on which, under the microscope, the grain boundaries proper appear to be superimposed. The fainter response of the sub-network to etching is due to the fact that the orientations within adjacent sub-grains are a nearer fit with each other than exists on either side of the ordinary grain boundary and may only differ in this respect by a degree or two of arc.

This type of grain boundary can be produced in various ways, for example, by cold working to a small extent and then annealing at a sufficiently low temperature to prevent new larger crystal grains from growing. They can also accompany a phase transformation. Their effect results in an appreciable increase in strength with respect to both yield stress and u.t.s. with very little loss in ductility.

To summarize, the types of lattice imperfections or dislocations so far dealt with are (a) point defects, such as vacancies, atoms in interstitial positions or the presence of impurity atoms, (b) line defects such as the simple dislocation formed by slip, which is a line imperfection forming a boundary of a slipped area within a crystal, and (c) plane defects of which grain boundaries and low-angle substructure grain boundaries are examples. A further type of dislocation is more complex. This is known as the 'screw dislocation'.

Screw Dislocations

If we picture a lattice imperfection as in Fig. 11, we have a different type of edge dislocation from that pictured by a pack of cards sliding over each other. In Fig. 11, looking down on the end surface, the crystal grain is not now composed of regular parallel planes each displaced with respect to the other, as in the pack of cards. The atoms now form a spiral ramp with *BC* as the axis in which the original bottom layer of atoms moves up one atomic distance when the semicircular path shown in the figure has been traversed. This is an example of a screw dislocation.

Obviously on the basis of minute interatomic distances involved, collections of dislocations may take the form of curves and may form networks very similar to grain boundaries in themselves. While, however, grain boundaries and low-angle grain boundaries are visible in the optical microscope, dislocations when 'decorated' by an etching technique can only be

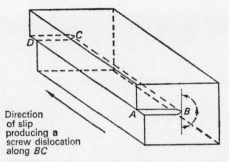

Direction
of slip
producing **a**
screw dislocation
along *BC*

FIG. 11. A screw dislocation. If *AD* slips one unit crystal with respect to *BC*, then unit crystal planes form a spiral ramp with *BC* as the axis.

seen by means of the electron microscope. Plates 3(*b*) and 4 show the appearance of typical collections of dislocations and the magnifications are to be noted.

The Dislocation Stress Field

It has been stated previously that the cohesive strength of a perfect arrangement of atoms in a lattice is some 100/1000 times that encountered in practice, and one of the original concepts of the dislocation theory was to explain this discrepancy. In a perfect cubic lattice, parallel layers of atoms are in the position of minimum energy. The energy curve is at a maximum midway between each pair of adjacent atoms. If, however, an edge dislocation is present between two adjacent layers of atoms as in Fig. 12 then while the end atoms in the two planes are at a minimum energy position, the middle one in the lower plane is at a position of maximum energy, while corresponding ones on each side of this atom are at intermediate energy positions which are equal and opposite. To move therefore the centre atom in the lower plane through one atomic distance the energy required is theoretically zero. A crude analogy would be to compare the centre atom in the lower plane with a soft iron bar

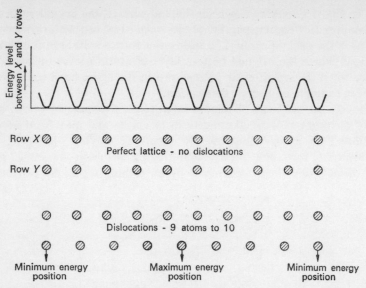

FIG. 12. Energy curves between adjacent atoms, showing ease of movement of a dislocation. (After F. Seitz, *The Physics of Metals*. McGraw Hill Inc., New York, 1943.)

just balanced in the field of two magnets of equal strength. The energy required to unbalance the bar so that it is attracted to either one or the other of the magnets is very small compared with the magnetic field energy of each magnet. A dislocation can therefore move easily through a lattice volume. Deformation by the mechanism of slip therefore takes place.

The fact that in the perfect lattice regular cohesive forces exist implies that any irregularity such as a dislocation is surrounded by a volume in which elastic stresses exist. These stresses can affect other dislocations in the vicinity and can influence separate atoms other than those of the basic lattice which may be present. As a result, a dislocation line may be considered as a path for diffusion, or a collector for solute atoms until some barrier is met and a so-called 'atmosphere' is developed around the dislocation. This is basically a concept which explains the hardening effect of one metal on another when dissolved in it by alloying to form a solid solution (as distinct from an alloy between two elements which may separate into two distinct phases).

Atoms on either side of a dislocation are oppositely in a state of tension or compression. This state of strain can be reduced by larger atoms (if available) collecting in the tension region and the smaller atoms (also if available) in the compression region. The local stress field in the vicinity becomes lowered by this collected atmosphere of other atoms, and consequently the dislocation becomes locked. To move it when locked a higher stress is required than in the absence of interaction with the atmosphere atoms.

The above mechanism of immobilizing dislocations is not the only way to prevent them from spreading. Dislocations will pile up at a grain boundary for instance in a polycrystalline structure. Plate 2(a) shows that slip bands are confined to the crystal grain in which they originate, and the initiation of these by dislocation in a single plane have been observed to form a pile-up in a manner shown in Plate 4. There is obviously an increasingly high stress towards the head of the pile-up. This may become sufficiently high to break down the barrier (e.g. grain boundary) if the tensile stress is sufficient to produce a crack. Alternatively, the intensified stress at the head of the pile-up may produce further slip on another plane or in the case of a point obstacle the dislocation may climb round it. A crude analogy to the effect of piling up against barriers such as grain boundaries is to visualize the different energies needed to tear a coarsely woven cloth of the same thread strength as distinct from that for a finely woven cloth. The higher yield stress obtained in fine grain structures can be visualized as arising from the greater number of barriers in the path of piled-up dislocations.

Cottrell[6] has postulated a further combination of dislocations which may operate in the body centred lattice structure, for example, in ferrite. A dislocation may move along the (101) plane in a crystal while another may move along the (10$\bar{1}$) plane which intersects. If the two move together and join, then a final dislocation results which is now stationary due to reaction, and is in effect equivalent to a minute crack which is only one interatomic distance thick. The interesting fact is that the (001) plane on which the dislocation has become stationary is that plane which forms the so-called cleavage surface apparent in a fracture occurring in a brittle fashion. There is an obvious possibility that such a crack may grow by further dislocations travelling over the {110} planes, and an interesting hypothesis for brittle behaviour is apparent since by such a mechanism we arrive at a condition which now enables a spread of the crack by the Griffith theory to take place.

The foregoing has provided an outline of the modern concepts of faults in both single and polycrystalline metals. Whereas the original Griffith crack theory was more easily visualized because of its association with larger magnitudes, the electron microscope has provided evidence of basic imperfections in the atomic lattice which, while not in themselves constituting discrete cracks may be the origin of minute microscopic cracks which can then grow under the applied stress so resulting in final failure. All bulk metals contain dislocations which are consequential on the change of state from liquid to solid. There is a lack of perfection in the formation of the lattice structure as the atoms become stationary. These dislocations are permanent unless heat and energy are applied to alter them. If heat energy is sufficient to cause recrystallization, those originally present are obliterated but are replaced by others on cooling down again. Cold work shifts them and adds to them by producing others. A fully annealed material is estimated to contain between 10^6 and 10^8 dislocation lines per square centimetre. Cold working the metal will multiply them by some 10^4 times. The only known exception to this state of affairs is provided by metallic 'whiskers' already mentioned. Their possession of near theoretical strengths indicates the almost complete absence of dislocations.

The Propagation Velocity of a Crack

The failure of a steel in a brittle manner implies that complete fracture takes place suddenly; there is no slow tearing. Hence the initial small crack leading to failure must lengthen and spread through the material at a high velocity.

Robertson[7] has made actual measurements of the velocities encountered. The test he used is described more fully in chapter 13, since it concerns the determination of a 'crack arrest temperature' for a given material. The stressed testpiece is struck by a bolt gun at the end which contains a purposely introduced notch, and by using a camera capable of photographing 4000 frames/ sec he found that while on one frame no crack was apparent the next frame showed a full-length crack. Hence the speed of crack propagation was some value in excess of 2000 ft/sec.

An improvement in this technique made use of an electronic timer, operated by the fracture as it lengthened, the growth of the fracture causing, in turn, the fracture of brittle strips of graphite-coated paper which acted as resistances and which were attached to the testpiece near the notch at 1 in. intervals by a very thin coat of cellulose varnish. The electronic counter was thereby triggered as the resistances themselves were successively fractured. Velocities of about 6000 ft/sec were recorded near the notch for stresses of 10 tons/in². These velocities fell to about 4000 ft/sec as the stress was reduced to 6 tons/in².

Such velocities emphasize the meaning of the term 'catastrophic failure'. The breaking in two of a large tanker such as the *World Concord* would occur therefore in a fraction of a second.

Previous to the practical determination of the velocity involved in the propagation of a crack, Mott[8] in 1948 made a theoretical study of the possible velocity assuming its propagation through an isotropic material.

In such a material the movement of an initiated crack releases elastic energy. This elastic energy is in turn balanced by (*a*) the kinetic energy accompanying the movement outwards of material on each side of the crack as the crack opens up, and (*b*) the surface energy of the newly formed surfaces of the crack itself. Mott evaluated this as:

$$v = Bv_0\left(1 - \frac{l}{L}\right),$$

PLATE 3

(a) Formation of sub-grain boundaries separate from the original grain boundary network. Three - dimensional network of dislocations within the sub - grains. × 40,000. Reduced by ⅓ on reproduction. Iron creep-tested to 50% elongation (near fracture) at 550° C under load of 3 tons/in². (K. F. Hale and D. McLean, *The Stress Sensitivity of Creep Structural Processes in Creep.* J.I.S.I. 1961.) (*Courtesy of Director N.P.L. and J.I.S.I.*)

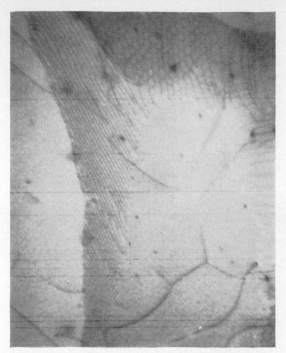

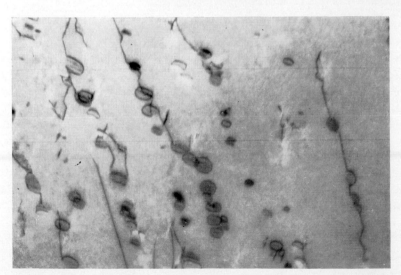

(b) Iron containing 1% Mn, 0·028% N₂ creep-tested 600 hr at 500° C and 7 tons/in² (plastic strain 1–2%). Shows precipitation of disc-shaped Mn-nitride on moving dislocations. × 80,000. Reduced by ⅓ on reproduction. (*Courtesy of Research Dept. Colvilles Ltd.*)

PLATE 4

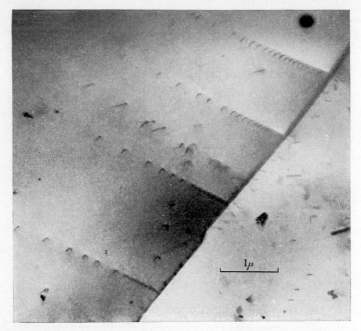

Piling up of dislocations against a grain boundary in stainless steel. × 17,500. M. J. Whelan, P. B. Hirsch, R. W. Horne and W. Bollman. *Proc. Roy. Soc.* (*Lond.*), **240** A (1957), 524; Cambridge University Press.

where $\qquad v_0 = \left(\dfrac{E}{\rho}\right)^{\frac{1}{2}} = $ velocity of sound in the material;

$\qquad\qquad\quad l = $ length of a Griffith crack;
$\qquad\qquad\quad L = $ actual length of the whole crack;
$\qquad\qquad\quad B = $ a constant;
$\qquad\qquad\quad E = $ Young's modulus for the material;
$\qquad\qquad\quad \rho = $ density of the material.

In the first equation, if the crack resulting from the propagation of a Griffith imperfection is very large, then the term l/L becomes extremely small and may be neglected so that in the limit $v = Bv_0$. The constant B has been evaluated by Roberts and Wells[9] and found to be approximately 0·38.

Hence $\qquad\qquad\qquad\qquad v = 0\cdot38v_0,$

or alternatively, $\qquad\qquad v = 0\cdot38 \left(\dfrac{E}{\rho}\right)^{\frac{1}{2}}.$

If we substitute Robertson's experimentally determined value of 6000 ft/sec in the above equation, then for steel the ratio v/v_0 is found to be 0·36 which agrees very well with the value for the constant B as evaluated by Roberts and Wells.

The Effect of Temperature on the Formation of Micro-cracks

The development of an increasing degree of brittleness as temperature is lowered is shown by the ordinary impact transition curve. While cracks of the Griffith type have not been found in unstressed metals, considerable evidence exists to show that micro-cracks can be formed under a stress which is just sufficient to produce a degree of plastic deformation. Moreover, the degree of micro-cracking encountered is temperature dependent. This leads to a link between the change-over from toughness to brittleness as the temperature is lowered.

Experimental work demonstrating the relationships between temperature yield stress, fracture stress, ductility and micro-crack formation has been carried out by Hahn, Owen, Averbach and Cohen[10]. Two steels were tested under tensile stresses at ambient and various lower temperatures down to $-200°$ C. By plotting the values obtained against the testing temperature the characteristics shown in Fig. 13 were obtained for fine- and coarse-grain structures. It is to be noted that the steel in Fig. 13(a) contains 0·21% C and therefore the structure contains ferrite + pearlite. In Fig. 13(b) the coarse-grain material is ferritic only, that is, it is substantially pure iron. The curve showing the increase in micro-cracks was obtained by counting the number of crystal grains which contained cracks and converting to a percentage value in a known size of field under the microscope.

D

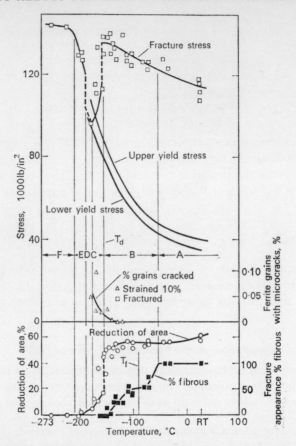

FIG. 13(*a*). Summary of tensile properties, fracture appearance, and micro-crack data for fine-grain (A.S.T.M. grain-size no. 7) steel containing 0·21% C. (Reprinted from *Fracture* by G. T. Hahn *et al.*[10]; by permission of The M.I.T. Press, Cambridge, Mass.)

In Fig. 13 the diagrams are divided into regions of decreasing temperature based upon characteristics of the curves and from a consideration of these the following statements can be made (Fig. 13(*a*)).

(1) At room temperature fracture produces the normal cup and cone appearance indicating considerable ductility. This is accompanied by a high value for the reduction of area.

(2) As the temperature is lowered the outer rim of the testpiece shows increasing signs of brittleness indicated by the presence of cleavage facets. An increase in tensile strength is apparent. This is accompanied by an increase in both the upper and lower yield stress values while there are also signs of the appearance of increasing numbers of micro-cracks.

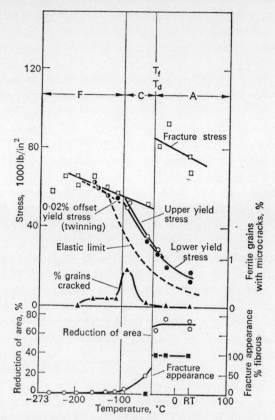

FIG. 13(b). Summary of tensile properties of very coarse-grained ferrite ($d = 0.409$ mm). (Reprinted from *Fracture* by G. T. Hahn *et al.*[10]; by permission of The M.I.T. Press, Cambridge, Mass.)

(3) At T_d there is a sudden change, indicated by a sharp drop in the fracture stress and the percent reduction of area. Also the area previously occupied by the fibrous portion of the fracture has fallen to zero. At this stage, however, the micro-cracks have not reached a maximum figure but they are increasing at a rapid rate.

(4) The micro-cracks now reach a maximum at a temperature which is lower than that at T_d. The fracture stress now falls to a minimum and indeed coincides with a value equal to that of the lower yield stress. When the number of micro-cracks are at a maximum the reduction of area is almost negligible.

(5) Subsequently, at still lower temperatures (region D) the lower yield stress continues to coincide with the fracture stress although both are now increasing as the temperature decreases further.

(6) After the region D completely brittle fracture occurs by cleavage since there is no distinctive yielding of the material.

(7) At the lowest temperatures fracture is found to occur by twinning.

In Fig. 13(b) there are certain differences apparent in the coarse-grain steel. For the coarse-grain material, the minimum fracture stress (which, it may be noted, occurs at an appreciably higher temperature than for the fine-grain steel) does not coincide with the yield stress and there is a considerably greater percentage reduction of area at this point. Also to be noted is the fact that at the minimum fracture stress the micro-cracks have not reached a peak value as they have in Fig. 13(a).

The two diagrams do correspond, however, at the point of the peak value for micro-cracks because for both steels at this point the yield stress and fracture stresses are coincident. It is to be noted in Fig. 13(b) also that micro-cracks at successively lower temperatures tend to lessen.

From both examples it is apparent that cracks which give rise to the brittle type of fracture are not necessarily inherent in a steel. If the material is deformed they can, and do, develop, so that brittle facture involves first plastic deformation to some degree, followed by the initiation of cracks and finally the propagation of these, resulting in failure. The significance of the different amounts of energy to initiate and to propagate a crack in various steels is discussed elsewhere.

Owen, in a discussion of this work on the two different steels, endeavours to identify the mechanism whereby the cleavage type of crack in Fig. 13(a) is nucleated, that is, where the fracture stress falls rapidly to meet the yield stress. He states that micro-cracks form first in the pearlite component of the steel in range B, and their rapid increase in range C and at still lower temperatures is also probably due to failure of the pearlite. Certainly the absence of pearlite in Fig. 13(b) appears to eliminate the range indicated by B in Fig. 13(a) covering those temperatures down to that at which the fracture stress drops very sharply. Above this temperature the coarse-grain ferritic material has a higher degree of ductility and shows a completely fibrous fracture, whereas the steel containing pearlite has a lower degree of ductility and considerable crystallinity is apparent in the fracture. Owen concludes, therefore, that the absence of pearlite reduces the tendency to form an internal crack of critical size (from which propagation may result) in the neck of the specimen. He further attempts to explain the superior notch toughness of high manganese steels on the basis of the behaviour of the modified form of pearlite, which they contain. In a high manganese steel the pearlite becomes much finer and the carbide component tends to spheroidize. Owen concludes that the tendency for micro-cracks to form in the range between room temperature and that at which the fracture stress suddenly falls, is decreased in consequence.

Some evidence for this is provided by one of the author's higher tensile steels described in chapter 9. This steel is essentially a high manganese steel, modified by an increased silicon content above that required to deoxidize completely and made with a fine grain by the addition of aluminium. When this steel is normalized an extremely fine form of pearlite is produced. This structure gives a remarkably good transition curve as determined by the Charpy test.

That the initial failure of pearlite in ordinary steels is responsible for the initiation of cleavage fracture in all cases cannot be firmly established without further work. A strict requirement for the purpose is that two sets of specimens of the same composition and grain-size, one with and one without pearlite, should be tested at progressively lower temperatures. Such a requirement can only be satisfied by applying two different heat-treatments to a single suitable composition. Air cooling from the normalizing temperature would give a ferrite-pearlite structure, while quenching from the same temperature to retain carbon in solution followed by tempering would result in the same austenitic grain-size. It is indeed known in practice that if a steel is subjected to these two heat-treatments, lower transition temperatures and greater resistance to brittle fracture are secured by the latter heat-treatment. The absence of pearlite as a separate entity in the steel is therefore desirable, a fact which offers some support to the concept that it is this component in which brittle fracture is initiated. The explanation is unsatisfactory, however, since quenching (and tempering) involves only a shift of the tough-brittle transition to some lower temperature. The change to a brittle condition may still occur and is not eliminated by the absence of pearlite.

Propagation of a Micro-crack

The concept of dislocations renders possible a mathematical treatment of their implications. Zener[11] first stated that dislocations may pile up and initiate a fracture by reason of the high stresses produced. The pile-up, under some critical stress value, results in the formation of a cavity by coalescence, and the work of Petch[12] and Cottrell[13] has resulted in the means of evaluating a stress required to propagate a micro-crack formed in this way when the grain diameter d is known.

Petch found by examination of experimental data on mild steel, a soft 'ingot iron' and spectrographically pure iron that the following formula could be applied:

$$\sigma_f = \sigma_i + Kd^{-\frac{1}{2}}, \tag{1}$$

where σ_f = stress to produce fracture (the cleavage strength);
σ_i = frictional stress resisting motion of the dislocations;
K = a coefficient of strength;
d = mean grain diameter.

Now the form of (1) is similar to that defining the relationship between yield stress and grain diameter, that is,

$$\sigma_o = \sigma_i + K_y d^{-\frac{1}{2}}, \tag{2}$$

where σ_o = the yield stress:
K_y = a constant.

Cottrell has defined the force necessary to propagate a micro-crack as

$$\sigma \simeq \frac{2S}{nb}, \tag{3}$$

where σ = stress to propagate;
S = surface energy of the crack;
n = number of dislocations;
b = Burger's vector.

The term b may be defined as the amount of displacement occurring between the two planes of atoms involved in the edge dislocation. As a vector quantity it defines both the magnitude of the slip and its direction.

Cottrell also showed that if an applied stress t is equal to $\frac{1}{2}\sigma$ and acts upon a slip plane L whose length is $\frac{1}{2}d$, then

$$nb \simeq \frac{(t - t_i)d}{E}, \tag{4}$$

where t_i = the frictional resistance to slip.

Now (2) the 'yield equation' can be expressed in terms of the applied shear stress thus

$$t_0 = t_i + k_y d^{-\frac{1}{2}}, \tag{5}$$

where t_0 = shear stress;
k_y = a constant.

Also (3) can be expressed in terms of the shear stress t_0 which is equal to $\frac{1}{2}\sigma$ as stated in (4).

Thus substituting $2t_0$ for σ in (3) we have

$$t_0 = \frac{S}{nb}$$

or $$S = nbt_0. \tag{6}$$

We can now substitute two values in (6):
(i) the value for nb from (4),
and (ii) the value for t_0 from (5).

This gives $$S = \frac{(t - t_i)d}{E} \times (t_i + k_y d^{-\frac{1}{2}})$$

or $$ES = dt_i(t - t_i) + k_y d^{-\frac{1}{2}}(t - t_i),$$

but since from (5) $t - t_i = k_y d^{-\frac{1}{2}}$,

then $$ES = dt_i k_y d^{-\frac{1}{2}} + k_y{}^2. \tag{7}$$

This equation is modified by the introduction of a coefficient β, i.e. ES becomes $ES\beta$, where β expresses the ratio of the maximum shear stress to the maximum normal stress which may not coincide. For torsion $\beta = 1$, for tension $\beta = \frac{1}{2}$, and for a region which is plastically constrained at the root of a notch $\beta = \frac{1}{3}$.

The equation therefore becomes

$$ES\beta = t_i d^{\frac{1}{2}} k_y + k_y^2. \tag{8}$$

This equation defines the equilibrium limit at which a crack will just propagate. If the term $ES\beta$ is greater than the right-hand value a crack can result from the piled-up dislocations but it does not propagate further. If, however, the right-hand term is greater than $ES\beta$ and the shear stress is equal to the yield stress, then the crack will continue and a cleavage fracture results. The equation also indicates that a change from a ductile to a brittle state will take place as the temperature decreases, since the yield stress approaches the shear stress under these conditions.

We can further modify (8) if we rearrange (5) thus

$$t_i = t_0 - k_y d^{-\frac{1}{2}}. \tag{9}$$

Substituting for t_i in (8) we have

$$ES\beta = t_0 k_y d^{\frac{1}{2}}. \tag{10}$$

Now at the point when the gliding dislocations coalesce into a crack the frictional resistance t_i becomes 0.

Hence at this point (4) becomes

$$nb \simeq \frac{td}{E}. \tag{11}$$

By substituting (11) in (3) we obtain

$$\sigma = \frac{2ES(\beta)}{td}. \tag{12}$$

Now $t = \frac{1}{2}\sigma$. Hence by substituting for t in (12) we get

$$\sigma \simeq 2\left(\frac{ES(\beta)}{d}\right)^{\frac{1}{2}}. \tag{13}$$

This expression gives the stress which will propagate a micro-crack.

In (7) and (8) the parameter k_y is extremely significant. Cottrell gives the value of $\frac{k_y}{E} \cdot cm^{\frac{1}{2}}$ as 0.4×10^{-4} for iron at room temperature, a value much higher than that for niobium which is 0.1×10^{-4}. It is known from experience that metals with lower values are less prone to brittle fracture. Also, as a metal is cooled the internal friction t_i increases, thus increasing the right-hand sides of (7) and (8). It is obviously desirable therefore, in order to avoid brittleness, to decrease the value of d in order to compensate. Steels intended for low-temperature service are therefore purposely made 'fine grain'. The cleavage strength of polycrystalline iron therefore depends on strength near the grain boundaries where dislocations can pile up, and on the grain-size.

The Transition from the Brittle to the Ductile State

Dislocation theory may be considered as a means of describing and accounting for possible atomic mechanisms. While, as in the previous section, the theory is capable of predicting changes of properties which can occur as temperature is lowered, actual experiments do not always indicate precise agreement. Petch states that because the region near the grain boundary is involved then composition can affect characteristics of the cleavage, yield and plastic strain because solute atoms tend to segregate in the vicinity of grain boundaries. The presence of very small percentages of impurities, for example, nitrogen, can therefore be significant. The presence of a discrete precipitate such as iron carbide in the pearlite, which can affect the stress concentration locally in a different way, obviously interferes with the conclusions.

In equation (8) whether one side exceeds the other depends, for example, on the increase in internal friction taking place as the temperature decreases —for some particular grain-size. Hence a sudden change should occur at a specific temperature—the *transition temperature*.

This is indeed true for substantially pure iron (see Figs. 3(a) and 3(b)). Commercial materials blur the perfect theory and even for compositions which are as nearly identical as is humanly possible, exact registration of their ductile–brittle characteristics will not occur. It is a fact that for commercial materials complete transition from ductile to brittle state takes place over an appreciable range of temperature—the *transition range*.

It must be remembered, therefore, that the fracture of one grain of ferrite by reason of piled-up dislocations implies the involvement of the ferrite only. Also, while the transition from ductile to brittle is a characteristic of the (b.c.c.) structure, the (f.c.c.) metals do not show this change. The increase in stress required to cause yielding or plastic flow increases very markedly in (b.c.c.) structures. Between room temperature and $-196°$ C, this increase may be some 3 to 8 times (see Fig. 13). For (f.c.c.) metals the change in yield stress is considerably less (about 2 times) over the same temperature range.

Davidenkov and Wittman[14] in 1937 proposed that a transition temperature could exist if temperature changes alter the resistance to fracture by shear and fracture by cleavage to different degrees. Essentially, this theory implies that above the transition temperature the fracture stress is well above the stress necessary to cause plastic flow. Conversely, below the transition temperature the fracture stress comes first. Decreasing temperature and increasing the strain rate are factors which raise the stress to cause plastic flow without raising the fracture stress. For mild steel the strain rate has a considerable effect on the yield stress. In an impact test this rate is enormously greater than that used in the ordinary tensile test. It can be suggested therefore, that in a notched-bar test, the rate of strain being so high, the yield stress is increased so as to coincide with the fracture or cleavage stress. This may be expressed schematically as in Fig. 14, where curve (a) indicates how the yield stress varies with temperature when a notch is present. This curve cuts the fracture or cleavage strength line (b) towards the higher end of the temperature scale at point P. Below this intersection there is brittleness, and

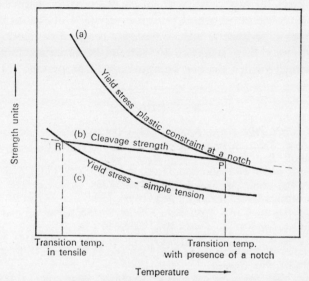

FIG. 14. Occurrence of 'transition temperature' when curve of flow stress intersects that of the cleavage strength (schematic). (After N. N. Davidenkov and F. Wittman[14].)

above, increasing ductility. The fracture strength line (b) is known to be less sensitive to temperature change. Curve (c) shows how the yield stress in simple tension and in the absence of a notch varies with temperature. This curve also cuts the fracture strength line (b) at point R to give a transition temperature considerably lower than that obtained when a notch is present.

It is to be noted that the intersection between (b) and (c) is more clearly coincident with a sharp drop in the reduction of area in Fig. 13(a) for a fine-grain steel than it is for a coarse-grain ferrite, Fig. 13(b), and occurs at a lower temperature. In the latter the sharp reduction in area occurs before the yield stress has reached the value of the fracture stress. We know, however, that generally the transition occurs over a temperature range in most materials and not at a specific temperature except in the case of very pure materials.

Such an explanation does not take into account the dislocation theory and its mathematics, but presents a much simplified view. It appears doubtful indeed, when the complexities and micro-variations which occur in materials for construction are taken into account, whether a completely satisfactory explanation can be arrived at. This state of affairs, while undesirable, does not interfere with or prevent the practical achievement of significant improvements in materials. While much of this improvement is gained through empiricism it is nevertheless effective and contributes to the sought-after technological advances. An interesting example is provided by the development of 9% Ni steel for use at temperatures down to −196° C. The development of this steel, the properties of which are described in chapter 12, was not founded on any theoretical considerations involving dislocations but resulted from numerous experimental melts covering a range of compositions. These compositions were then subjected to various heat-treatments to discover conditions which yielded the best combination of properties.

REFERENCES

1. A. A. Griffith. *Phil. Trans. R. Soc.*, **221** A (1920), 163.
2. C. E. Inglis. *Trans. Instn nav. Archit.*, **55,** pt. 1 (1913), 219.
3. W. Weibull. *Roy. Swed. Inst. Eng. Res.*, (1939), no. 151.
4. J. C. Fisher and J. H. Hollomon. *Trans. A.I.M.E.*, **171** (1947), 546.
5. W. S. Pellini. *A.S.T.M. Stand.*, 1954. Spec. Tech. publ. 158, 216.
6. A. H. Cottrell. *Trans. A.I.M.E.*, **212** (1958), 192.
7. T. S. Robertson. *J. Iron Steel Inst.*, **175,** pt. 4 (1953), 361.
8. N. F. Mott. *Engineering, Lond.*, **165** (1948), 16.
9. D. K. Roberts and A. A. Wells. *Engineering, Lond.*, **178** (1954), 820.
10. G. T. Hahn, W. S. Owen, B. L. Averbach and M. Cohen. *Weld. J.*, **38** (1959), 367-S (*Weld. Res. Suppl.*).
11. C. Zener. 'The Micro-mechanism of Fracture', *Fracturing of Metals*, Amer. Soc. Metals, Metals Park, Ohio, 1948.
12. N. J. Petch. *J. Iron Steel Inst.*, **174** (1953), 25.
13. A. H. Cottrell. *Dislocations and Plastic Flow in Crystals*. Oxford Univ. Press, New York, 1953.
14. N. N. Davidenkov and F. Wittman. *Phys. Tech. Inst. (U.S.S.R.)*, **4** (1937), 300.

CHAPTER 3

HEAT-TREATMENT OF STEELS: GENERAL PRINCIPLES

It is well known that many ferrous alloys undergo an increase in hardness if heated to a temperature above the Ac_3 point and then quenched in water or oil to remove the heat from the mass at a rapid rate. While water or oil—the latter being less severe—are the common media for industrial quenching there are various solutions (e.g. of 2% or 5% caustic soda)—or H_2 gas which, by virtue of their superior heat conductivity, are capable of exerting a still more rapid abstraction of heat from the heated mass and therefore have special applications.

A little thought will indicate that a requirement of any quenching medium to be effective is that its own volume must be very large in relation to the volume of the article to be quenched, otherwise the rate of abstraction of heat from the steel will be slowed down by the rapid rise in temperature of the quenching medium itself. This would result in failure to achieve the maximum hardness. In addition, liquid-quenching media are usually agitated or may even be renewed by continuous pumping of fresh solution through the quenching tank while the article is immersed in order to remove the vapour layers surrounding the article, thus ensuring a more efficient heat transfer.

Hardenability

Assuming these requirements for the quenching medium are satisfied let us examine the characteristics which the steel itself may possess after quenching. The maximum surface hardness which may be secured becomes a function of the composition of the steel and Fig. 15 shows approximately how this degree of hardness varies in the normalized condition with the carbon content only.

A steel containing 0·15 to 0·20% C can be hardened to a level of 400/450 D.P.N. In the normal hot-rolled condition, such a steel would possess a hardness of approximately 150 D.P.N. which corresponds to an ultimate tensile strength of 32 tons/in². For a hardness of 400/450 D.P.N. the tensile strength is 85/98 tons/in² and the author has actually obtained these tensile

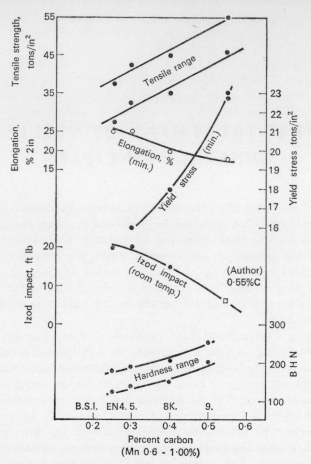

FIG. 15. Variation in properties with increasing carbon content for C–Mn steels in the normalized condition.

strengths by quenching ordinary mild steel plate up to $\frac{3}{4}$ in. thick in a 2% caustic soda solution after heating to 920° C for austenitizing.

The term surface hardness has so far been referred to and an obvious question is whether or not this surface hardness is a satisfactory measure or indication of the hardness throughout the thickness of the section. If in a thick forging or plate the hardness midway between two outside surfaces is not the same as that of the surfaces, then other mechanical properties, for example, tensile strength, cannot be the same and the steel is non-uniform with respect to these properties. In fact, it is established that different types of steel have differing depth hardenability characteristics and this is important when considering material for specific applications. Fig. 16 shows the manner in which hardness varies for SAE. 1045 and SAE. 6140 steels when rolled into bars of various diameters which have been austenitized and water quenched. The plain carbon steel 1045 is seen to diminish in hardness between surface and centre to a much greater extent than does the low-alloy steel 6140, in the smaller diameters. The converse holds true for the larger diameters, the fall in hardness, surface to centre being greater in these. Also the achievable maximum hardness at the surface falls off rapidly.

The low-alloy steel shows conversely less difference surface to centre in the smaller diameters and the hardness achieved, even in the largest diameter, is

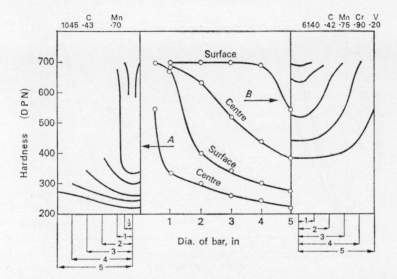

FIG. 16. Effect of size and alloy content on hardenability of a 0·4% C steel.

higher than that for steel 1045. This comparison shows the effect of chromium and molybdenum on hardenability—the steels having the same carbon content.

Hardenability as a term therefore implies the depth to which a steel may be hardened—or alternatively it may be defined as the sectional thickness of a mass which may be hardened under some given cooling conditions to a narrow range of hardness throughout. It does not refer to the maximum hardness which it is possible to obtain. Maximum hardness obtainable is governed mainly by the carbon content, but the depth to which hardening can be achieved for a given carbon content depends upon two separate factors, (i) the amounts of alloying elements other than carbon, and (ii) the grain-size of the austenitic solid solution produced by heating to above the Ac_3 point.

Effect of Alloying Elements on Hardenability

Systematic work on the quantitative effects of the various steelmaking elements on hardenability was carried out by Grossman[1] some twenty years ago. By using a pure Fe–C alloy and adding increasing quantities of a chosen element and then quenching the resultant products in a standard size, measurable changes in hardenability were produced. From the results, a multiplying factor could be evaluated by dividing the hardenability value for any content of the added element by the hardenability value of the pure base Fe–C alloy. A relationship between the content of the added element and multiplying

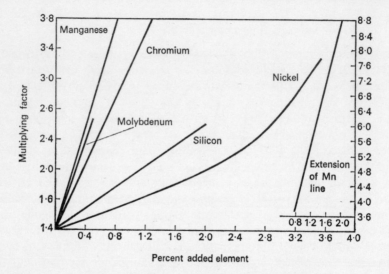

FIG. 17. Multiplying factors for hardenability.

factor was thereby established. The effect on hardenability of the most useful steelmaking elements yields a graph of the form shown in Fig. 17.

The fundamental usefulness of this work is that it assists in evolving combinations of added elements which will produce desired hardenability characteristics in low-alloy steels intended for quenching and tempering. In general the properties obtainable can be practically equivalent for different combinations of different quantities of the alloy additions. Opportunities therefore arise to develop cheaper alloy steels by substituting say a larger percentage of a cheaper element for a smaller amount of a very expensive metal—or vice versa depending on relative costs, or by adding small quantities of several elements which become additive in their effect. This procedure was carried out during the Second World War as a means of conserving the scarcer and more valuable alloying elements for more specific purposes. It is known that Germany substituted some of the expensive Ni-Cr-Mo-V steels by silico-manganese steels for tank armour-plate on this principle.

Grain-size

It has been emphasized that, in order to secure the maximum degree of notch toughness for any particular steel, the finest grain-size possible in the finished condition ready for use, is a requirement. Grain-size is a function of two factors (see Plate 12):

(1) The temperature above the upper critical temperature Ac_3 to which the steel has been heated and the time held at this temperature.
(2) The history of the steel with particular reference to the deoxidation procedure adopted during manufacture.

Considering (1) the solution of carbides above Ac_3 results in the formation of austenite, or the γ solid solution, the structure being characterized by polyhedral grains. If the temperature is much in excess of the actual Ac_3 temperature, these grains will enlarge by absorption of neighbouring grains, with both time and increasing temperature. As a result, on subsequent cooling in air (normalizing) or quenching, the structure will be composed of coarse grains and the alloy much less tough than one possessing a uniform fine-grain structure. This coarsening occurs in all single-phase metals and alloys when a certain temperature is exceeded. The danger of producing an overheated coarse-grain structure must be avoided in practice and is particularly to be guarded against in heat-treating some potentially fine-grain steels which usually display a tendency towards extremely rapid grain growth when a certain critical temperature above Ac_3 is reached. An example is provided by the plain C-Mn steels to which sufficient aluminium has been added to produce a fine-grain structure. Such steels have their superior notch toughness drastically reduced when heated in excess of 1050° C. It is to be noted that an inherently coarse-grain steel, that is, not treated with a 'grain refiner' during manufacture, coarsens steadily as temperature increases above Ac_3 but it does not achieve the same degree of coarseness as an inherently fine-grain steel when heated above its critical coarsening temperature. Practical heat-treatment for normalizing or quenching is therefore aimed at heating to as little in excess of the true Ac_3 temperature as possible, followed by the minimum time necessary to ensure uniform temperature throughout the mass. This time depends on the mass and thickness of the object and the relationship of these to the heat capacity of the furnace. It is important, however, particularly for low-alloy steels, to allow adequate time for the complete solution of the more complex carbides which may be present. The assessment of time is therefore a matter of experience. If, prior to quenching, a minimum time for complete austenitizing or solution of the carbides is not given, then the resulting hardness on quenching may be considerably below the maximum obtainable and properties in the tempered state may be inferior.

With reference to (2) all steels have an inherent grain-size which depends upon their method of manufacture. Grain-size is visually determinable by microscopic examination of a plane polished surface which has been suitably etched to reveal (in hypo-eutectoid steels which have been relatively slowly cooled, e.g. normalized) the ferrite-pearlite network. The grain-size of quenched steels may be revealed by etching with special reagents which show the different orientations in the martensitic structure. Knowing the magnification of the image (usually $\times 100$), the size of the grains can be compared with standard 'grain-size charts' and the grain-size so nominated. Conventional standards are those of the A.S.T.M.[2] in which the normal range of grain-sizes is covered by the numbers -3 to 10, the latter being the finest. Table 4 gives a relationship between A.S.T.M. grain-size numbers and areas.

Table 4. *Size relationships for A.S.T.M. grain-size numbers*

A.S.T.M. no.	No. of grains in 1 in² of image at 100 × 's
−3	0·06
−2	0·12
−1	0·25
0	0·5
1	1
2	2
3	4
4	8
5	16
6	32
7	64
8	128
9	256
10	512

Referring now to factor (2) the inherent grain-size of a steel is determined at the time it is made by the method of deoxidation employed. Normal methods of partial or complete deoxidation involving the addition of silicon only (viz. 0·025 to 0·25% approx.) produce coarse-grain steels, and the familiar semi-killed or silicon-killed mild steel has a grain-size of 2–3 on the A.S.T.M. scale in the hot-rolled condition. To produce a fine-grain steel special additions of aluminium, titanium, zirconium, or vanadium must be introduced. These grain-refining elements are used in small quantities only (i.e. up to say 0·1% each) and are in effect powerful deoxidizers which provide minute particles for initiating crystallization. At the same time they possess an ability to combine with N_2 also. A grain refiner of more recent introduction is niobium—now added to B.S. 968 steel to the extent of 0·025/0·065%. This steel, although 'balanced' (i.e. it is not completely killed with silicon), is thereby amenable to grain refinement by normalizing and the effect is discussed in more detail elsewhere.

As a result of such additions the grain-size usually becomes no. 6–8 on the A.S.T.M. scale. This is nominated as a fine-grain steel. Practical methods for achieving this degree of inherent fineness are relatively simple in that for steels leaving the furnace at 0·1% C or less some 3 to 5 lb of aluminium per ton of steel are added to the ladle along with other required alloys. Aluminium may sometimes be added to the mould while teeming, in order to secure the same result, although this requires caution since in a large mould in which the metal surface may rise more slowly, films of Al_2O_3 may cause laps at the ingot surface and corners where the metal is relatively stagnant. It is not wise to use mould additions for ingots larger than about 7 tons, otherwise 'dirty' steel may result. Alsimin (an alloy containing Al and Si) can also be used for grain refining in the mould. The ferro-alloys of zirconium, titanium or niobium should not be added to the mould since these have too high a melting point to be uniformly and satisfactorily dissolved and distributed.

Quantities of these refiners necessary have been determined empirically in practice. It is a general rule that to achieve the same final effect, the nearer the liquid steel is to solidification the smaller the quantity that is required. Grain refining in the furnace requires larger additions of the agent than when refining is done in the ladle. The smallest amount of the agent is required when the refining is carried out in the mould during teeming, but at the same time greater care is needed to secure homogeneity. It is also a general rule that the lower the carbon level of the liquid steel at tapping (i.e. the more highly oxidized is the steel) then the greater the amount of grain refiner necessary.

It is now customary to produce fine-grain steels as a specification requirement. Fortunately in practice only two grades on the A.S.T.M. scale are required in the majority of cases, for example grain-size no. 2–4 or grain-size no. 6–8. Intermediate grain-sizes are not often requested and are difficult to control and achieve. It is the fine-grain steels which are more important in this book.

The fact that a grain-refined steel suddenly coarsens at a particular temperature in the austenitic range suggests that the particles of Al_2O_3 or AlN (or both) act as obstructions to the movement of grain boundaries until grain growth reaches a critical speed in areas free from obstructions. Thorium oxide particles act similarly in the heat-treatment of tungsten metal. These particles are by no means of the normal inclusion size encountered in steel.

E

Inclusions in the steel are present as a result of other deoxidizing and alloying additions and it appears, if the 'obstruction' theory is correct, that the particles which matter are practically colloidal in their dimensions. The development of a small inherent grain-size by Al additions to steel constitutes an example of a practical achievement without a complete knowledge of the full mechanism responsible.

Effect of Grain-size on Steels

The importance of grain-size is made clear by the following effects:

(1) A coarse-grain steel possesses a greater depth hardenability than a fine-grain steel. From the point of view of uniformity of properties in fully heat-treated steels this may be an advantage because it becomes easier to obtain a greater uniformity of properties throughout the thickness. Fine-grain steels are generally less depth hardenable—hence the thickness or mass (which may also prejudice the quenching efficiency) may determine whether such steels can be used for a specific application.

(2) A fine-grain steel is definitely tougher and more resistant to impact than a coarse-grain steel of otherwise similar composition. The development of notch tough steels suitable for low-temperature use over the past 10–15 years has almost entirely depended upon grain refinement as a basis—improved toughness being secured by normalizing after hot rolling to refine the grain-size to the greatest extent possible, or by producing fully-killed steels to which aluminium or other grain-refining agents have been added and normalizing these steels additionally.

These two principal characteristics (1) and (2) above, become incompatible under certain circumstances of mass or thickness, the fine grain preventing uniformity of mechanical properties such as tensile strength throughout thickness of the steel if quenched and tempered in thick sections but a greater degree of resistance to impact particularly in the outer layers. The coarse-grain steels can under similar circumstances give greater uniformity but inferior toughness. It is for this reason, amongst others, that in certain specifications (e.g. B.S. 1501, etc., and B.S. 970, the EN series of steels) for any range of composition there are limiting thicknesses (ruling cross-sections) beyond which the stated properties are not guaranteed.

In such circumstances, therefore, we must turn to other compositions to satisfy both toughness and uniformity of other properties. If a fine-grain steel of maximum toughness is required then it becomes possible to secure a considerable increase in tensile strength by the introduction of elements on the basis of Fig. 18. It becomes apparent therefore why some of the modern low-alloy steels are so complex in composition.

There are certain other concomitant effects due to grain-size. Fine-grain

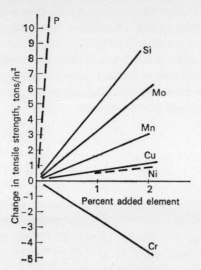

FIG. 18. Effect of various elements, when in solid solution in ferrite, on tensile strength. (Pickering and Gladman[11].)

steels are usually considered to distort less on quenching, but this is relative only in that shape also exercises an influence. They are generally somewhat more resistant to the development of quenching cracks. The reason for this can be appreciated. Because the depth hardenability is less than that of a coarse-grain steel of the same composition, the stresses produced internally during the quench are 'let down' through the thickness to a greater extent than occurs in a steel which hardens through more uniformly to the centre.

A distinct advantage of the fine-grain steels is the greater resistance to 'ageing' effects which they possess. This is dealt with subsequently.

Quenching and Tempering of Steels

The solid solution of carbon in iron (or iron containing elements such as nickel or copper, which in themselves are present in solution) is achieved by heating above the Ac_3 critical temperature and results in the production of austenite which forms polyhedral grains at the elevated temperature. This constituent is not retained as such in plain carbon or low-alloy steels by normal quenching. The alloy content has to be very high in order to render austenite sufficiently stable for it to be present at ordinary temperatures after quenching, for example, as in the 'austenitic' stainless steels and Hadfield's 13% Mn steel. All practical and normal rates of heat abstraction during quenching (with the exception of the true austenitic steels) permit a transformation of the austenite to martensite. Martensite is the hardest and least tough of all the microstructural forms which can be secured in steel by heat-treatment. The maximum hardness which it can attain is principally a function of the carbon content. Plate 5(a) illustrates a typical martensitic structure for a steel containing 0·70% C.

From the point of view of notch toughness, therefore, a totally martensitic steel is useless and although possessing a maximum static strength by virtue of its hardness such steels obtained by quenching are not applied where shock under varying loads is encountered.

The suitable modification of this martensitic structure constitutes the reason for tempering by re-heating to some temperature lower than the quenching temperature. Such a treatment results in a partial or complete transformation of the structure to a degree, which is time and temperature dependent. This transformation effects a degree of softening which also improves toughness. Isothermal transformation diagrams describing the microstructural changes occurring on tempering have now been worked out for a large range of standard steels[3]. These have been evolved by quenching small metallographic samples from the austenitic range in liquid baths held at different constant temperatures and retaining the samples in these baths for different times. Removal at varying time-intervals followed by quenching and microscopic examination then shows how the structure transforms. Similarly on suitably larger specimens, mechanical properties associated with these transformed structures have been ascertained.

As an example of the transformations which occur in a simple steel containing 0·7% C approximately we have, during quenching, the formation of hard martensite from the solid solution of carbon in iron, at temperatures below 230° C (the M_s point). This is the least time dependent of all the modified structures which can be secured. The same steel can, however, transform to bainite over the temperature range 540–230° C. This bainite structure is still acicular (see Plate 5(b)) but tends to etch darker than martensite. Both the martensite and bainite are in a metastable and highly stressed condition due to the quench, and are hard and brittle. Tempering between 540° C and below the Ac_1 point (ca. 700° C) results in forms in which stresses are relaxed and carbides are emerging from solution. This results in a degree of softening depending on time at the tempering temperature with the development of ductility and toughness. It is found that tempered martensite has the best combination of strength and toughness. Bainite may be designated as 'upper' or 'lower' bainite, depending on the velocity of the quench and the temperature at which the transformation from austenite took place— this temperature varying for different steels. Bainite formed in the upper region of the range 540–230° C is designated 'upper bainite'. When tempered this form gives a somewhat inferior toughness to that obtainable from 'lower bainite' formed towards the lower end of the 540–230° C range.

When transformed on cooling between 700° and 540° C the original solid solution breaks down completely to yield a pearlite structure in which the carbides are now precipitated as lamellar pearlite. Considerable structural modifications are possible within this temperature range as in the case of the bainitic transformation range. When tempering is carried out at the low-temperature end the pearlitic lamellae are extremely fine and hardness is greater. As the tempering temperature increases coarsening takes

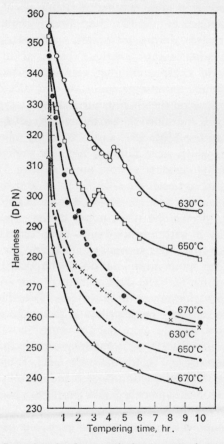

FIG. 19. Secondary hardness peaks in a tempered vanadium steel.

place, resulting in some softening. Holding for extended times at the higher end of the range results in the disintegration of the carbide lamellae which 'ball up' and form spheroids of carbide. By tempering to just below 700° C therefore, the steel becomes fully tempered and exhibits a degree of softness and toughness much greater than that possessed by the material when produced by hot working (forging or rolling) and followed by normal air cooling.

While the foregoing constitutes a brief survey of the order of events in tempering at different temperatures the temperature ranges and tempering times associated with characteristic microstructures differ in detail for steels of different compositions and reference to the appropriate isothermal diagrams[3] for steels becomes necessary. Alternatively for a particular steel composition a painstaking investigation, in which test coupons are variously treated and their physical properties actually ascertained, may be carried out for the purpose of securing some required optimum set of properties.

In addition to the effects of microstructure already dealt with, other effects may manifest themselves during tempering—particularly with regard to specific properties. An important example of this occurs in the production of secondary hardness in steels containing complex carbides. Vanadium (a grain refiner), chromium and molybdenum are examples of elements which produce a peak hardness on the cooling curve during tempering.

Fig. 19 illustrates this and shows the hardness curves of specimens tempered at different temperatures, 630°, 650° and 670° C for different times (up to 10 hr) for two steels which were designed for high strength coupled with a high degree of notch toughness at low temperatures. The two steels are practically identical in composition except for the absence of vanadium in steel B. The three lower curves were obtained from this steel. Steel A, which contained 0·12% V, yielded the three upper curves. The humps on these indicating an increase in hardness are due to the precipitation of vanadium carbide and are distinctive. This secondary hardening occurs after a shorter time (2 hr) at the higher temperature, but does not appear until after 4 hr at a lower temperature of 630° C. The development of this secondary hardness, therefore, delays the achievement of maximum softening with respect to tempering time. The steel may be described as temper resistant.

From Fig. 19 it will also be seen that to secure the same hardness (and tensile strength) in both steels the vanadium steel requires tempering at 670° C for 5 hr as against 640° C for the other steel. Table 5 gives details of the two steels which were production casts made for rolling into 3 in. thick plates to be supplied in the quenched and tempered condition.

Table 5. *Two low-alloy plate steels for quenching and tempering*

Steel	C	Mn	Si	Ni	Cr	Mo	V	S	P
A	0·175	0·97	0·23	1·82	0·80	0·52	0·12	0·018	0·015
B	0·19	0·95	0·11	1·90	1·04	0·52	0·02	0·034	0·024

Other Forms of Tempering

Modifications of the simple quenching procedure followed by tempering by re-heating and subsequent cooling have been developed in order to achieve specific characteristics. The following procedures briefly described are not as yet applied to large repetition masses such as plates. They are usually confined to costly 'one off' forgings, small tools, and dies where maximum shock resistance in service is of importance.

Martempering

During the quenching operation large temperature gradients exist at any instant within the mass and consequently residual stresses are very high. If therefore instead of quenching down to room temperature the article is quenched in a molten salt bath whose temperature is just above the temperature at which martensite forms—say 230/240° C—and allowed to attain this temperature throughout, then subsequent removal followed by air cooling produces a martensitic structure in which the internal stresses are much lower. A tempering operation may then be applied by re-heating to a certain temperature which will modify the martensite to give requisite toughness and strength and a much-reduced risk of distortion or cracking.

Austempering

For some applications, when reasonable toughness coupled with high strength is required, a tempered lower bainite is to be preferred. This can be achieved by 'austempering', which, like martempering, is best achieved by quenching the chosen steel in a molten salt bath to the temperature at which the lower bainite structure is known to be stable. The steel is then held at this temperature for a generous length of time to ensure that all micro-areas are completely transformed. The operation is then completed either by quenching or air cooling to room temperature. A further tempering may be given subsequently to lower the hardness and strength still further to a required level.

While the austempering operation yields a combination of exceptional toughness with strength, it is expensive and time consuming, which precludes its use on economic grounds except for very special products, usually of small mass. Small masses are advantageous in that the times required to raise (or lower) the temperatures to the required levels are short. The operation may be applied to products such as strip or wire which can be processed continuously by moving through an austenitizing furnace followed by a quenching bath at the correct temperature and then passing through a second furnace for austempering—the emerging product being finally coiled.

Temper Brittleness

The quenching operation which changes the austenite to martensite confers the maximum hardness on the steel—the level of this hardness depending principally on the carbon content. This maximum hardness is accompanied by the minimum ductility and toughness. Hence the necessity for tempering which reduces the hardness (and hence the tensile strength) but which also toughens.

Unfortunately the toughening process is not smoothly progressive over the whole range of temperature down to room temperature. Certain steels if held within, or are slowly cooled from, say 680° C through a particular range of temperature below, develop an increased degree of brittleness known as temper brittleness. This is shown very markedly by notched-bar impact test results for steels so treated and Fig. 20, which gives results for a 9% Ni steel,

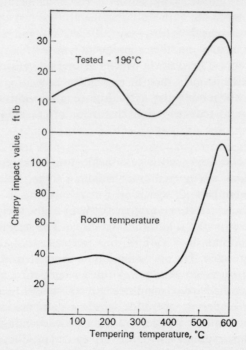

FIG. 20. Trough in impact curve. Temper brittleness in 9% Ni steel. (After Hardwick[12].)

shows the characteristic form of impact strength curve obtained at the lower end of the tempering range. The low impact strength trough is not located at precisely the same temperature for all steels but generally occurs between 230° and 330° C. While it is possible, therefore, by tempering at such low temperatures to secure a desired high tensile strength from a particular steel, in practice this would not be done. To secure a required high tensile strength a different steel necessitating tempering at a higher temperature above this range would be chosen. It is also possible for certain alloy steels to become brittle if slowly cooled from about 540° C when tempering after quenching. Provided it is physically possible, it is always preferable to cool rapidly by quenching from the tempering temperature as a means of avoiding temper brittleness. Plain carbon steels containing between 1% and 2% Mn, certain chromium steels containing 0·75% Cr or over, certain nickel-chromium steels and 3–5% Ni steels, exhibit temper brittleness while a high phosphorus content also emphasizes the feature. An element which is entirely beneficial by reducing this form of brittleness is molybdenum, and for this reason chromium steels are usually supplemented by an addition of molybdenum (as little as 0·25% is effective). Generally, however, the higher the alloy content of the steel the greater is the amount of molybdenum required to counteract this brittleness.

Generally, in production tempering, the critical brittle range is passed through fairly quickly—both in heating up and cooling down afterwards during which the steel is not subjected to severe stressing. There are service conditions however which can accelerate the development of temper brittleness. The author has encountered its occurrence in bolts for high-pressure steampipe flanges, and it is fortunate that all bolts do not fail simultaneously. In service the bolts are highly stressed and failure can arise when a change in temperature occurs at a plant shutdown. Toughness may be perfectly satisfactory at operating temperatures but brittleness develops on cooling with consequent fracture under certain conditions of stress. Room temperature testing reveals the existence of brittleness.

The mechanism of the development of temper brittleness is not completely explained. The fracture is usually intergranular, which suggests a grain boundary weakness, and although no films or precipitates have been detected in embrittled steels under stressed conditions a general assumption is that a segregation of impurities to the grain boundaries does take place. It seems probable that N_2 enters into the mechanism and the brittleness which may be associated with pipe fastenings is also associated with the notches at the base of screw threads. Ordinary static tensile tests, that is, without the presence of notches may not disclose any change in this property. It is obvious that heat-treated bolts for high-pressure systems, particularly for service at elevated temperatures, must be carefully chosen with respect to composition and heat-treatment and they invariably incorporate molybdenum and/or vanadium as counteracting agents.

Blue Brittleness

An analogous phenomenon to temper brittleness is blue brittleness, the term being derived from the fact that the temperature range in which reduced ductility and brittleness occurs is that in which blueing of a polished ferrous surface due to an oxide film occurs on heating, that is, between 150° and 260° C. This form of brittleness differs from temper brittleness in that within the blue brittle range of temperature the tensile strength increases and ductility decreases. It is produced by the existence of stresses within the temperature range, and the ageing effect or degree of change in properties which follows from the resultant strain and temperature conditions can be time-dependent. Plastic deformation at room temperature followed by heating to within the blue brittle range results in a marked decrease in notch toughness. The rate at which a steel will strain age increases in this temperature range and this suggests that blue brittleness is an accelerated form of strain ageing.

Strain-ageing Embrittlement

There are various practical consequences in many fields of the behaviour known as strain ageing. Strain-ageing embrittlement can occur, even at room temperatures, after prolonged times and an example of this occurs in low-carbon rimming steels which are used for sheet and strip intended for deep stamping and drawing. Often, such sheet is given a final 'skin' or temper pass in the rolling mill, and this very slight deformation purposely applied to achieve an accurate final gauge results in a greater hardness and loss of ductility which increases with time. Unless finished stampings and pressings are produced within a certain time after the rolled sheet is produced therefore, rejects may result due to fractures and stretcher strain markings which arise from the brittleness developed. Ordinary rimming steel sheets intended for deep drawing operations are used within a short time-interval after final rolling to avoid this.

A further practical example is provided by rimming steel strip used for the production of automobile wheel rims. Strip of suitable width is cold rolled to produce the trough-like cross-section into which the tyre fits. At the same time the rolled section is coiled into a helix which is then cut at intervals to give circumferential lengths which result in wheel rims when the two ends are flash welded. This rim blank is then trued to size by slightly stretching, by means of an expanding die. While this cold working increases the inherent strength and rigidity of the wheel rim, some risk is implied if the steel is very susceptible to strain ageing. Brittleness may develop to a degree sufficient to cause the rim to crack in its more highly stressed parts. These cracks may occur at the sharpest bends of the section shortly after manufacture. Manufacturers of automobile wheels are therefore extremely careful in their selection of steel for this purpose and failure in actual service is extremely rare. Comparatively simple tests in the environment of everyday usage of one type of steel, for example, rimming, serve to differentiate grades within that type which while nominally identical with respect to composition may respond very differently to the development of blue brittleness by heat-treatment or by strain ageing. The following simple experiments show this.

Two coils of hot-rolled rimmed steel strip $8\frac{5}{8}$ in. wide × 0·128 in. thick, each from a different cast, were examined relative to each other by machining from each coil sub-standard Charpy testpieces 10 mm × 55 mm × 0·128 in. thick. The 55 mm dimension was transverse to the direction of rolling.

Specimens from strip A in groups of three were heated to predetermined temperatures for 15 min., cooled in air and then tested in a modified Charpy impact machine. Testpieces were placed on the anvil blocks so that they were struck by the knife edge of the pendulum on the 10 mm dimension. The

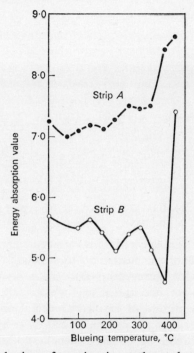

FIG. 21. Impact behaviour of two rimming steels tested at room temperature.

specimens were therefore suddenly bent by the impact to a constant angle determined by the distance between the anvil blocks. Relative energy absorption values for bending through a definite angle were obtained. A second version of the test conducted on strips A and B was to introduce a Charpy V-notch at the centre of one edge of each specimen of another series, these specimens being in effect Charpy sub-standard testpieces. The results obtained are shown in Table 6 and Fig. 21. It is seen that strip B has much lower energy absorption values than strip A and there is a marked drop in the value for strip B at 380° C. This result was confirmed by further tests. It is seen from Table 6 that results for notched and unnotched specimens from strip A

Table 6. *Relative impact values of two rimming steels, showing different brittleness characteristics*

Type of specimen	As rolled	Heated to −°C for 15 min. and air cooled									
	20	60	100	140	180	220	260	300	340	380	420
Strip *A* Unnotched	7·2	7·2	7·3	7·5	7·2	7·6	7·9	7·8	8·1	8·1	8·3
Strip *A* Notched	7·2	7·0	7·1	7·2	7·1	7·3	7·5	7·5	7·5	8·4	8·6
Strip *B* Notched	5·7	—	5·5	5·6	5·4	5·1	5·4	5·5	5·1	4·7*	7·4

* This test was repeated confirming the result shown.
NOTE: Numerical values are arbitrary and relative only as a result of modification of the impact machine.

do not differ from each other significantly, but energy absorption differences between *A* and *B* are quite significant and the extremely low value for strip *B* obtained after heating to 380° C is to be noted. Carbon, manganese and sulphur values in these two coils from separate casts of steel were nominally identical. Further investigation revealed the following analytical differences:

Strip *A* N_2 0·0045%   As 0·068%   P 0·024%
Strip *B* N_2 0·0065%   As 0·135%   P 0·044%

The development of brittleness in rimming steels can be due to the presence of residual elements and it is customary to stipulate that these be low for satisfactory performance during deep drawing or stamping operations. It is known that nitrides are precipitated over the temperature range concerned and while a complete picture of the mechanism is not established on any quantitative basis other elements such as oxygen, arsenic and phosphorus contribute to the effect. High N_2 contents in steel have been associated with the development of brittleness since the early days of Bessemer steelmaking.

From the foregoing section it will be noted that rimming steel has been used as an example of embrittlement produced by heating to within a critical range of comparatively low temperatures. It has also been stated that the effect is a form of accelerated strain ageing. Other steels show this behaviour to a less marked degree. It is well known that the more completely a steel is deoxidized when made then the less is the deterioration in impact values under 'blue brittle' conditions and the less marked are the strain-ageing effects. Hence a semi-killed or balanced steel is somewhat superior to a rimming steel and the least susceptible of all is a fully silicon-killed steel which has been grain refined by the addition of aluminium or other suitable elements such as vanadium, titanium or niobium.

The nearest approach therefore to a non-ageing steel is the latter and the effect is attributed to the combination of the N_2 with aluminium to form AlN, that is, the removal of interstitial N_2 from the iron lattice to form a stable compound. The phenomenon is characterized by causing successive yielding in a tensile test. A plain carbon steel when tested before ageing displays a yield point as the load increases and permanent deformation takes place. If, when the yield stress is exceeded, the load is removed before fracture and the specimen is then aged at a certain temperature, the interstitial atoms present, for example N_2, diffuse towards dislocations in the structure much quicker at the ageing temperature than occurs during the ordinary tensile test. As a result, locking of the dislocations takes place and on subsequent retesting a new higher yield stress results.

Ageing, and the development of a higher yield stress value results in an increase in brittleness, and since conditions in service may sometimes result in ageing, a test for the susceptibility of a particular steel may be mandatory in some specifications. An example of the effect of ageing on impact strength is given in Table 17.

The precipitates referred to in connection with ageing embrittlement are not visible under the optical microscope which is limited to about 2000 magnifications. The electron microscope, capable of magnifications of 20,000 to 200,000, has of recent years assisted considerably in the elucidation of some of the principles underlying the changes of properties with differing heat-treatments and conditions of deformation.

Quench Ageing

An elegant investigation into the structure of quench-aged alloys of Fe–C and Fe–N has been conducted by Hale and McLean[4]. Quench ageing differs from strain ageing in that it is a type of true precipitation hardening which occurs on quenching a low-carbon steel from about 700° C. This is the temperature of maximum solubility of carbon and N_2 in ferrite. Using binary alloys of extreme purity (a) 0·05% C + 0·0005% N_2 + Fe, and (b) 0·004% C + 0·01% N_2 + Fe, specimens were heated to 690° C for (a) and 550° C for (b) and quenched in water. They were then aged at 20° C and 100° C for periods up to 27 months. Electron microscope examination revealed that carbon in (a) precipitates in the form of minute platelets of ε-iron carbide ($Fe_{2\cdot4}C$) and nitrogen mainly as platelets of α-$Fe_{16}N_3$. The size of these precipitates was up to 5000 Å across and only 40 Å thick, and they were found to precipitate at dislocations in the matrix. Evidence was found that the α-nitride was a weaker barrier to slip than the ε-iron carbide. This would be expected since the α-nitride is practically identical in crystalline form with the iron matrix. The precipitates were also found to occur along the {100} cleavage planes and while they might be expected to induce brittleness thereby as a result of their forcing-apart action, the embrittling effect is actually attributed to the increase in yield strength of the material since it had been proved previously that single crystals of iron in the aged condition do not break at any less stress along cleavage planes as a result of precipitation effects.

Generally the tensile strength of low-carbon steels shows a peak at about 200° C as a result of strain ageing during the actual test. If the N_2 in the steel is fixed by combination with aluminium, no peak occurs. This constitutes a sensitive test for the presence of N_2 dissolved in the ferrite.

General Comments on Ageing Phenomena

It is possible to generalize with respect to elements that give rise to ageing effects in steels and ferrous alloys. If the solubility of an element in ferrite increases appreciably as the temperature rises to the Ac_1 point, then at room temperature or a sub-zero temperature it is possible to secure by heat-treatment (sometimes coupled with stress or actual deformation), a precipitation of the element in some form which exercises the observed effect on mechanical properties. A qualification is that there must be more of the element present than is indeed soluble at room temperature. Consequently certain elements associated with steel are ruled out as a cause of ageing. Manganese has a much higher solubility in ferrite than the amounts normally used in steels. Similarly, phosphorus and sulphur are never present in the steel to the extent of their maximum solubilities at room temperature, hence they do not of themselves give rise to ageing effects.

Carbon and N_2 can be present in excess of their room temperature solubilities in ferrite and therefore as shown by Hale and McLean do give rise to ageing effects.

Manganese and silicon can enter indirectly into the ageing mechanism if they form compounds which are subject to the above solubility qualifications. It is postulated for this reason that MnS does contribute slightly to ageing because it has a small solubility in ferrite, while Arrowsmith[5] has recently shown that silicon nitride is responsible for some deterioration in the mechanical properties of a silicon-killed steel when stress-relieved at 590/600° C.

Other elements of importance in connection with heat-treatment (in addition to aluminium) are titanium, vanadium and niobium. All these elements added to steels in relatively small quantities (viz. 0·03/0·12%) exercise powerful grain-refining effects and therefore develop the superior notch toughness associated with fine-grain steels when correctly normalized. While the two former like aluminium are extremely powerful deoxidizers as indicated by the high free energies of formation of their oxides, all three possess the ability to form stable nitrides (and carbides with the exception of aluminium). Hence their use in the production of so-called non-ageing steels.

For this reason vanadium can be added to rimming steels to achieve non-ageing characteristics. In very low carbon steels containing only 0·03/0·06% C titanium can prevent ageing effects by 'fixing' carbon as well as nitrogen, if present in a sufficient quantity. For this purpose the titanium content must be at least 4·5 times that of the carbon content.

Another alloying element which has a solubility in ferrite at elevated temperatures in excess of its solubility at room temperatures is copper. At room temperature the solubility is 0·35% Cu. Hence, if present in excess of this amount precipitation effects can be secured. It is interesting to record these effects on the hardness and notch ductility of a steel produced by the author for use in the construction of reactor spheres for the generation of nuclear power. The early reactor vessels at Calder Hall and Chapel Cross were relatively small and fabricated from 2 in. thick plate made from a low-carbon high-manganese fully silicon-killed and grain-refined steel which would now be classified as B.S. 2762–ND IV grade. Subsequent reactors required 3 in. and 4 in. thick plates of larger sizes and in order to compensate for the usually poorer notch toughness encountered in thicker material it was decided to introduce copper and a small quantity of molybdenum (approx. 0·25%), the latter being added to improve resistance to creep at elevated temperatures. Small additions of copper are generally acknowledged to improve tensile strength and yield stress values, and copper-steels are much used in the U.S.A., where most proprietary high-strength structural steels contain 0·20/0·60% while several specify 1·0% or more. The knowledge however that copper can produce precipitation hardening raised doubts as to the stability of properties of large pressure vessels held at elevated temperatures over a period of years, and special importance was attached to the possible deterioration in toughness. Extended tests, up to 10,000 hr duration, in which samples were held at constant temperatures between 350° and 450° C inclusive, were carried out, hardness measurements being made at suitable intervals. The samples were cut from 3 in. thick plates of the following composition (all percentages):

C	Mn	Si	Mo	Cu	Al (sol.)	Al (insol.)
0·12	1·08	0·08	0·26	0·43	0·04	0·01

N_2	S	P	Cr	Ni	Sn
0·004	0·044	0·026	0·11	0·08	0·013

The steel was fully killed and grain refined (A.S.T.M. grain-size 6–8). The level of N_2 is typical of the open-hearth furnace product. The small amounts of nickel, chromium and tin are 'residuals' arising from the scrap used in the change. The plates were normalized at 910/920° C and samples were stress relieved at 600° C for $2\frac{1}{2}$ hr followed by slow cooling in the furnace.

Changes in hardness resulting from time at different temperatures are shown in Fig. 22. From an initial 130 D.P.N. corresponding to a tensile strength of 28 tons/in^2, 168/170 D.P.N. is reached after 3000 hr approx. at 375° C. At the higher temperatures of 425/450° C the peak hardness reached is lower—155/160 D.P.N., but this hardening is attained in under 1000 hr. In the latter temperature range softening subsequently occurs with a return to near the original hardness.

The highest hardness achieved is equivalent to 34 tons/in^2 tensile strength. At the lowest temperature the initiation of hardening is protracted and contrary to the others is apparently still increasing after 5000 hr approx.

The effects of ageing on toughness are shown in Table 7. There is an appreciable deterioration in notch toughness as measured by the Izod test at room temperature in most specimens, particularly those held at 400° C. The

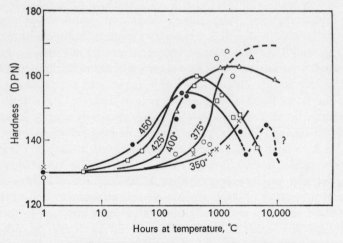

FIG. 22. Precipitation hardening in a Cu–Mo steel with time.

maximum decrease in toughness coincides in general with the highest hardness values and is evidenced by the appearance of some crystallinity in the fracture. The important point, however, is that the decrease in toughness (even after one year at an elevated temperature) was not as serious as might result from other causes and it was concluded by the present author, therefore, that the precipitation effects arising from the presence of copper in this steel are not prohibitively harmful and must be weighed against other advantages to be gained from the steel, such as a higher yield stress and improved resistance to creep owing to the presence of molybdenum. Chemical examination of the heat-treated specimens revealed that no precipitated metallic copper or other constituent could be isolated which might be associated with age hardening in the temperature range of 350/450° C. This result suggests that the room temperature solubility of copper is greater than 0·35% previously stated.

In considering results of this type the conditions of testing must be borne in mind. Deterioration was indicated by room temperature tests after heat-treatment has been applied. This does not necessarily imply that when operating at the service temperature a pressure vessel made from the steel would be unsafe. An increase in hardness with time could be regarded as compensating for the normal reduction in tensile strength and yield stress value which

Table 7. *Izod impact tests after prolonged ageing at 400° and 450° C. Low carbon–copper–molybdenum steel*

Heat-treatment		Izod value ft-lb at room temperature	Appearance of fracture	D.P.N.
Temperature (°C)	Duration (hr)			
As rec.	—	56, 59, 55	Fibrous	128
400	300	59, 50, 54	Fibrous with small crystalline patch	135
400	1602	50, 40, 55	Fibrous with small crystalline patch	150
400	1692	54, 38, 61	Fibrous, crystalline centre	164
400	2500	38, 42, 39	Fibrous, crystalline centre	163
400	4056	38, 41, 38	Fibrous, crystalline centre	166
400	10,386	42, 49, 44	Fibrous small crystalline areas	160
450	1694	54, 76, 53	Fibrous, no crystallinity	150
450	2500	64, 58, 63	Fibrous, no crystallinity	143
450	7019	49, 62, 49	Fibrous, no crystallinity	145
450	10,386	40, 62, 50	Fibrous, no crystallinity	136

a non-ageing steel undergoes at an elevated temperature. A possible risk, however, in its use lies in cooling down from, or heating up to, a service temperature subsequent to a vessel being commissioned. Uneven or exaggerated stresses may occur locally as a result of the cooling or re-heating. As a result of this investigation it was decided to limit the application of the steel to the lower portion of the spherical reactor where temperatures were lower than those of the tests due to the natural temperature gradient existing from top to bottom of the vessel in service.

The Effect of Irradiation on Steels

The relatively recent and rapid development of the production of electric energy in large atomic power stations necessitated early studies of the effects of neutron bombardment on steels and other materials for reactor and plant construction. Wigner[6] first indicated that damage could result from irradiation of solids and obviously the effect on the toughness of metals is of considerable importance.

F

The intensity of the radiation is a prime factor and, since the total amount of dosage also involves time of exposure at a particular degree of intensity, the two are combined and measured as the integrated neutron flux *n.v.t.* where $n = $ no. of neutrons/cm^3 in the beam; $v = $ velocity in cm/sec; $t = $ time in seconds (total). Hence as an example we may have:

$$\text{Intensity} \times \text{Time} \qquad\qquad \text{Total dose}$$
$$10^{12}\, n/\text{cm}^2 \times 6 \text{ months } (1\cdot5 \times 10^7 \text{ sec}) = 10^{19}\, n/\text{cm}^2$$

The temperature at which the irradiation takes place is also defined.

Essentially the principal effect of irradiation is to harden the material as shown by an increase in yield and tensile strengths. This is accompanied by a shift of the ductile/brittle transition range towards higher temperatures and a reduction in energy absorption in the impact test. Irradiation effects on single crystals of pure iron have been shown to be sensitive to cold working prior to exposure—the greater the extent to which cold work (plastic deformation) has been applied the less is the yield stress raised for a particular dosage. Polycrystalline pure iron responds similarly and Sutton and Leeser[7] have shown that ferritic steels from 0·10 to 1·0% C, if irradiated in the softest condition (i.e. annealed), harden to a greater extent than when the steels were initially hardened by quenching. A very high dosage of $10^{20}\, n/\text{cm}^2$, can cause the yield stress of the steel to approach the ultimate tensile strength —a feature which one associates with a steel in the quenched and untempered state. It was also found that irradiation hardening was more severe when conducted at room temperature than when carried out at elevated temperatures (about 200° C). Other workers have confirmed this; identical dosages at different increasing temperatures produce diminishing increases in the yield stress shown by subsequent tests at room temperature.

For an identical dosage at say 80° C the yield stress of a steel may increase by over 100%, but at 400° C the increase may only be of the order of 40%. Fine-grain steels have been found to be considerably less sensitive to radiation damage.

The increase in hardness and yield stress as a result of neutron bombardment accompanied by an increase in the transition temperature is shown in Fig. 23 for an ordinary silicon-killed boiler steel to A.S.T.M. Specification No. 212/B (Bergren and Wilson)[8].

These general effects of irradiation apply to low-alloy steels, although to different degrees for various compositions. When certain high-alloy ferritic steels are irradiated, however, a marked difference in response is apparent. Both before and after irradiation these steels reveal no distinct ductile brittle transition temperature down to −200° C. The change which irradiation produces is a progressive lowering of the energy absorption when impact tested. The degree of reduction is a function of the severity of the dose and the temperature. A low-carbon steel containing 0·10% C and 9% Ni (see chapter 12) which, in the double normalized and tempered condition, consists mainly of a nickel-ferrite and some austenite behaves in this way.

An exception in the high-alloy ferritic steels is provided by a high chromium steel (A.S.T.M. Specification No. 336) which in the normal condition shows no transition temperature between +300° and −185° C, but after irradiation, develops a very high transition temperature between 175° and 205° C.

Tests for irradiation embrittlement have apparently not been conducted on ordinary plain carbon steels in other than the normalized or as-rolled condition. Low-alloy steels of the types which are normally used in the quenched and tempered condition and not in the ferritic condition, reveal

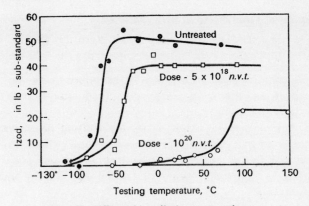

FIG. 23. Effect of irradiation on toughness.

that when irradiated, the former condition possesses superior resistance to damage. Unfortunately the structure (bainitic) is not the best for elevated temperature applications where creep may take place, and the quenched and tempered steels are therefore more useful for ambient or sub-zero temperatures.

The increased resistance to damage possessed by a quenched and tempered structure compared with ferrite-pearlite suggests that fully austenitic steels, that is, some stainless steels, would be still more resistant. This has indeed been confirmed by Bergren and Wilson[8].

Recovery from Irradiation Damage

Irradiation damage is obviously of serious consequence, if any steel so damaged is likely to be stressed in service at ambient or low temperatures. It is fortunate that this does not occur in any known practice. Fortunately, also, the recovery of the original properties and a restoration of the original transition temperature can be effected by annealing the damaged material.

This recovery commences at a temperature of 300° C. Meyer[9] has shown that a mild steel in the irradiated condition had a transition temperature of +18° C. After annealing at 315° C the transition temperature was lowered to 9° C and further annealing at 480° C lowered this temperature to −1° C (its original value). Austenitic stainless steels, while suffering less damage, require considerably higher annealing temperatures to restore the original properties. Murphy and Paine[10] showed 600° C to be effective. Provided therefore that irradiation under service conditions takes place at elevated temperatures there is substantially a cancelling out effect. This fact has enabled the construction of nuclear reactors in steel to be accepted with confidence.

The Mechanism of Embrittlement by Irradiation

Damage to any solid material may result from irradiation. For a non-fissile material such as steel the damage arises from the following causes:

(a) Undesirable impurity atoms may be introduced into the structure as a result of the capture of neutrons and radioactive decay. This cause is the least damaging.

(b) More serious damage results from the shifting of atoms from their regular positions. These atoms, unless they are pushed into an already vacant site in the lattice, may assume interstitial positions—hence resulting in increased rigidity of the lattice, thereby increasing the tensile strength.

(c) Vacant sites may be produced in the lattice.

(d) While only a small part of the ingoing energy is absorbed by the formation of vacancies or interstitials the remaining energy produces, in the vicinity of the collision, an increased vibration of the immediately surrounding atoms. This results in an enormous local temperature rise, such that the region behaves as a liquid until the intense temperature is lowered by heat dispersion.

Such effects are sub-microscopic in scale but their accumulation with time explains the deterioration of initially satisfactory properties.

The Effect of Stress-relieving on Steels

An important requirement for welded pressure vessels intended for service at ambient or low temperatures is that of stress-relieving after fabrication. Forming the cylindrical barrel out of rolled plate may be done either hot or cold—usually the latter for plates up to 3 in. thick. For very thick plates 3 in. and upwards, hot forming is usually adopted because power requirements and weight of equipment for cold bending become excessive. With care, hot forming can conveniently be arranged so that, as in rolling, final working coincides with the normalizing temperature, in which case a normalized structure results on cooling down. In cases where shaping is done by hot pressing this procedure is conveniently adopted and the petal plates for atomic energy reactor spheres were formed in this way. Under these conditions residual stresses are at a minimum in the individual plates, but if cold forming is adopted the effect of cold work involves the introduction of severe stresses which are considerably augmented in a non-uniform manner by welded joints during assembly. These stresses are prejudicial to toughness particularly at low temperatures. Endeavours are made therefore to reduce or eliminate these residual stresses by the stress-relieving operation which for plain carbon steels is usually carried out at $580/620°$ C, that is, below the Ac_1 point. This treatment does not radically alter the structure of the ferrite-pearlite steels, except that in the case of large vessels which by their size and mass involve long heating (and cooling) times some spheroidization of the carbide component of the pearlite may take place. While stresses can be relieved by holding for a longer time at a lower temperature, the $580/620°$ C range represents an economic and convenient compromise. Very large furnaces are necessary, and special furnaces may even be built round the construction itself. The attainment of the required temperature uniformly over the whole mass simultaneously, while desirable, is not so important as in tempering a quenched steel. The time factor is not so critical, and slow cooling in the furnace completes the operation. Reactor spheres 60 ft approx. in diameter have been successfully stress-relieved after construction *in situ*, by insulating the outside and lining the inside with stainless steel resistors which were then heated electrically. A temperature of $590/600°$ C was maintained for 72 hr, subsequent cooling occupying a fortnight.

Stress-relieving exerts a considerable effect on the mechanical properties of the steel which fact is now acknowledged in standard specifications.

For ordinary carbon steels an appreciable drop in the yield stress occurs together with an increase in the ductile/brittle transition temperature. The yield stress subsequent to stress-relieving is usually some $1\frac{1}{2}$ tons/in^2 below the 'as-rolled' or normalized value, while the transition temperature may shift downwards by $10°$ C or more depending on whether the steel is fully killed or not. This deterioration in properties must now be compensated for by the steel producer who must ascertain and satisfy the required physical properties on test coupons which have been stress-relieved (i.e. heated to $580/620°$ C) and not in the condition in which the plate itself is supplied to the fabricator. This presents no difficulty if the steel, in the 'as-rolled' or normalized condition is in the top half of the permitted tensile strength range, but if the tensile strength of the 'as-rolled' or normalized plate is near the bottom of this range then the results in the stress-relieved condition may cause rejection.

Table 8. *The effect of stress-relieving on the properties of three steels*

Type of steel	Condition	U.T.S. (tons/in²)	Yield stress (tons/in²)	Elongation %	Impact values in ft-lb at —° C (Longit.)								
					R.T.	0	−10	−20	−30	−40	−50	−60	−70
C–Mn Si-killed Al grain refined	N. 920° C	29·9	18·6	38	88	88	67	59	—	—	22	—	—
	N. 920° C	32·0	20·5	34	95	92	72	74	—	—	31	—	—
	S.R. 610° C (5 hr)	29·7	18·6	35	59	46	34	29	—	—	13	—	—
		29·8	19·6	35	62	49	41	32	—	—	12	—	—
C–Mn–Si + Nb treated Al grain refined	N. 900° C	40·2	29·3	28·5	100	80	—	—	—	61	—	—	46
	N. 900° C S.R. 625° C (2 hr)	38·4	27·5	30	95	86	—	—	—	55	—	—	42
Ni–Cr–Mo–V Si-killed only	D. Norm 920°–880° C	43·4	26·3	20	49	42	35	—	—	—	—	—	—
	D. Norm S.R. 600° C (72 hr)	44·8	36·1	23	41	30	25	20	15	12	10	—	—

An example of the effect of stress-relieving on properties of three steels is given in Table 8, from which it can be seen that certain complex low-alloy steels may differ from carbon steels in their response to a stress-relieving treatment at or about 600° C. While a deterioration of impact values occurs the yield and tensile strengths may increase appreciably as a result of precipitation hardening effects.

As in the case of other effects which can arise from sub-critical heating, for example, effects which can arise from ageing and the development of blue brittleness—the change in properties brought about by a stress-relieving treatment is the result of some mechanism involving the precipitation of a discrete phase and nitrogen appears to be involved. The previously mentioned work by Arrowsmith has revealed that in a silicon-killed commercial steel heated at 600° C for 36 hr there is precipitated a silicon nitride which is isomorphous with AlN. The fine precipitate is only detectable by means of the electron microscope at magnifications of 40,000 to 100,000. It appeared in the form of flakes and occurred extensively at the grain boundaries while the grains themselves contained finely dispersed particles. The steels examined also included a semi-killed variety containing 0·05% Si, and in this material there was no precipitation within the grains and very little at the grain boundaries after heat-treatment at 600° C. All steels examined contained 0·005% N and the conclusion was reached that this is removed from solution by precipitation in the silicon-killed specimens as silicon nitride, the identity of this compound being established by X-ray analysis.

While this modification of the structure, resulting from heating silicon-killed steels (containing about 0·15% Si) at 600° C, may account for a change in properties it does not explain the fact that the semi-killed steels also undergo a similar deterioration in properties when stress relieved. The whole problem of sub-microscopic precipitations of small quantities of compounds of silicon, aluminium, nitrogen and carbon still requires investigation before a complete explanation, which will account for all the characteristics encountered in the sub-critical heat-treatment of steels can be given. Obviously, both the physical form of any precipitate, its size and distribution, are factors of importance. In any consideration of the effects of nitrogen it must be borne in mind that while generally considered disadvantageous at the higher levels encountered in basic Bessemer steels (viz. 0·010/0·015% N) there are conditions in which physical properties may be improved by its presence when accompanied by a nitride former such as vanadium or aluminium. On the Continent, where until recently the basic Bessemer process has been predominant for so many years yielding a product high in nitrogen, the development of steels equivalent to those of the open-hearth furnace was achieved by deoxidizing with silicon and introducing aluminium as a grain-refining agent, thereby tying up the nitrogen as a compound. There are indications that certain proprietary continental and American steels, intended for fabrication and having properties superior to those of mild steel, do indeed depend on a relatively high nitrogen content in a combined form, but this field is not completely explored at present.

REFERENCES

1. M. A. Grossman. *Trans. A.I.M.E.*, **150** (1943), 227.
2. E. C. Bain and J. R. Vilella. 'Austenitic Grain Size in Steel', *Metals Handbook*. Amer. Soc. Metals, 1948 edn., 399.
3. 'Atlas of Isothermal Transformations', Iron and Steel Inst. Spec. Rep. no. 40 (1949).
4. K. F. Hale and D. McLean. *J. Iron Steel Inst.*, **201** (1963), 337.
5. J. M. Arrowsmith. *J. Iron Steel Inst.*, **201** pt. 8 (1963), 337.
6. E. P. Wigner. *J. Appl. Phys.*, **17** (1946), 857.
7. C. E. Sutton and D. O. Leeser. *Nucleonics*, **12,** no. 9 (Sept. 1954), 8.
8. R. G. Bergren and J. C. Wilson. Oak Ridge Nat. Lab. Report No. CF-56-11-1, Jan. 1957.
9. R. A. Meyer. *J. appl. Phys.*, **25** (1954), 1369.
10. W. F. Murphy and S. H. Paine. *A.S.T.M. Stand.*, 1956–7. Spec. Tech. publ. 208, p. 162.
11. F. B. Pickering and T. Gladman. B.I.S.R.A. Carbon Steels Comm. Harrogate Conf. May 1963.
12. J. Hardwick. *Iron and Steel* (Sept. 1961).

PART II

THE TECHNOLOGY OF STEELS

CHAPTER 4

HISTORICAL SURVEY OF THE DEVELOPMENT OF BESSEMER MILD STEEL AND THE OCCURRENCE OF BRITTLENESS

It is obvious that brittleness, or the inability to withstand shock which results in a special type of fracture betraying little or no deformation or sign of ductility, has indeed occurred at various times since metals have been used by man. Catastrophic failure is not a modern phenomenon, but it must be borne in mind that the seriousness of present-day failures is often enhanced by the size of the structures involved.

Early Bessemer Steel

Very little information is available on the general behaviour of wrought iron under low-temperature conditions in the early days preceding its displacement by Bessemer steel. Bessemer's early experiments date from 1856 and his first attempts were directed to the production of malleable iron. His announcement of 'The Manufacture of Malleable Iron and Steel Without Fuel' from hematite pig iron at the Cheltenham meeting of the British Association in 1856 was followed by enthusiasm, but indiscriminate trials in many places, using pig irons containing phosphorus, resulted in failures to achieve a tough product. It took nearly another quarter of a century to establish the 'basic' process (associated with Gilchrist and Thomas) for converting iron containing appreciable quantities of phosphorus into a satisfactory steel. Meanwhile, however, the acid Bessemer process using hematite pig iron developed rapidly. To gain a proper perspective of the significance of this advance 'the greater tenacity of the steel as compared with wrought iron allowed the use of steam at a pressure of 80 lb/in² with marked economy of fuel'. This may be contrasted with today's pressures of 650–1250 lb/in² made possible by using alloy steels. In 1863 a clipper ship of 1250 tons constructed of Bessemer steel plate was launched. An account[1] of the behaviour of this vessel pays a compliment to the toughness of the steel as evidenced by its encounter with a cyclone in Calcutta in October 1864.

75

'The ship was struck fairly on end by a vessel of 1000 tons—the plates were beaten in but not fractured. Forward—the continual hammering of several large vessels bent the bulwarks level with the deck. The plates forming them were nevertheless so tenacious that they were prised back to their original position to do duty again—without the aid of a riveter. In another part of the bulwarks a plate had been partially knocked out, and catching the side of the other vessel was rolled up as perfectly as a sheet of paper could be. In the stern between the upper deck and the poop several plates were driven in by repeated blows from a heavy wooden ship. These and the angle irons were twisted into a thousand fantastic forms—in some cases doubled and redoubled and in no case was there a crack or fracture that indicated any brittleness in the metal!'

This description pays a remarkable tribute to the suitability of the properties possessed by the steel. It is an excellent example of 'toughness' and the implications of the word, although no low temperature was involved. Nothing is known of the source, composition or uniformity of properties of these plates, nor any details of the design of the vessel, and certainly not all steel produced at that time behaved in this way.

Occurrences such as these, involving a new material, obviously assisted in the rapid displacement of wrought iron. The Paris Exhibition of 1867 displayed cast steel boiler plates[2]. Progress was not however without some sense of caution. Fairbairn[3] in 1869 stated that 'for several years past attempts have been made to substitute steel for iron on account of its superior tenacity in the construction of boilers, bridges, ships, etc., and there can be no doubt as to the desirability of employing a material of about the same weight and of double the strength provided it can at all times be relied upon. Some difficulties exist and until they are removed it would not be safe to make the transfer from iron to steel. These difficulties may be summed up in a few words—viz. the want of uniformity in the manufacture in cases of rolled plates and other articles which require perfect resemblances in character, and the uncertainty which pervades its production.'

Bessemer himself remarked that 'in no case was this change in material [from wrought iron to steel] more important than in the construction of ships, for in no instance are lightness and strength more essential'. He stated that 'vessels of a large size constructed to Class A1 (12 years) at Lloyds weigh, when built of iron, 12 cwts/ton measurement, whereas when built of steel they weigh 7 cwts/ton measurement'.

From this historical background and from records of tests the tensile strength of early Bessemer steel varied between 25 and 35 tons/in². Sharp[4] stated that the most satisfactory range was 33/35 tons/in², as steel plates within this range possessed sufficient ductility to render them safe under all circumstances. This level of strength can be contrasted with the average of

18/30 tons/in² for wrought iron. Hence the basis of Bessemer's claim previously referred to for weight-saving in ships. Experience and satisfactory service for conditions in those days therefore resulted in the evolution of the so-called mild steel. Sharp[4] in 1869 revealed some of the troubles encountered. He mentioned that plates of inferior or brittle quality had been supplied and of too high a tensile strength (at the expense of ductility). He showed that punching holes for rivets was more harmful than drilling and his steel boiler plates suffered more than wrought-iron plates of 20/22 tons/in² tensile in this respect. In the same year Vickers[5] tested steels of different carbon contents. A steel containing 0·33% C gave a tensile strength of 30·4 tons/in² with an elongation of 1·37 in. on a gauge length of 14 in. (about 10%). A carbon range of 0·05–0·15% gave tensile strengths of 28·7–34·4 tons/in².

Development of 'Mild Steel'

From the preceding notes it is seen that history itself constitutes a partial reason for the existence of mild steel. It was the first reasonably strong material to be produced in larger quantities than previously possible and possessing some degree of consistency. To complete the picture of its early development we must recall that the refining of crude iron obtained from ores in the blast furnace is achieved by the preferential oxidation of impurities such as carbon, silicon, manganese and phosphorus which are initially present. The removal of these elements down to levels which characterize mild steel as now known is accompanied also by the oxidation of some of the iron itself. Generally the more carbon eliminated, the greater is the degree of elimination of other impurities and the greater is the oxidation of the iron itself. Because of this it was natural that a lower carbon steel should in the early days be more consistent in properties. For this reason also it was comparatively easier to produce and this steel became a standard product. During the past century this product has become established as 'mild steel' which is definable as follows: 0·12/0·26% C; 0·55/0·65% Mn; 0·02/0·07% Si. The objectionable impurities sulphur and phosphorus are limited to maximum levels of 0·06% each, but may also be still lower in many specifications.

Steels lower than 0·12% C are made. These possess a lower strength and are produced mainly in the form of thin sheet. Much of this low carbon material is produced as rimming steel—so called because of its composite structure. Because little or no deoxidant such as silicon is added the steel 'rims' during solidification in the mould, that is, as cooling occurs the carbon in solution reacts with FeO in solution to evolve carbon monoxide. A rim of solid material develops from the mould wall inwardly. This solid material is lower in carbon than the initial carbon content of the liquid. After a time the overall fall in temperature is sufficient to inhibit this reaction and the remaining internal liquid solidifies as a relative spongy mass which consolidates on rolling. This last core to solidify is higher in carbon content than the rim, resulting in a composite structure. The softer rim has useful properties in that it is more easily deformable without fracture—hence the use of the steel for deep stampings in the form of sheet.

The analysis range of the mild steel given above is known in Britain as a 'balanced' steel, that is, the degree of deoxidation effected by the amount of silicon is not enough to suppress all gas evolution during solidification. Consequently, an ingot of this steel does not shrink fully to give a pronounced primary pipe as would a fully-killed steel but solidifies with a spongy top which consolidates and welds up during rolling. This enables a maximum percentage weight of the ingot to be obtained as a saleable product.

In the hot-rolled condition, steel of the composition range given will possess a tensile strength of 24/34 tons/in^2 and a yield stress which is approx. 0·53/0·58 of the tensile strength. Modern design requirements necessitate a smaller range of properties with stipulated minimum values, which must be equalled or preferably exceeded—but still within the range. The degree of control necessary to give narrower property ranges is achieved by adjusting the carbon content of the liquid steel before pouring, since carbon has the most pronounced effect on strength. The carbon level must also be altered to suit various thicknesses. In the broad chemical specification given, a hot-rolled 2 in. thick plate would have a tensile strength of up to 25 tons/in^2 at the 0·12% C level but a strength of 29/31 tons/in^2 at the 0·26% C level.

Strength in Relation to Composition

Many investigations have been carried out on strength in relation to composition. These have consisted of statistical examinations of results obtained from actual tests made on 'as-rolled' material. From these statistics formulae have been derived which relate the two.

An example is as follows:

$$\text{Tensile strength (lb/in}^2) = 38{,}000 + C[800 + 4(C - 20)]$$
$$+ Mn[100 + 2(C - 20)] + P[1000] + Si[120] + K.$$

Values of K are

Thickness	K	Thickness	K
1 in.	−2000	$\frac{5}{8}$ in.	+1000
$\frac{7}{8}$ in.	−1000	$\frac{1}{2}$ in.	+2000
$\frac{3}{4}$ in.	0	$\frac{3}{8}$ in.	+3000

K is an empirical constant which varies with thickness and rolling mill conditions. Carbon, manganese, phosphorus and silicon are the amounts of these elements present in units of 0·01%.

From the formula the effect of an increase of 0·01% C on the strength is roughly equivalent to that of an increase of 0·08/0·10% Mn. It will also be noticed that the factor for phosphorus is high. It is therefore a powerful strengthener and indeed is used as such in a number of American high-tensile steels in spite of its normal designation as an undesirable impurity.

Welding

Steel of the composition range given has a history therefore of approximately 100 years and constitutes the basis of B.S. 15 'Mild Steel for General Structural Purposes'. It is only during the past fifteen years that considerable modifications to its composition have been introduced and to these changes the introduction of welding as a means of fabrication has probably contributed most. Welding has obvious technical and economic advantages. It received a considerable impetus after the First World War when the tonnages of various navies were limited by international agreement. During the period 1930/40 welding increased rapidly, and in 1940 a Swedish shipyard constructed a 6000-ton oil tanker which was 98% welded. The subsequent enormous growth of welding made possible the maintenance of adequate shipping capacity during the Second World War and the term 'Liberty Ships' is a reminder of this. These vessels were built from large prefabricated sections which were assembled on the stocks.

The Problem of Brittle Fracture

This change from riveting to welding emphasized the serious problem of brittle fracture, but it is erroneous to associate the problem with welding only. Riveted ships such as the *Berengaria, Leviathan* and *Majestic* all developed brittle fractures in different plates at various times. The occurrence of this type of fracture dates back to the early development period of mild steel. In 1879 it was stated that certain Bessemer steel plates exhibited brittleness. Occasionally plates fractured when dropped from a height in cold weather— an early indication of the effect of low temperatures. In 1900 both Charpy and Izod were evolving tests to determine the degree of resistance to shock possessed by various steels, and in 1905 Charpy showed that lowering the temperature of a specimen produced a brittle type of fracture as distinct from a tough one. This type of brittle fracture was found to require less energy than the tough type occurring at a higher temperature.

A survey of the interval to the present time indicates a rapid growth in the physical dimensions of structures such as bridges, tanks and ships. Consequently the failure of a structure owing to brittle fracture has become correspondingly more serious and costly. A new descriptive term—catastrophic failure—is now used. Its relevance can be appreciated since, in a large completely welded structure, a local failure can result in a complete destruction of the whole fabrication. Moreover such a failure can be practically instantaneous subsequent to its initiation.

Details of the more striking failures involving large structures and subsequent investigations carried out have been described at intervals over the past thirty years. Probably the most prominent early example of the occurrence of brittle fracture in steel was the collapse of the Hasselt Bridge (over a canal) in Belgium in 1938[6]. In 1943 an all-welded tanker, the *Schenectady*, broke in two while in dock after undergoing sea trials. A similar tanker, the *Ponagansett*, also broke in two while moored in calm water. A British tanker, the *World Concord*, broke in two under different circumstances in the Irish Sea on 27 November 1954. The ship was in ballast only, but the weather was rough, wind force 8–9. She was some 625 ft long and her dead weight tonnage was 31,800 tons, being launched only 2–3 years previously (see Plate 6).

The most recent notable failure has been that of the Kings Bridge, Melbourne, which collapsed on 10 July 1962. The bridge carried at the time a load of approximately 28 tons total in the form of a low-loader truck and trailer. On reaching a certain span this collapsed and sagged to a depth of about 1 ft—being fortunately prevented from collapsing further by the concrete deck and the vertical walls which existed underneath. This particular span was near one end of the bridge. Examination revealed many fractures characterized by a brittle appearance and these originated from toe cracks in the parent metal of the flanges and transverse fillet welds. The official report[7] states that the final collapse was a last stage in a cascade pattern of small fractures which took months to develop sufficiently to result in the final failure. A distinctive feature of this casualty was that the material used for construction was of a higher tensile strength (32–38 tons/in²) than the normal mild steel.

Serious failures of the magnitudes mentioned are obviously subjected to the most rigorous inquiries as to the causes and contributing factors. Details of these inquiries are not always freely available but the official report on the Kings Bridge failure may be regarded as a classic example of the thoroughness which characterizes such inquiries. Appropriate bodies in Europe, America and elsewhere have concerned themselves with ship failures, and probably the greatest mass of information exists in connection with these. Failures in the past have given an impetus to the development of improved notch tough steels with which this book is concerned. It is possible to record that while failures in storage tanks result in total destruction of the fabrication not all failures end so disastrously. The *World Concord* has since returned to service with a somewhat increased length, the two halves being subsequently joined together.

PLATE 5

(*a*) Martensite in a 0·70% carbon steel. Quenched in a 2% NaOH solution. × 700.

(*b*) Lower bainite in a 0·45% carbon steel. Quenched in water. × 700.

PLATE 6

The *World Concord* which broke in two off the coast of Pembrokeshire, 27 November 1954. (*Photograph: United Press International (U.K.) Ltd.*)

REFERENCES

1. T. Turner. *The Metallurgy of Iron* (C. Griffin: London, 1908), p. 44.
2. F. Kohn. *Iron and Steel Manufacture* (W. Mackenzie: London, 1869), p. 193.
3. W. Fairbairn. *Iron* (A. and C. Black (Edin.), 1869), p. 314.
4. H. Sharp. See Ref. 2 above (*ibid.*), p. 255.
5. T. E. Vickers. See Ref. 2 above (*ibid.*), p. 242.
6. O. Bondy. *Engineering, Lond.*, **145** (1938), 670.
7. *Report of Royal Commission into Failure of Kings Bridge*, by Authority (A. C. Brooke, Govt. Printer: Melbourne, 1963).

CHAPTER 5

THE INFLUENCE OF METHODS OF STEEL MANUFACTURE ON NOTCH TOUGHNESS

Factors which Affect the Energy-Temperature Transition Curve

Curves relating the energy to fracture a specimen, and its temperature as derived from an impact test such as the Charpy, do not always show a sharp changeover from a tough to a brittle type of fracture as the temperature falls. They vary in shape depending on the material and its condition. In some cases (as in Fig. 3) the transition point is sharply defined and in others (see Fig. 2) the energy curve is gradual. Unless some assessment of an additional criterion such as the percentage of crystallinity in each fracture is made, in order to adhere to an arbitrary but common standard which may be 50% crystallinity, then it is difficult from the energy curve to say what the transition temperature is. Materials such as stainless steel and 9% Ni steel indeed show only a gradual drop in the fracture energy from ambient to the lowest temperature achieved.

There are many variants of these two extreme types of curve and it has been found that certain factors can cause changes in the general shape.

The types of change can be defined as

(1) change of slope;
(2) maintenance of slope but a shift towards higher or lower temperatures;
(3) changes incorporating both (1) and (2).

Both (1) and (2) above are influenced principally by factors which may be listed under two principal headings, (a) composition, and (b) structure.

Composition

With regard to composition, while elements such as carbon, silicon, nitrogen and phosphorus generally flatten the slope, the elements manganese, nickel and oxygen tend to shift the curves—the latter element adversely towards higher transition temperatures. Manganese is an obvious example of a beneficial effect which was taken advantage of, in developing the notch

82

tough steels N.D. I to N.D. IV designated in B.S. 2762. In these steels the manganese content is increased substantially from 0·5/0·6% to 1·2/1·4% and the carbon decreased in order to secure transition temperatures lower than those of ordinary mild steel. A Mn/C ratio of 8/1 to 10/1 is used. The impact strength of pure Fe–Si, Fe–Ni, Fe–Cr and Fe–Mo alloys has been investigated by Rees *et al.*[1].

Structure

The type and condition of microstructure resulting from different heat-treatments also modifies the shape of the curves and alters the position of any

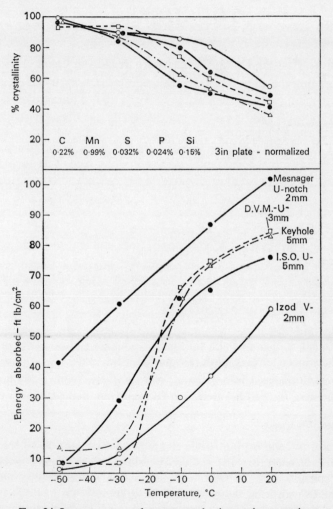

FIG. 24. Impact tests on the same steel using various testpieces.

arbitrary transition point with respect to temperature. A fine-grain steel with a ferrite/pearlite structure will possess a lower transition temperature than a coarse-grain steel of the same composition, while quenching and tempering both lowers the transition temperature and alters the shape and position of the curve.

While these broad principles hold, there are other factors present in practice which complicate the effects, for example, a change of slope can be effected by changing the type of testpiece. A familiar example of this lies in the distinctly different curves obtained on the same material when using a Charpy V-notch testpiece and the D.V.M. U-notch testpiece. Reference may be made to Fig. 24. A change in dimensions of a testpiece also alters the slope of the curve when compared with the standard 10 mm × 10 mm Charpy V-notch results. By altering rates of application of stress or by neutron irradiation of the specimens, standard curves for most materials can be altered in ways involving both change of slope and shift of the curve. It is doubtful, however, if the toughness properties of all alloys were indeed defined specifically with respect to the influence of every single factor whether in practice much usefulness would be served. While one might evolve the best degree of notch toughness, this would not automatically imply that other engineering properties would indeed be best at the same time.

Apart from composition and the effects of microstructure, certain inherent influences result from the methods of manufacture, that is, the processes used and the various forms of the product. A brief review of these is therefore pertinent.

Ferrous alloys may be divided into three categories with respect to their end uses, these categories being defined by their initial mode of production. A finished structure or design is most frequently composite in that it involves numerous components (often formed by welding). Each component may have been produced in one of three forms: (1) rolled material, (2) forged, or (3) as a casting. By the third is implied the achievement of the finished component by casting liquid metal into a mould of the desired shape. These three categories of rolled, forged and cast materials have inherently different characteristics with respect to toughness properties even if all three forms are of identical composition. These different characteristics result from their mode of manufacture, the process used and the heat-treatment applied.

Steelmaking Processes

The major portion of the world's steel is at present produced by the basic open-hearth process but increasing quantities are being produced by the basic oxygen processes (either L.D. or Kaldo). Considerable tonnages of alloy steels are made by the basic electric furnace process. The 'acid' forms of these processes are relatively negligible in magnitude of production since the bulk of the world's ore supplies contain sufficient phosphorus to render them inoperable. Each of the three major processes has characteristics of its own.

The Basic Open-hearth Process

Mass production of steel by this method involves the melting and refining of different proportions of steel scrap together with pig iron (usually charged into the furnace as a liquid). Heating is by gaseous or liquid fuels (oil or tar) and some gaseous oxygen may be used to enrich the air for combustion of the fuel. Oxygen may also be used to reduce the level of carbon in the bath after melting down. The feature of the process is that it necessitates the use of strongly oxidizing slags at all times. Hence the metal before tapping may contain variable amounts of oxygen for this reason and also as a result of a degree of deoxidation applied during the adjustment of the required composition. Consequently it may be characterized by different degrees of cleanness arising from the presence of non-metallic inclusions which are the products of deoxidation. These inclusions exert a pronounced effect on notch toughness, particularly in relation to directional properties in rolled products. Because of the access of air to the furnace a certain equilibrium is also established between nitrogen from the air and the liquid steel.

In consequence, basic open-hearth steels usually contain 0·004/0·006% N. Also, because of the presence of moisture in the fuels used and in the air for combustion, the steel may absorb considerable quantities of hydrogen during refining. Other sources of H_2 are from moisture in the lime used as a slag former and from rusty scrap. The use of liquid fuels (hydrocarbons) in which the weight ratio between H_2 and carbon is greater than in gaseous fuels such as producer gas, gives rise to a greater concentration of water vapour in the furnace atmosphere, and modern steels produced in liquid fuel fired furnaces do indeed tend to contain higher levels of H_2 in consequence. The harmful effects of the presence of this gas on the toughness properties of steels intended for low-temperature service are dealt with elsewhere.

The growth of the use of vacuum degassing processes to reduce the hydrogen and to a lesser extent the nitrogen level in liquid steel is directed to the improvement of physical properties. Normal hydrogen levels in basic open-hearth steel at tapping are of the order of 3·5/6·0 c.c. per 100 g and these levels may produce hydrogen flaking or cracking in rolled and forged material depending on subsequent treatment of the ingot. The strongly oxidizing character of the slags necessary to effect purification of the bath precludes for economic reasons the complete addition of all alloys to the furnace before tapping. Excessive losses of certain of these alloys by rapid oxidation would render the steel prohibitive in cost, and in some cases, for example those containing a high proportion of silicon, the amount would also so upset the slag composition as to cause a reversion of phosphorus back from the slag to the bath thereby exceeding a maximum level permitted by the specification. Hence it has become customary to add the major portion of the alloys necessary to the ladle during tapping. This method automatically limits the maximum amount of alloying elements which can be added in this way, since there is insufficient heat in the liquid steel running from the furnace to melt and mix adequately more than a certain weight proportion of cold material. It is not possible, for instance, to produce a 4% Cr steel by the basic open-hearth process by adding all the chromium to the ladle because the heat necessary to melt all the chromium alloy and still maintain adequate pouring temperature is not available in the liquid steel. Low-alloy steels of the Ni–Cr–Mo–V types can be produced since both nickel and molybdenum can be added to the bath without any substantial loss, thus relieving the burden of additions to the ladle. A good steelmaker will, however, endeavour to make his steel in the furnace itself as far as limitations permit. Much greater skill and judgement is required in this case but superior results with respect to uniformity of properties and quality repay this. The steel can be much cleaner, and the subsequent grain refining by additions of aluminium to the ladle is more effective. This can be reflected in the increased toughness of the product.

The Basic Oxygen Processes

These post-war processes, which are rapidly gaining ground, were rendered possible by the production of gaseous oxygen on a 'tonnage' scale. Oxygen-producing plants are now working which are capable of producing 100/300 tons of almost pure oxygen per day.

Both the L.D. (Austrian) and Kaldo (Swedish) processes use converter vessels somewhat similar in shape to the old Bessemer converter. The L.D. process uses an upright converter which is stationary during the blowing period. A water-cooled lance from which oxygen at a high velocity strikes the surface of the liquid bath is lowered into the converter, thereby effecting, in conjunction with slags of suitable composition, preferential oxidation of the impurities in the charge. Steel scrap can be charged with liquid pig iron to an extent limited by the amounts of initial impurities: carbon, silicon, manganese and phosphorus in the pig iron. The oxidation of these can only produce a limited amount of heat which depends upon the quantities present. This available heat must serve to melt both scrap and slag components and also raise the temperature of the whole to the required degree for tapping. At present no external source of heat is used during the whole process. Large converters of 100/120 tons capacity can melt some 25/30% of steel scrap.

The Kaldo process uses a similar-shaped vessel which rotates inside a cage during blowing. This cage is inclined some 15° to the horizontal. The oxygen lance enters the mouth of the vessel at an approximately similar angle so that the oxygen jet strikes the surface of the bath at a relatively shallow angle. In the L.D. process impingement is normal to the surface. The Kaldo arrangement prevents the formation of a symmetrical pattern of gas flow which is present in the stationary L.D. converter and consequently it is possible to develop more heat within the vessel by better mixing of oxygen with the carbon monoxide generated. This demands a somewhat greater oxygen consumption per ton of steel produced but the extra heat available within the vessel enables a greater percentage of scrap to be absorbed. This results in certain economic advantages.

Both these processes are also strongly oxidizing in character under all conditions but they have potential advantages from the point of view of steel quality. Because of the absence of moist air which is required for combustion, in a fuel-fired furnace, hydrogen concentrations are considerably lower than those of the open-hearth process. Hydrogen available for absorption by the steel is limited to that contained by the materials only, namely, lime and rusty scrap. Further, the absence of air during blowing tends to reduce the nitrogen content of the steel. Hence nitrogen levels in the steel of $0.0015/$ 0.003% can be secured while hydrogen levels of $1.5/3.5$ c.c. per 100 g are obtained. The lowest levels of H_2 are characteristic of steel plants in which freshly burnt lime is produced on the site. If moist lime from distant sources is used, the hydrogen contents can rise above the range given. Hydrogen contents of liquid steel can also depend on the development and use of proper slags during the refining period.

The Basic Electric Furnace Process

This process is distinct from the foregoing processes in that an electric arc between carbon electrodes and the bath provides the heat required. Because of relative stagnancy, the atmosphere above the bath can contain appreciable quantities of carbon monoxide which is reducing in character. Moisture is not entirely excluded while making additions through an open door but there is not the continuous access of moisture as in a gas-fired furnace. As a result of the predominantly reducing atmosphere it is possible (in addition to using an oxidizing slag for impurity elimination) to finish the refining operation with a reducing or 'white' slag in which the oxygen carrier (FeO) can be reduced to a very small concentration, this being achieved by additions of anthracite or graphite dust.

An oxidizing slag can be used up to the point of tapping the charge (single slag process). This procedure approximates to the basic open-hearth process. However, the oxidizing power of this slag can be less than that of the open hearth because of the absence of the continuous oxidizing effect of the gas or oil flame in the latter. If the charge is finished under a white slag conditions can be so reducing that it is possible to add all required alloys to the bath before tapping, practically without loss due to oxidation, and no limitation on the quantities of these alloys which can be added becomes necessary. Hence it is by this method that stainless steels with 18% Cr and 8% Ni, etc., are made. This avoidance of alloy loss compensates appreciably for the increased cost of electricity as a heating medium.

Because lime is necessary for refining, moisture (and hence H_2) is not entirely excluded and H_2 levels in the steel are generally highest for those charges finished under reducing slags, namely, 4·0/6·0 c.c. per 100 g steel. Under oxidizing slags throughout H_2 levels may be from 2·5/5·0 c.c. per 100 g steel.

Generally, steels made in the electric furnace tend to be somewhat higher in nitrogen than those of the open hearth. The accepted explanation for this is that, in spite of a lesser concentration of nitrogen being present in the furnace atmosphere, the amount present is more easily absorbed by the metal bath via the arcs because of the transient formation of cyanides (CN) by combination with the carbon of the electrodes. Nitrogen levels in steel made by the electric arc process are of the order of 0·007/0·012%.

Because of the ability to secure high metal temperatures and to produce the required composition in the bath before tapping, electric furnace steel commands a reputation for superiority with respect to cleanliness, that is, freedom from non-metallic inclusions while possessing superior mechanical properties, particularly ductility. This is important in steels for low-temperature applications, particularly in hot-rolled products, since greater freedom from inclusions can reduce the differences with respect to directional properties which may exist in 'dirtier' steels. Notch toughness as measured by energy to fracture differs considerably in plates and sections depending on whether the specimen is taken in the direction of rolling (longitudinal) or at right-angles to this (transverse), or through the thickness, that is, normal to the other two axes.

Highly alloyed electric furnace steels may also contain high levels of H_2 and N_2 because of the introduction of these gases by heavy additions of ferro-alloys under reducing conditions. While these elements can exercise an adverse effect on notch toughness H_2 and some N_2 can be removed by vacuum degassing before casting.

The Basic Bessemer Processes

The Bessemer processes, air blown from the bottom (as originally evolved), or the modified forms in which a mixture of steam and oxygen, or air enriched with oxygen is used, may be mentioned briefly. These processes produce mainly low-carbon steels (0·05/0·10% C) for the manufacture of thin sheet. By reason of the form and fields of application of this product, that is, extreme thinness and large surface area, problems of brittleness at ambient or low temperatures do not arise in its applications. Low-carbon rimming steels, which are deoxidized in manufacture to a lesser extent than the semi-killed mild steels, are prohibited in specifications for large pressure vessels and for use as ship plate since they undergo ageing and display poor notch toughness characteristics. In the form of thin sheet failure is more likely to occur through buckling and distortion. While cracking can, and does, occur through fatigue from high or low amplitude stress-variations the result is not catastrophic. Evidence of this may be found in a particular type of sheet-steel pressing in a motor-car body in which cracks spread gradually.

REFERENCE

1. W. P. Rees, B. E. Hopkins and H. R. Tipler. *J. Iron Steel Inst.*, **177** (1954), 93.

PART III

FORMS OF FERROUS PRODUCTS AND THEIR CHARACTERISTICS IN RELATION TO TOUGHNESS

CHAPTER 6

HOT-ROLLED PRODUCTS

The most familiar forms of hot-rolled products are plates, sheets, angles, joists (or sections), broad-flanged beams, billets (usually of square form in section but with rounded corners), rounds and flats or slabs. Some of these products, particularly sheets produced in continuous mills as strip, may be finished hot, or subjected subsequently to 'cold rolling' in which a further reduction in thickness is effected at room temperature. For the purpose of considering low-temperature property characteristics, hot-rolled plates produced in a plate mill, as distinct from a strip mill, may be considered separately on the basis that all other products are characterized by a very large length to width ratio and length to cross-sectional area ratio.

While plates, angles, sections and beams represent the finished product when cut to size or length, the other products are usually classed as 'semi's' in that they are most frequently subjected to further re-heating and are then rolled in smaller mills into a final finished form; for example, the square billet may become a round or square rod or bar of a smaller size while slabs may become thin strip. Similarly, the rod or bar may be drawn into wire or it may be accurately sized and its strength improved by cold drawing through a die.

The length/width or length/cross-sectional area ratio has an important bearing on the degree of notch toughness at low temperatures as measured by the energy required to fracture when considered in two directions at right-angles to each other—representing length and width.

Plates

For large, thick plates, e.g. 4 to 6 in. thick, for very heavy pressure vessels, it may be necessary to produce a single plate from each ingot. On the other hand, a dozen or more lighter plates may be rolled from the same-size ingot. The solid portion of the ingot has a coarse cast structure since it originates from the relatively slow cooling of the liquid steel. This implies a degree of directionalism in its properties. For example, there may be some segregation of carbon, sulphur and phosphorus down the vertical central axis from the

93

top because of progressive solidification inwards from the mould walls. At the bottom there may be a cone-shaped distribution of fine non-metallic particles. If, therefore, a single large plate is rolled from the ingot one can expect this pattern characteristic of the ingot to persist in the plate to some lesser degree owing to its dilution by extension in both length and breadth directions. Mechanical tests, sulphur prints and careful chemical analyses confirm this lack of complete uniformity. This inability to secure a complete micro-uniformity is indeed one reason for stipulating a range of certain

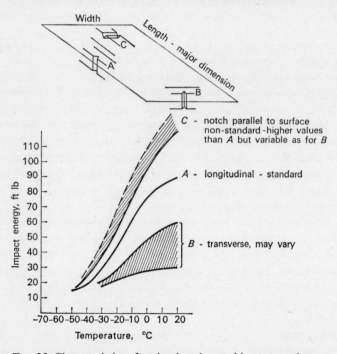

FIG. 25. Characteristics of variously orientated impact specimens.

properties in any specification, e.g. 26–32 tons/in² for the tensile strength. For design purposes minimum values for other properties such as yield stress, elongation, etc., are also specified.

It is possible to apply to a thick plate a variety of tests in three different orientations. One may test in the direction of rolling (longitudinally) or at right-angles to the direction of rolling (transversely) or through the thickness of the plate, as shown in Fig. 25. From the diagram given the three impact curves obtained in these directions differ very considerably at ambient temperatures but tend to close up at the lower temperatures. Tensile properties taken longitudinally and transversely do not reveal these marked differences, but the tensile strength through the thickness of a plate may be less than half the strength of that in the longitudinal direction. The reason for this is not difficult to visualize since some non-metallics, being plastic at the rolling temperatures (the rolling of mild steel commences at 1280°/1300° C), become flattened out and elongated into 'stringers'. Viewed from above through the plate thickness, they may occupy a larger total cross-section of a testpiece than they do when viewed from the other two directions in which they are present edgewise. An inevitable discrepancy in test values therefore becomes apparent, this discrepancy being greater the 'dirtier' is the steel.

There is obviously no constant ratio between the results for differently orientated tests taken from plates. The reason for this becomes apparent when we consider that one single plate can be rolled in two ways from the ingot or slab.

(a) The length of the ingot (or slab) can become the width of the finished plate, or

(b) the width of the ingot can persist as the width of the finished plate depending on how the slab enters the rolls, even though the initial width may be increased by a certain amount of 'cross-rolling'.

Smaller and thinner single plates are likely to have more uniform properties within themselves because each plate is a smaller fraction of the original ingot. Such plates may be rolled from slabs in either of the above ways, the ingot being first rolled into a long slab by increasing its length. The long slab is then cut into several lengths, each of which will be inserted into the plate mill in one of the two ways indicated.

The best possibility of securing uniform properties in both the longitudinal and transverse direction results from rolling a square slab into a square plate so that the amount of hot work applied is equal in both directions This, however, is uneconomic and prohibited in most cases by the required plate dimensions. Even if square plates are required it is cheaper to roll a rectangle and subsequently cut it into squares. The liberty to roll in either direction in relation to the vertical axis of the ingot must be the prerogative of the steelmaker since it enables him to plan sizes (areas) and thicknesses of slab from suitable ingots in the most economic manner.

Irrespective of the relationship the final plate length may bear to the vertical axis of the ingot, the longitudinal properties are always superior to the transverse because the greater extension taking place in this direction develops a 'fibre' through the elongation of plastic non-metallics. A further factor in plate rolling that influences the relative notch toughness is the finishing temperature. This is normally variable depending on the finished thickness. It is obviously desirable to achieve the required final thickness at a temperature as little above Ar_3 as possible so that subsequent air cooling results in a normalized structure having a fine grain. Neither this, however, nor separate normalizing, eliminates directional differences in properties although it may lessen them by improving both transverse and longitudinal toughness to differing degrees. 'Controlled' rolling can be carried out. This implies distribution of the total deformation necessary by waiting for cooling to take place at various passes through the rolls. The final thickness can then be achieved in the last pass at a temperature just above, but close to the Ar_3 point for the steel. Theoretically this should give the finest grain-size. There is, however, the possibility of 'cold' rolling below the Ar_3 resulting in deformation of the grains. This is detrimental to toughness although advantageous to strength properties. Additionally, in a modern high-speed mill with only one rolling stand the rate of output is considerably reduced. The method is more suited to multistand continuous mills. Ordinary rolling speeds followed by standard normalizing appears preferable therefore.

Sections

If now we consider sections, flats and beams, the length of the finished product must always correspond to the vertical axis of the ingot. Because the elongation produced by the rolling of sections may be so much greater than that produced in the rolling of a plate, the differences between longitudinal and transverse properties, particularly notch toughness, are at a maximum. This does not imply that the gap between the two widens to an absurd degree. There is obviously a maximum obtainable in the longitudinal direction and a minimum in the transverse, which is characteristic of the material. It is customary to test both products in the longitudinal direction since failure in service, if it occurs, is likely to be initiated at right-angles to this direction. Problems arise from the amount of work imposed at certain temperatures during rolling, particularly in the case of modern broad-flanged beams, as a consequence of the development of the final shape. The flange is usually much thicker than the web. Hence the flanges not only remain hotter during rolling while developing the section in the various passes, but differential cooling in air takes place after the finishing pass, the toes of the flanges remaining hotter for a longer time. In the case of sections, therefore, it is customary to test for notch ductility by means of specimens taken from the flange in a longitudinal direction because values obtained are lower than those encountered in the faster cooling web.

Differences in toughness can also be caused by the various designed thickness of the cross-section. These differences arise from the varying amounts of deformation during rolling. Brittle failure, should it occur in a beam, is likely to be initiated at some point in the toe of the flange. Some correction of this cross-sectional non-uniformity and improvement in low-temperature toughness can be achieved by normalizing. This is more feasible for large, costly

PLATE 7

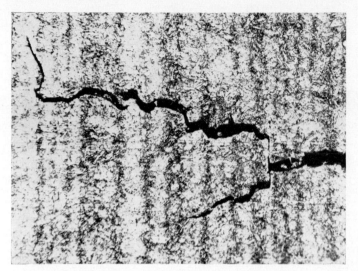

Internal 'shatter' crack in 9% Ni steel caused by hydrogen during cooling below 300° C. Etched nital. × 100. Note fracture along a 'stringer' inclusion.

PLATE 8

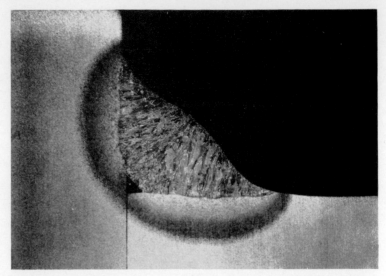

(*a*) Photomacrograph of fillet weld using low hydrogen mild-steel electrode in nickel-molybdenum steel showing relatively poor penetration. × 5.

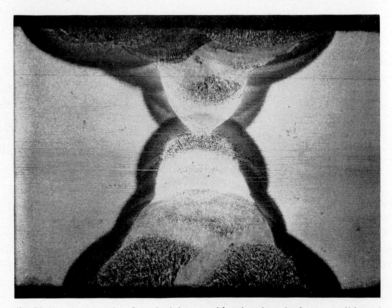

(*b*) Photomacrograph of typical butt weld using low hydrogen mild-steel electrode in nickel-molybdenum steel. × 3.

sections. The complicated profile of many sections causes warping during heat-treatment. This involves expensive cold straightening.

In billets also, the elongation produced in rolling relative to the ingot axis is very large. In consequence, low temperature and other properties of billets are ascertained only in the longitudinal direction. In the case of a square

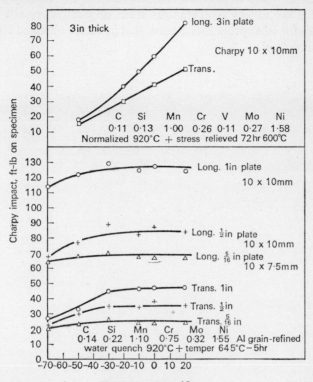

Fig. 26. Longitudinal and transverse Charpy values in 3 in. thick and 1 in. and below plates showing long./trans. ratios depending on thickness of plate and effect of inclusions.

billet it is obviously immaterial which side of the square (unlike the rectangle of the plate section) carries the notch for test purposes.

This variability in the isotropy of hot-rolled products does not prevent the achievement of satisfactory low-temperature properties for service but it is most important to associate any ascertained property with direction. The reconciliation of different levels of low-temperature characteristics in one type of product can then be achieved. Fortunately the longitudinal direction is well established as a basis for the determination of properties because, as previously stated, failure, should it occur in use, is likely to be initiated at right-

H

angles to a length, for example, as in a girder in a bridge, or a strake of plates in a ship's hull, where the rolled length of the plates is always disposed along the length of the ship. Typical differences in Charpy impact values for the longitudinal and transverse directions in a rolled plate are given in Fig. 26. It can be seen that, depending on the test-temperature, the transverse values vary between 40% and 60% of the longitudinal ones. In assessing the value of a steel for use at low temperatures from impact test results the same convention as for other properties is used, that is, values obtained must exceed some minimum level.

CHAPTER 7

CASTINGS AND FORGINGS

In the previous chapter emphasis has been given to features affecting notch toughness of hot-rolled products. These products form by far the largest proportion of the world's output of steel and because they are the raw materials of all large constructions, the importance of their properties at low temperatures cannot be overemphasized.

There are, however, other forms of ferrous products, the low-temperature properties of which may be of equal or of lesser importance for more specific applications. These are castings (both 'iron' and steel) and forgings. Their range is so extensive as to render a detailed survey impossible. While a large helical gear and pinion in a turbine speed-reduction unit must obviously possess toughness, this unit is not called upon to operate at sub-zero temperatures, whereas a cast-steel ship's propeller intended for arctic service is, as are the relatively small pipe flanges, valves and fittings for a liquefied gas-storage tank.

Iron Castings

The basic material of iron castings is initially the product of the blast furnace. This primary material, remelted in the foundry, can be modified by reducing the carbon content, or by partial purification. Alloying elements may also be added and heat-treatments applied to improve specific properties.

Both iron and steel castings are produced in sand moulds shaped to be as near as possible to the finished size and form, with suitable allowances for machining. The general term 'cast iron' covers a very wide range with respect to composition and properties. The extensive range of properties also depends on the fact that the material is 'composite' in that graphitic carbon (occurring as flakes or nodules) is a separate phase embedded in a metallic matrix which itself may be ferritic, pearlitic, austenitic or martensitic.

The three basic elements which affect strength and hardness are 'total carbon' (i.e. graphite plus carbon existing as a carbide, or in solution), silicon and phosphorus, and these may be interpreted in terms of a 'carbon

99

equivalent'. This is not to be confused with the carbon equivalent of steels, a term which defines weldability.

$$\text{Carbon equivalent (for cast iron)} = \text{total C\%} + \frac{\text{Si\%} + \text{P\%}}{3}.$$

The structure and thereby the properties of a cast iron are influenced by the rate of cooling from the liquid state. For equal rates of cooling, however, such as would apply to castings of equal cross-sectional thicknesses, a carbon equivalent greater than 4·3 would result in a coarse flaky graphite and mechanical weakness. As the value decreases below 4·3 the graphite flakes decrease in size and strength increases.

British Standard 1452 : 1961 lists seven grades of 'grey' iron. These are based on the minimum tensile strengths of 10, 12, 14, 17, 20, 23 and 26 tons/in² obtained on a 1·2 in. dia. test bar. Extensive work on the low-temperature properties of cast irons has been carried out by Gilbert[1] of the British Cast Iron Research Association, and his classification of types forms a convenient basis on which the properties may be considered.

Grey Irons

These are used for general engineering purposes in the 'as-cast' condition. The structure is graphitic (flake) with variable amounts of pearlite and ferrite in the matrix. Compositions are covered by the following ranges:

Total C%	Graphitic C%	Si%	Mn%	S%	P%
3·4/3·8	2·25/3·25	1·65/2·25	0·5/0·9	0·06/0·10	0·1/1·10

Room temperature properties depend on the quantity, size, form and distribution of the graphite. Gilbert[2] has shown that down to −100° C the tensile strength increases by 10/15% over that at room temperature. Testing at −269° C (liquid helium) revealed that the strength of a grey iron with a pearlitic matrix decreased only slightly as compared with that at room temperature, while the strength of an iron with a ferritic matrix increased from 13 tons/in² to 20 tons/in², that is approximately 50%.

Impact tests on unnotched bars ($\frac{5}{8}$ in. dia. with 3 in. between supports) revealed low values of 3·4–10 ft-lb at room temperature, and generally these values decreased by 30% at −100° C. While, in terms of the Charpy V-notch test used for steels, the energy absorbed to fracture is low, the author states that provided suitable design factors are adopted such castings may be safely used down to −40° C. Still lower service temperatures can be tolerated if shock loading is not encountered. It is to be noted that the specimen for impact tests on cast irons is unnotched, this type of specimen gives finer grading of results over the smaller range of energy values encountered.

Malleable and Nodular Cast Irons

These two forms are distinct from the common grey irons in that the graphite is present in the form of rounded nodules. Malleable iron (first introduced in 1722) is still used extensively for small repetition castings. It is produced by annealing an originally hard and brittle white iron, containing little or no graphite, at 920/950° C for several days. Castings are packed in boxes containing an oxidizing agent such as iron ore, and the carbon combined as cementite is precipitated in nodular form. This results in a product called 'blackheart'—its name deriving from the black and silky appearance of the fracture. The resulting matrix is ferrite and the castings are relatively soft, tough and can be cold deformed.

Nodular irons are produced in the original casting during initial solidification by inoculation of the liquid metal with special alloys containing magnesium and cerium. They usually contain about 1% Ni as an alloying element.

Both malleable and nodular irons show a change from the ductile to the brittle state as the temperature is lowered. Gilbert[3] states that the temperature of this change depends on test conditions, the highest temperature occurring when a notched impact specimen is used. Annealed ferritic irons show an increase in tensile strength down to −100° C. If, however, the matrix is pearlitic, strength increases down to −80° C and thereafter decreases.

Charpy impact values for malleable irons vary from 12 to 27 ft-lb at room temperature falling to 3–6 ft-lb at −100° C, the lower value in each case applying to the notched specimen and the higher to the unnotched specimen. The tensile strength of blackheart malleable iron is relatively low (25 tons/in²); its 0·2% proof stress being of the order of 13 tons/in² and its elongation about 20%. For use at sub-zero temperatures much stronger irons have been produced by developing a pearlitic matrix in place of the ferrite after annealing. This can be done by varying the composition, for example, by increasing the manganese content from 0·4% to 1·0% and also by arresting the annealing operation and allowing the casting to cool in air. Such castings may also be quenched and tempered (similarly to a steel). As a result tensile strengths of 30–40 tons/in² and 0·2% proof stress values of 27–36 tons/in² can be achieved.

In spite of these appreciable strength properties, the malleable irons are generally inferior to the cast nodular irons with respect to low-temperature toughness. By oil hardening and tempering a cast iron of the following basic composition—

Total C %	Si %	Mn %	S %	P %	Ni %
3·55	1·5	0·38	0·020	0·020	0·85

—the following properties are obtainable:

Table 9. *Properties of hardened and tempered and annealed ferritic iron*

Treatment	0·2% proof stress (tons in²)	Ultimate strength (tons/in²)	Elongation (%)	Impact properties (unnotched testpiece)	
				Transition temperature (°C)	Max. energy absorbed (ft-lb)
Oil hardened, tempered, furnace cooled	33·9	43·3	8·5	−100	31·5
Hardened in oil, tempered, water quenched	39·4	49·4	6·5	−100	38·0
Fully annealed and furnace cooled	16·3	25·6	28·0	−110	97·0

The effect of increasing the silicon and phosphorus contents above the values shown is detrimental. The ductile/brittle transition temperature is increased and temper brittleness is developed in a manner identical with that encountered in steels.

Alloy Cast Irons

According to their microstructures these materials can be classified as follows:

Acicular Irons. This type of cast iron is produced by the addition of 1·5–3·0% Ni and 0·5–1·5% Mo. The structure consists of graphite and a matrix of acicular (needle-like) ferrite with some retained austenite. Tensile strengths vary from 21 to 30 tons/in². Charpy values (using a $\frac{5}{8}$ in. diam. round specimen) range from 13 to 20 ft-lb at room temperature. These irons are characterized by a phase change between −47° C and −64° C, the retained austenite changing to martensite. In consequence, the impact values decrease to 5–10 ft-lb at −130° C.

Martensitic Irons. An iron containing about 3·0% total C and 1·5–2·0% Si, if alloyed with 4·5–5·0% Ni, consists of graphite and martensite. It is very hard (340 B.H.N.) and is not used for low-temperature applications. Charpy values range from 10 ft-lb at room temperature, falling to 5 ft-lb at −130° C.

Austenitic Irons. These irons usually contain 2·5–3·0% C, 2·0–3·5% Si and 0·5–5·0% Mn. The alloying elements used to produce a graphite-austenite structure are 10–15% Ni, 1–2% Cr and 6–8% Cu. Small quantities of free carbides may be present in the structure. At room temperature the tensile strengths are low, from 6 to 11 tons/in², as compared with other cast irons. Their impact resistance may increase depending on composition, with decreasing temperature down to $-120°$ C if the structure contains no free carbides. A progressive decrease of impact resistance (due to the austenite-martensite transformation) follows at lower temperatures. The austenite phase is, however, much more stable than in the acicular irons, transformation temperatures being as low as $-175°$ C. It is this class of alloy cast irons, therefore, which is used for extremely low-temperature applications. Room temperature impact values may be 16–18 ft-lb, rising to 28 ft-lb between $-70°$ and $-100°$ C, thereafter falling to about 15 ft-lb at $-130°$ C ($\frac{5}{8}$ in. diam. specimen).

Steel Castings

Steel castings involve the production of liquid steel with or without alloy additions by any of the usual methods. As in the case of iron castings there is no deformation by subsequent hot work; therefore required metallurgical and mechanical properties can only be developed or improved by heat-treatment, which may consist of annealing or normalizing, or, in the case of certain alloy compositions, by quenching and tempering. The weights of iron and steel castings may range from a few ounces to 100 tons or more. Cross-sectional areas of various parts of the same casting may vary considerably and consequently their cooling rates may also vary. It is obvious therefore that there must be different degrees of segregation of non-metallics in various parts of a large casting of intricate shape.

The bulk density of a casting cannot equal the density of a wrought product of the same composition and therefore low or ambient temperature properties tend to be slightly inferior.

Engineering castings are made of steels of widely different compositions—from a killed mild steel, in which the carbon content is 0·25% max. (to ensure weldability) to complex steels containing up to 0·45% C with additions of nickel, chromium and molybdenum in varying proportions. The cast steels cover a tensile strength range from 28/35 tons/in² to 50/55 tons/in². Non-alloy steels are usually fully annealed between 850° and 950° C depending on composition and are furnace cooled. Alloy castings are normalized and tempered between 600° and 650° C.

Annealed or normalized mild steel castings have the same transition characteristics as hot-rolled mild steel and an Izod impact value of 20 ft-lb at room temperature is an average level.

Castings such as propellers, or propeller blades intended for ice-breaking ships, are subject to more stringent requirements, 15 ft-lb Izod at $-10°$ C being a minimum. This improved level is secured (as in hot-rolled steels) by grain refining with aluminium.

The plain C–Mn cast steels display increasing brittleness as the carbon increases. At low-carbon levels the transition temperature is lowered as manganese increases. Fine grain practice ensures the maximum notch toughness but since Izod values are only within the range 10–30 ft-lb at room temperature, the simple ferrite-pearlite steels are limited in their applications to low-temperature service conditions.

Satisfactory toughness properties down to $-50°$ C can be secured by using alloy compositions in the quenched and tempered condition, thereby producing a bainitic structure. There are limitations as to size and thickness since, depending on the composition used, depth hardenability will vary. Nickel is the principal alloying element used (from 1 to 4%) with 0·75–1·0% Cr and 0·25–0·50% Mo. Oil quenching is applied to avoid distortion. Low-alloy castings up to 2·5 in. thick, oil quenched and tempered have Izod impact values of 30–50 ft-lb at room temperature and, depending on the carbon content (up to 0·30%), yield and tensile strengths of 25 to 45 tons/in² and 35 to 50 tons/in² respectively.

For the most severe low-temperature service conditions it is essential to produce the casting in one of the austenitic steels (see chapter 14) in which the structure is f.c.c. and therefore does not pass through a ductile-brittle transition range. Suitable alloys are low in carbon content (0·10% C) and contain 18–20% Cr and 8–10% Ni. Additions of 2–3% W or Mo may be made and such steels are usually 'stabilized' by the addition of 0·15–0·25% Ti. The castings are readily weldable and may therefore be attached as fittings to vessels made from rolled plate. As a result of stabilization by titanium, the migration and deposition of carbides to grain boundaries, which would otherwise occur in the heat-affected zone of a weld, is inhibited. Consequently, weld decay through localized corrosion does not occur.

Austenitic castings have an Izod value of 50–60 ft-lb at room temperature and their impact level shows only a small decrease down to $-190°$ C.

It is observable that castings of all kinds are generously designed—an ordinary valve body being a familiar example. Apart from any intrinsic level of mechanical properties at low temperatures, there is some assurance against the initiation of brittle fracture by reason of total strength. Castings are designed purposely with very generous fillet radii, which considerably reduce the possibility of high local stress concentrations in service. Generous fillets are also necessary to avoid hot tears in the casting during solidification in the mould.

Steel Forgings

Small forgings are made from hot-rolled blooms or billets cut to suitable unit lengths. Large forgings are produced from individual cast steel ingots. The fact that both materials undergo hot work to develop the required shape guarantees a greater uniformity of structure than that produced in a casting. When followed by a suitable heat-treatment: normalizing, or quenching and tempering, low-temperature properties equivalent to those of a rolled steel of the same composition are secured.

In the case of massive forgings of large cross-section a further qualification is necessary. These forgings possess limitations in the degree of uniformity of properties similar to those encountered in very large thick plates. Increase in total mass obviously widens the range limits of the properties. An example is a very large shaft for a turbine forged from a 100-ton ingot. The shaft must be forged so that its central axis coincides with the axis of the ingot. If the maximum diameter of the shaft at some part is appreciably larger than in other parts, the low-temperature properties near the surface will differ from those nearer the axis. These properties will also differ from end to end of the shaft on account of 'ingotism'.

Test specimens may be radial, longitudinal or circumferential. In spite of this, some forgings may possess certain advantages over fabricated plate. A hollow forged boiler drum is made from an ingot which has been pierced down its central axis and the heavily segregated material thereby removed. The pierced blank is then placed on a mandrel and expanded into a hollow cylinder of uniform wall thickness. Circumferential properties of the wall are therefore likely to be more uniform than if the cylinder is constructed from a number of plates, hot pressed and welded together to produce the same size.

In order to limit the range of properties which would otherwise occur in large masses, rules and practices such as those laid down by Lloyd's, apply to the manufacture of forgings. A prime requisite is that a fully-killed steel must be used. The ingot must be poured 'wide end up' and provided with an adequate feeder head to eliminate pipe within the ingot proper. Top and bottom discards must be sufficient to ensure freedom from shrinkage cavities and harmful segregation. The forging itself must be as near as possible to the required finished shape and size and the ingot must be worked (if practicable) so as to ensure that the metal flows in the most favourable direction to suit the mode of stressing to be encountered in service. This is particularly important in large crankshafts.

An adequate amount of hot work is ensured by limiting the maximum cross-sectional area of any part of the piece to some fraction of the cross-section of the ingot used, for example, to one third where the length of any section is greater than its diameter, or to two thirds if the length of any section is less than its diameter. For forged discs or rings the finished thickness must not be more than one half of the rolled or cast length from which it was forged.

While many forgings are provided from mild steel, the range of compositions available is identical with that for rolled steels. Standard compositions are given in B.S. 970 which includes both plain and alloy steels in bloom and billet form. Minimum requirements for mechanical properties, including room temperature impact values, are given together with 'ruling sections' in which these properties are securable. The ruling section for a particular steel governs its properties by reason of its depth hardenability, the larger the section the lower being the properties.

In the above specification all impact values are those obtained by the Izod test at room temperature. While such values are not directly convertible to Charpy equivalents, this test is also capable of placing steels in an order of merit with respect to notch toughness. The more recent adoption of the Charpy test as a standard for plate testing has created an anomaly with respect to the impact values of forgings and castings.

REFERENCES

1. G. N. J. Gilbert. *Symposium on Brittle Behaviour of Metals at Low Temperatures.* A.S.T.M. 1954, Spec. Publ. 158.
2. G. N. J. Gilbert. *Iron Steel.* April, May, June, 1964.
3. G. N. J. Gilbert. *J. Br. Cast Iron Res. Assoc.*, 6 (1957), 484.

CHAPTER 8

THE SIGNIFICANCE OF HYDROGEN WITH RESPECT TO STEELS FOR AMBIENT AND LOW-TEMPERATURE USE

Sources of Hydrogen in Steel

Hydrogen is introduced unavoidably into steel during its manufacture in the furnace while the bath is in the liquid condition. Contamination by hydrogen may arise from the use of rusty scrap in the charge and from damp lime and ore or mill scale used to work the charge. By far the biggest source, however, is the atmosphere in a fuel-fired furnace. Open-hearth furnaces fired by gas, oil or tar, generate water vapour as a product of combustion and the slags used to effect purification of the metal, particularly those in the basic processes, are capable of absorbing large amounts of water vapour. The slag in turn, by contact with the metal below, is capable of passing hydrogen to the steel, the amount depending on conditions. Basic open-hearth slags are known to be capable of dissolving up to 20 c.c. H_2/100 g of slag, and steel at tapping may contain 3 or more c.c. H_2/100 g of metal.

According to work done by the author it is important, in order to secure a low hydrogen content in the steel, to develop a slag with a low FeO activity. One would expect that severely oxidizing conditions (i.e. a high FeO activity) would prevent the entry of hydrogen to the bath, but a detailed study of a number of open-hearth charges indicates that it is more important to use a slag with a low FeO activity (which does not necessarily prevent hydrogen from entering), because such a slag facilitates the escape of hydrogen from the bath to the atmosphere above. The vigour of the 'boil' in producing carbon monoxide gas then acts as an effective cleanser—the bubbles of CO sweeping out the hydrogen from the metal.

It has been noted previously that the general level of hydrogen existing in the steel varies with the process used. The L.D. process using pure oxygen and a relatively uninterrupted blow, produces the lowest hydrogen content (about 1·5–3·5 c.c./100 g), while the Kaldo process also using oxygen produces somewhat higher levels because blowing is interrupted more frequently.

During these interruptions the vessel becomes filled with humid air. The hydrogen may be 2·5–4·5 c.c./100 g. The basic open-hearth furnace, particularly when fired by oil atomized with steam, may produce steel with 3–6 c.c. H_2/100 g of metal at tapping. The acid open-hearth furnace, because it uses slags which are chiefly silicates of iron and manganese (in which hydrogen is soluble to a much smaller degree), generally produces steels lower in hydrogen than those produced in the basic furnace. In the past, the superior ductility of good acid steel has been attributed to this fact.

The Mechanism of Hydrogen Damage

Hydrogen is present in solution in steel in the monatomic form. The hydrogen atom is small in comparison with that of iron and therefore it occupies interstitial positions within the lattice. It can diffuse both inwards and outwards at elevated temperatures. The embrittlement which occurs as a result of a high hydrogen content is generally held to be due to the gas coming out of true solution during cooling and accumulating as molecular hydrogen at various sites within the metal such as at true voids or actual cracks and as cloud precipitates in the vicinity of dislocations. This diffusion to local sites builds up internal pressures which can produce minute internal fractures. When a steel specimen high in hydrogen is completely fractured, as in a slow bend test, these internal fissures become apparent as small silvery areas— variously called flakes, fissures or grey spots. Examples of these are seen when weld metal high in hydrogen is fractured.

Non-metallic inclusions present in steels may also act as nucleation sites for the precipitation of molecular hydrogen. This might be expected, since the ability of some non-metallics to dissolve hydrogen is greater than that of the metal. Hence there are local high concentrations in the vicinity of inclusions. The hydrogen may conceivably form a film round the inclusion therefore during cooling. Some evidence for this appears to be indicated by the fact that microscopic cracks in the metal are indeed associated with inclusions (see Plate 7).

The Effect of Steel Composition

Early occurrences of damage to steel by hydrogen were first noted in medium- and high-carbon forgings and rails containing 0·50/0·70% C. An association resulted, therefore, between hydrogen and a fairly high carbon level. It was assumed, because the higher carbon steels were not so severely oxidized in the furnace during manufacture, that hydrogen was more easily absorbed.

This is now known to be erroneous since hydrogen is evolved during the solidification of low-carbon rimming steels. Ordinary semi-killed mild steels containing 0·18/0·25% C and 0·55/0·70% Mn apparently do not suffer from severe hydrogen trouble. It may be that evidence is not revealed because of less detailed testing than is applied to other steels. Also, the manganese level is not as high as that of the notch tough varieties now made for use at sub-zero temperatures.

Experience however with the notch tough steels containing over 1% Mn and a relatively low carbon level has proved that H_2 is a source of trouble and the author has concluded that this level of manganese appreciably increases the solubility of the steel for H_2. A contributory factor is that ferro alloys, such as ferro-manganese, contain appreciable amounts of H_2 and the addition of larger quantities of this alloy to achieve the higher manganese level results necessarily in higher hydrogen contents in the steel.

No recent work is available on the additions of alloying elements to steel and their effects on its solubility for hydrogen. It is a fact, however, that low-alloy steels generally are prone to more difficulties which arise from hydrogen. Steels containing appreciable quantities of nickel ($> 1\cdot0\%$) are particularly prone to hydrogen pick-up. The consequences of contamination by hydrogen are some of the factors which contribute to the cost of the final product. The increased cost is consequently not proportional to the value of the alloys added. In many cases an increased level of rejections becomes inevitable.

Critical Parameters

Damage from hydrogen results when transformation stresses are present, that is, when cooling down from the austenitic state. The actual minimum content of hydrogen which will cause damage cannot be stated precisely. Depending upon a particular set of processing conditions 3 c.c. H_2/100 g metal may be a threshold value, below which damage will not occur, while in other cases 5 or 6 c.c. H_2/100 g may give no trouble. Flaking varies considerably with the composition, alloy content, thickness, rate of cooling and the degree of non-metallic segregation present in any mass. The rate of cooling is especially important. The slower this rate is, particularly when passing through the Ar_1 transformation range, the smaller are the resulting stresses. Very slow cooling below the Ar_1 temperature also favours diffusion of hydrogen outwards from the steel and the longer is the time occupied in cooling below this temperature the more effectively is the hydrogen content lowered. Diffusion is known to be easier (both into the metal and out of it) when the steel is in the body-centred (or α) state and a safeguard adopted with large forgings is to anneal for long periods at a sub-critical temperature, say 600/650° C. Diffusion outwards does not take place so easily in the austenitic (γ) state.

While a reduced cooling rate is always desirable, cracking can still occur on cooling within the 300/200° C range if the time taken is not long enough to allow sufficient hydrogen to diffuse out. There are also instances in which cracking has not occurred down to room temperature but has subsequently taken place after the mass has been at room temperature for some time, known as an 'incubation' period. If cracks do form under these conditions they indicate too short a cooling time. Hence an insufficient reduction of the hydrogen concentration still leaves the remaining concentration above the threshold value. Vacuum degassing of the steel while liquid is a modern method of overcoming difficulties due to hydrogen but where this is not possible then special cooling conditions and heat-treatments are necessary. These are best evolved empirically to suit the particular type of product and its mass in combination with the processing schedule.

Test Characteristics of Hydrogen-embrittled Steel

The state of hydrogen embrittlement is rendered apparent in a steel if the rate of straining during tensile testing is slow. Embrittlement, if present, is particularly marked at and about room temperature. Very slow tension or bending tests will then indicate a marked decrease in ductility. This is particularly evident in thick plates tested in tension through the thickness. However, results may be prejudiced adversely by the degree of cleanness. The more usual longitudinal or transverse tensile tests taken parallel to the surface do not show the effect of hydrogen so markedly, neither do the conventional Charpy tests even at relatively low temperatures. It is not impossible to visualize hydrogen as being one of the factors contributing to the spread of results obtained when testing commercial steels for impact characteristics, though no present proof exists that this is so. Cold straining to some degree, followed by testing at some period afterwards, will result in a marked decrease in ductility and this is usually attributed to the precipitation of hydrogen atoms as clouds in the vicinity of dislocations.

By far the most significant test which reveals the presence of hydrogen flakes in plates or other products is that of ultrasonic examination. The importance of this test with respect to steels intended for use at low service temperatures is very considerable. Such steels are nowadays almost invariably required to be guaranteed 'ultrasonically sound'. The presence of minute flakes arising from hydrogen condemns the product. These minute cracks may be likened to Griffith cracks and can therefore be regarded as potential sources of brittle failure, even though the conventional mechanical test results on a plate containing them may be perfectly satisfactory and well above the specified minima.

Experiences Encountered in the Ultrasonic Examination of Steel Plates

During an early period covering the production of several thousand tons of a special low-alloy steel (0·15% C max., 1% Mn, 1% Ni, 1% Cr, 0·40% Mo, 0·1% V) in the form of large plates varying from 0·75 to 3 in. thickness, many examples of hydrogen embrittlement were encountered, resulting in serious rejections. Each plate was required to be examined ultrasonically, in addition to the usual mechanical tests to determine 0·2% proof stress, ultimate tensile strength and elongation. A minimum Charpy impact value of 60 ft-lb at −40° C was stipulated with a maximum fracture crystallinity of 75%. The plates were supplied in the quenched and tempered condition to produce the required properties.

For ultrasonic examination each plate surface was marked into 1 ft squares by chalk lines and each square systematically examined—a map of the results being drawn for record purposes because of the importance of the application. Obviously interpretable faults, such as distinctive laminations caused by the inclusion of a portion of the pipe in the original ingot, were remedied by increasing the amount cropped off in subsequent casts at the slab stage. Additionally, however, many isolated defective areas occurred which bore no obvious relation to any ingot structure pattern. Sampling of these areas was carried out and microscopic examination revealed in most cases the presence of non-metallic inclusions to which are usually ascribed the poor ultrasonic response obtained. The interruption of the metallic continuity through the thickness of the plate by inclusions at any point under the probe gives rise to intermediate reflections of the ultrasonic beam. However, previous experience with thick plates made from a low-carbon high manganese steel suggested that the defective areas might indeed be due to the presence of minute hydrogen flakes possibly associated also with inclusions.

A process schedule was therefore devised which involved slow cooling the slabs (after their production from the ingot) in an unfired pit over 3–4 days by which time the temperature had dropped to 300/320° C. The slabs were then removed and dressed while hot with minimum delay and immediately charged into a preheating furnace which raised their temperature to 900° C. They were then transferred to a slab re-heating furnace proper and rolled to the required plates which were allowed to cool for ultrasonic examination. This treatment resulted in an improvement by reducing the number of defective plates. The assumption was therefore made that, in spite of a preliminary slow cool in the slab form, the hydrogen content was not being reduced below the threshold value and that either (a) flaking had occurred in the slabs and re-heating and rolling to plate had not eliminated them, or (b) flaking still occurred during cooling of the plate itself or at some time after. An additional treatment was therefore given to the plate shortly after rolling, that is, it was re-heated to a normalizing temperature and then allowed to cool. Inauguration of this final treatment reduced the number of faulty plates still further.

An examination however of the time-interval between the final rolling pass in the plate mill and the insertion of the plate into the normalizing furnace revealed that if the plate was not normalized within 10 hr after rolling, ultrasonic 'defects' were still present. Obviously this indicated the incubation of cracks at some time after cooling to a low temperature, 200/100° C approximately. The practice of normalizing of plates within 2–4 hr after rolling was then instituted. This reduced ultrasonic rejects to negligible proportions.

The mechanism of the prevention of hydrogen cracks in plates by a normalizing treatment a short time after actual rolling is not clear. It has been stated that sub-critical (i.e. below 700° C) annealing permits a maximum rate of diffusion of the hydrogen outwards. The time-interval involved in reaching this temperature during the final re-heating process is unlikely to be sufficient to permit any substantial amount of hydrogen to escape, especially from thicker plates. A feasible explanation is that at the last rolling stage, there

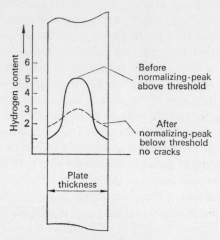

FIG. 27. Effect of normalizing on hydrogen gradient in a plate.

exists within the plate thickness a hydrogen concentration gradient shown schematically in Fig. 27. This gradient has developed and persisted from the slab stage and has resulted from slow cooling the slab. Subsequent re-heating in order to roll the plate has probably lessened the height of the peak concentration in the centre of the thickness, but to a degree insufficient to prevent the formation of flakes if allowed to cool in air. The final normalizing treatment therefore apparently reduces the peak concentration of hydrogen below the threshold value at which cracking occurs. This theory is difficult to prove, but the treatment adopted was undoubtedly effective and a final position was arrived at in which plates made from subsequent consecutive casts were entirely free from ultrasonic faults.

Such an experience raised doubts as to whether ultrasonic testing as carried out does indeed reveal non-metallic inclusions only. It is quite inconceivable

PLATE 9

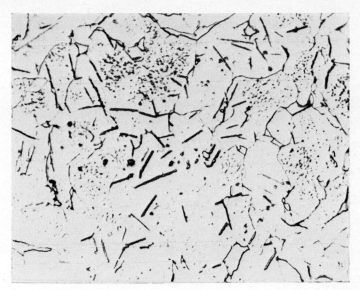

Brittle iron-nitride needles in weld metal from bare rod. Normalized.
$\times$ 750.

PLATE 10

$\frac{1}{2}$ in.

1 in.

$1\frac{1}{2}$ in.

2 in.

$2\frac{1}{2}$ in.

Base metal

0·04 in.
machined off

0·02 in.
machined off

Flame cut

Effect of cold bending on gas-cut and machined edges of plate.

that ultrasonic faults ceased under the final processing conditions because the steel became suddenly much cleaner and freer from non-metallic inclusions. Steelmaking experience precludes this possibility. All basic open-hearth steel contains inclusions. Dirtiness is a matter of degree and the cleanest steel can only be produced in the electric furnace using a two-slag process, the second one enabling the dissolved oxygen in the metal to be reduced to an extremely small level before final deoxidizing and alloying additions are made, thereby ensuring a minimum precipitation of non-metallics. An alternative method of securing a very clean steel is by vacuum melting and casting, which is costly on the commercial scale necessary for many common products, such as heavy plates.

A further doubt is introduced by the fact that when cutting the top slab from a rolled ingot, distinct evidence of piping may be revealed in the slab end nearest the ingot top. Because this is a discontinuity in the metal there are effectively two layers. Any trace of piping must be eliminated. The practice adopted therefore is to shorten this slab by further cutting until the visible lamination is just removed. The newly cut end therefore constitutes a section through the ingot just at the bottom of the shrinkage cavity. In large ingots there is always a considerable concentration of non-metallics below the bottom of the pipe, the metal in this vicinity being the last to solidify. A plate rolled from such a slab and given the described heat-treatment necessary to avoid hydrogen flaking will however reveal a perfectly acceptable ultrasonic standard in spite of an area of relatively concentrated non-metallics.

A Possible Explanation

A distinct lamination is plainly revealed by ultrasonic examination. Its shape may be accurately outlined and its position plotted. It must be realized, however, that the lamination involves two extra internal surfaces parallel to the two outer surfaces of the plate, these internal surfaces being separated by a film of gas. Hence a reflection indicating its presence is obtained on the oscilloscope tube. The wave impulse is here passing through metal to a gas layer and the change in relative density from that of the metal (approx. 7·8) to that of the gas (approx. 0·01) is very large. If, however, the impulse passes through the metal to an inclusion without an intermediate gas film, then the change in relative density is from 7·8 to 2·5/3·5 (the density of the slag inclusions). The difference in density is therefore much less, and unless the inclusion is backed up by numerous others forming layers below it, then the possibility exists that dirtiness due to normal inclusions gives no response.

In the case, however, of a plate having a sufficiently high hydrogen content to have caused permanent damage in the form of minute flaking, then gas films are present internally, both round the inclusions and as discrete films filling the minute cracks themselves. Such cracks are often associated

I

with inclusions as small tails which are not always easy to see under the optical microscope. Under these conditions we have the large change in density to initiate the oscilloscope response and 'faults' become apparent. In this connection it is interesting to note that the calibration of an ultrasonic testing set is accomplished by using standard steel blocks that contain drilled holes giving precisely the density change conditions instanced above.

For fuller information, B.S. 2704 (1956) 'Ultrasonic Reference Standards and Recommendations for their Use' may be consulted. This specification was under revision in 1964. Reference is made in it to 'flaw' detection without an attempt to define the nature of the 'flaw'.

To summarize, ultrasonic test results are significant with respect to steels intended for use at zero and sub-zero temperatures, in terms of both human safety and economics. The possibilities of brittle behaviour are enhanced by the presence of hydrogen flaking not only in plates intended for use in pressure vessels but in important forgings. While normal mechanical tests may fail to discriminate between acceptable and inferior material, the combination of these with ultrasonic examination probably provides the maximum assurance possible against brittle fracture.

CHAPTER 9

WELDING AND LOW TEMPERATURES

Introduction

Examination of any riveted structure, such as a bridge, ship's hull, storage tank or boiler reveals that, by reason of additional metal at the joints between the component plates, excess weight is introduced over that theoretically and practically necessary. Older types of horizontal boilers have longitudinal joints closed by butt straps, that is, additional strips of plate (usually of the same thickness as that of the shell itself) overlapping the joint between the two plate edges butted together. The straps are fastened by two or more rows of rivets with projecting hemispherical heads. Circumferential joints were usually lap joints, that is, one plate edge was flared and the adjacent plate edge fitted into it for a sufficient distance to allow rivets to be inserted at suitable intervals round the circle. Pressure tightness depended on accuracy of fitting and caulking of the joints. This was done by cold deforming the metal with a tool at the junction of the strap with the plate surface or at the junction of plate with plate in the case of the circumferential seam.

It is obvious that no theoretical need exists for this method of construction if a continuous metallic joint is securable between separate plate edges— always supposing that such a joint possesses properties equivalent to those of the parent plates which contain the joint. The vessel is then in effect made from one large plate.

Joining by welding possesses this objective and a valuable saving in weight results from the method. The growth of welding after the First World War developed rapidly as a consequence of restrictions imposed on the weight of the defeated nations' naval vessels. Welding offered a significant contribution to weight saving and at the same time permitted the development of other advantages such as higher speeds for equivalent horsepower.

Essentially, welding implies the incipient fusion of the two surfaces to be joined so that these are united by a liquid metal which subsequently solidifies. If the two surfaces are brought to a welding heat without the addition of liquid metal, then pressure between the two is necessary to unite them. An

115

example of this is the drawing of a flat strip preheated to a welding temperature through a conical circular die thereby producing a tube. The seam weld runs along the tube. For composite structures such a method cannot be adopted, and edges to be joined are usually prepared by machining or gas cutting to form a V-shaped trough which is then filled in with molten metal, provided from an external source.

For most structures, welding is carried out by the arc process, that is, an arc may be struck between an electrode and the base of the trough thereby progressively melting off the electrode and depositing the molten metal. At the same time the temperature of the sides of the trough is raised to incipient fusion point, thus ensuring a true metallic bond. This method is by far the most commonly used. Gas welding can also be employed, the necessary temperature being developed by an oxygen-gas blow-pipe, and in this process the metal to be deposited is supplied by a feeder or filler rod. A more recent process for the welding of thick plates is the electro-slag method in which an electrode, in the form of wire, is continuously fed into a gap between the two edges to be joined. This is done with the seam to be welded in a vertical position, the liquid metal being retained and cooled within the gap by water-cooled copper shoes which are automatically raised on both sides as the gap is filled in. For large gaps between very thick plates several electrodes can be used simultaneously, and joints 16 or more square inches in area can be made, thus enabling plates 6 or 8 in. thick to be joined. It is essential to refine the grain-size of electro-slag welds by normalizing, in order to secure adequate toughness.

Basic Characteristics of the Weld Joint

Edges of plates to be welded are usually chamfered suitably to provide a V- or double V-joint for filling in by successive runs of weld deposit. This applies where the edges of the plate are in the same plane, thus producing a 'butt' joint. If an edge is welded to a surface then a 'fillet' weld is produced (see Plate 8).

As a result of the deposition of molten metal at a temperature sufficiently high to fuse the adjacent solid surfaces to some depth which depends on the current-carrying capacity of the electrode used (i.e. its diameter), the final weld joint as a whole is characterized by the presence of three main zones.

(a) The parent metal is little affected a short distance back from the original edge.

(b) The heat-affected zone (or 'H.A.Z.') is the original edge which has been incipiently fused.

(c) The deposited molten metal forms the bond between two heat-affected zones.

The heat-affected zone usually possesses the greatest hardness because here the incipient fusion caused by the adjacent deposited liquid metal is accompanied by rapid heat abstraction by conductivity through the parent metal. In effect a quench is achieved. The weld itself is usually intermediate in hardness between that of the H.A.Z. and the parent metal. This volume, which may be built up by dozens of individual runs in the case of a thick plate, is in effect cast metal, that is, cooling has taken place from the liquid state giving relatively large crystal grains in the structure.

The hardness, however, of both the H.A.Z. and the deposit is also a function of the electrode used. Because the weld metal has a cast structure with

Table 10. *Composition of some weld deposits*[1]

A.W.S.* classification	Electrode coating	Type of alloy deposit	Composition of deposited metal						Stress-relieving temperature (°C)	Ductile-brittle transition temperature (°C)
			C	Mn	Si	Ni	Mo	V		
E 6010	High cellulose + sodium salts	C–Mn (mild steel)	0·07	0·47	0·02	—	—	—	None	−60°
E 6015	Low H₂ sodium salts	C–Mn	0·08	0·55	0·25	—	—	—	None	−60°
E 6020	High Fe oxide compounds	C–Mn	0·11	0·40	0·12	—	—	—	None	−50°
E 7010	—	C–Mn–Mo	0·07	0·34	0·15	—	0·52	—	None	−70°
E 7010	—	C–Mn–Mo	0·07	0·34	0·15	—	0·52	—	650° C	−65°
E 8015	—	C–Mn–Ni–Mo	0·08	0·61	0·15	2·15	0·45	—	620° C	−75°
E 8015	—	C–Mn–Ni	0·08	0·79	0·19	3·55	—	—	620° C	−125°
E 10015	—	C–Mn–Mo	0·16	1·97	0·41	—	0·43	—	None	−110°
E 10015	—	C–Mn–Mo	0·16	1·97	0·41	—	0·43	—	590° C	−70°
E 12016	—	C–Mn–Ni–Mo–V	0·06	0·90	0·30	1·80	0·80	0·25	None	−90°

* A.W.S. = American Welding Society.

its inherent weaknesses, then if the deposit were of the same composition precisely as that of the parent plate, inferior mechanical properties would result. Hence, in order that the properties of the weld metal in the cast state can equal (or be superior to) those of the parent metal, alloying elements are purposely introduced by means of the electrode. The electrode is usually a low carbon mild steel which may have a relatively high manganese content to compensate for loss of manganese by oxidation during its passage across the arc gap. Additionally, nickel and molybdenum can be introduced into the molten metal via the flux coating on the rod. This coating is primarily intended to produce a liquid slag to cover continuously the weld metal as a protection against oxidation and gas absorption.

Table 10 gives the composition of some weld deposits and their ductility-transition temperatures as determined by Charpy (keyhole notch) impact tests. The first three electrodes listed are suitable for the welding of mild steel. While both carbon and manganese contents are relatively low compared with those of a mild steel plate of 26–33 tons/in² tensile strength, deposited metal of these compositions achieves the strength of the parent plate because of the rapid cooling of the weld metal, that is, sufficient hardening takes place.

The remainder of the electrodes have the alloying elements nickel, molybdenum and vanadium introduced either singly or in combination—in order to achieve still higher tensile properties for welding high strength steels. It is to be noted that a stress-relieving treatment at 590°–650° C after welding significantly raises the ductility-transition temperature (e.g. E 7010 and E 10015) and this must be taken into account in considering the properties of any weld metal for low-temperature service.

Protection against Contamination

Oxygen and Nitrogen

Modified welding techniques other than by the use of a flux-coated electrode are designed to use a bare filler wire while at the same time providing protection against contamination by the gases O_2 and N_2. The submerged arc process is an example of a technique suitable for welding in the downhand position. The electrode, in the form of a bare wire, passes vertically through a continuously fed layer of granular flux which is melted so that the arc is submerged. In another process, carbon dioxide gas can be fed near the electrode

Table 11. *Izod impact results for welds made with bare and coated electrodes*

Electrode	Series I, as-welded	Series II, normalized
Bare wire	14, 4, 6 ft-lb —	1, 3, 1 ft-lb 1, 2, 2
Coated wire (a)	16, 9, 13	8, 4, 5
(b)	29, 17, 20	17, 10, 12
(c)	40, 26, 37	23, 26, 26
Parent metal (plate)	50, 87, 47 43, 70, 39	90, 40, 90 40, 70, 58

end to surround the arc, thereby exercising a shielding effect, while argon, a completely inert gas, can also be used as a shield—the argonarc process. This latter is far more costly but yields excellent welds.

Manual welding involves the use of special flux-coated electrodes to form the protective slag layer. Without such protection excessive quantities of nitrogen are absorbed by the deposited metal resulting in complete brittleness of the weld. The results shown in Table 11 were obtained by the present author many years ago.

Specimens of mild steel plate $\frac{1}{2}$ in. thick were edge machined to give a 60° single V-joint for butt welding. After welding with various electrodes, Izod V-notch testpieces were prepared so that the notch was located in the centre of the weld deposit. The impact tests were carried out at room temperature.

The experiments indicate that a flux cover is essential to keep out nitrogen and prevent excessive oxidation and that different fluxes can influence the weld toughness. Normalizing after welding, as shown by series II, resulted in a deterioration of toughness by precipitating the nitrogen in the form of brittle needles of iron nitride (see Plate 9).

Hydrogen

This gas can be absorbed by weld metal. If present in the deposit it can produce cracks which appear in the fractured testpiece as 'fish eyes' or flakes. These are areas of a silvery appearance quite distinct from the more fibrous appearance of the remainder. They possess this appearance because they are the boundary surfaces of ellipsoidal cracks and are not oxidized. Local accumulations of H_2 emerging from solution can build up pressures sufficient to cause rupture. Hydrogen cracking occurs at approximately 300° C and below, and an incubation period may intervene between reaching room temperature and the occurrence of cracking. The source of the gas can be a humid atmosphere and the composition of the flux on the electrode. Cellulose-type coverings are high in hydrogen. It is necessary, for all high-strength welds, to use special low-hydrogen electrodes baked just prior to use, at 350°/400° C to eliminate moisture.

Experimental evidence suggests that hydrogen in the weld metal increases notch sensitivity. If, therefore, hydrogen can be diffused out of the joint then increased notch toughness should result. Stress relief at 600/620° C assists in this diffusion, but it is of little use if cracks due to hydrogen are already present. As previously shown, there are precipitation effects which offset the benefit of stress-relieving, for example, an increase in the transition temperature of the weld metal (see Table 10—E 7010 and E 10015).

Low-hydrogen electrodes used without preheat can produce joints which are as tough as those obtained after stress-relieving welds produced from cellulose-coated electrodes. The best results are obtained by using low-hydrogen electrodes and some degree of preheat depending on thickness. These electrodes usually contain a fluoride in the flux coating, and fumes may be objectionable to operating welders when working in confined spaces, for example, the bilges of a ship. Ventilation is obviously important.

The Consequences of Welding

In relation to the service performance of composite structures required to operate at ambient or low temperatures, the presence of welds is accompanied by certain inherent features which have contributed in the past to the problem of brittle fracture. This does not imply that welding is dangerous in its consequences. It may prove to be so if not sufficiently well controlled and the quality of workmanship, properties of the parent metal and suitability of the electrode are extremely important.

Because the welding operation involves the application of liquid metal then shrinkage is involved during solidification. If therefore the two edges to be joined are constrained sufficiently during welding, shrinkage or thermal cracks can be produced on cooling. Even in their absence, stresses across the joint are set up and these may be sufficient to cause cracks subsequently when additional working stresses are superimposed under service conditions.

The possibility of producing thermal cracks as distinct from the previously mentioned hydrogen cracks is assisted by the enormous temperature gradient developed across the weld. This may be as large as 1500° C during the welding operation. It is to reduce this temperature gradient that preheating the edges to be welded is carried out. Successive layers, in multi-layer welds, can be deposited on preceding layers and the shorter the time-interval between the two operations then the higher is the effective preheat (or 'interpass' temperature). This may, however, introduce complications depending on whether the seam to be welded is 'vertical' or 'overhead'. Overheated weld metal may result in subsequent deposits remaining more fluid and the behaviour of the run in the vertical and overhead position is consequently more difficult to control. Such welds, therefore, can develop faults.

The proper time-interval between passes is therefore important. If the interpass temperature is too high and if the overall cooling rate is very low, the heat-affected zone may develop coarse grain-size and may transform to massive ferrite or upper bainite, both these structures possessing poor toughness properties.

Stress-relieving

Shrinkage stresses in a weld become important as the temperature falls to about 700° C. Above this temperature the stresses are absorbed by plastic flow of the weld metal. It is also above this temperature that ordinary steels are hot worked and consequently there is no loss of ductility. In order to lessen shrinkage stresses below 700° C, post-heating may be applied. This has the effect of retarding the overall cooling rate and so prevents the formation of underbead cracking. For important pressure vessels the whole structure is often stress-relieved by heating it in a furnace to 600/620° C for several hours. Existing atomic power station reactors in the form of large spheres some 70 ft in diameter made of 3 and 4 in. thick plates were stress-relieved after completion of welding, by heating to within this temperature range using stainless steel resistors.

In some cases, when, owing to size, stress relief of the complete fabrication cannot be accomplished, local stress-relieving can be achieved. A circumferential weld in a large vessel may be stress-relieved by wrapping the seam and some distance on either side of it with electrically heated resistors in the form of flexible blankets or tapes and then covering with light insulation material.

In other obvious cases, bridges, ships and very large field storage tanks (which may be 210 ft in diameter and 40/60 ft high) cannot be treated in any completely satisfactory way. The overall quality of the fabrication and its ability to withstand the locked-up stresses resulting from the various welds, must be accepted.

Fabrications which require to be machined subsequently are stress-relieved. In the initially fabricated job compressive and tensile stresses balance each other to give a stability of shape. Subsequent machining of various parts may disturb this balance and serious warping may result, unless the fabrication has been previously stress-relieved.

Other Weld Characteristics

A welded joint may display porosity (as distinct from cracking). This can arise from weld metal which is high in sulphur, i.e. above 0·06%. It may also arise from a high sulphur content in the parent plate, dirty surfaces contaminated by paint, rust or oil and moisture in the joint. The presence of slag inclusions caused by the failure to remove slag from a previous pass may also give rise to porosity.

Two further faults may be present under certain conditions: (1) there may be serious 'undercutting', or (2) the added weld metal may not penetrate sufficiently into the parent metal.

The former arises from the melting or burning away of the parent metal at the toe of the weld. In a butt weld this may reduce the effective thickness of the plate locally thereby forming a notch and it usually results from the use of both too heavy a current and electrode in an endeavour to secure good penetration. Lack of penetration is the reverse of this and results from too small a current and electrode gauge for the thickness of plate involved (Plate 8(a)). The rate of heat input in welding may be expressed by the arc power in watts (i.e. amps × volts) divided by the speed of travel of the electrode. Manufacturers of electrodes recommend voltage and current ranges which should be used. These recommendations have been evolved under test conditions to develop optimum properties. All welding conditions should be defined, that is, the electrode diameter, plate thickness, details of edge preparation and position of weld when conducting any comparative tests. An example might be $\frac{1}{4}$ in. plate, single V-joint, no preheat, $\frac{5}{32}$ in. coated electrode, 125 amps— 80 volts 10 in./min., single-pass weld.

The Concept of 'Weldability'

While all steels, both plain and alloy, are theoretically capable of being joined by welding, the statement is not universally true. In practice, conditions introducing difficulties may exist and these can prevent the achievement of an adequate and satisfactory standard.

It is, for instance, not economical to apply preheat to every joint in the welding of a ship or bridge. Welding must, in practice, be conducted often on sites where ambient temperatures may fluctuate considerably over the period of construction. Hence the rate of cooling of the weld at times may vary, cold weather obviously increasing the risk of cracking by rapid shrinkage. Fabrication inside a shop which has a more constant temperature is likely to produce more standard results. This adverse influence of a variable ambient temperature is obviously greater if the carbon content of the material is high. As the carbon content increases, rapid chilling approaches the effect of severe quenching and this may result in the formation of a hard and brittle martensitic structure in the vicinity of the weld. The superimposition of variable stresses as the structure grows in size may then be sufficient to initiate a crack in this vicinity which can give rise to a brittle fracture. Such fractures can occur in ordinary mild steel during winter and are not unknown during ship fabrication.

An accompaniment of a weld crack under severely stressed conditions may be the propagation of the crack through the adjacent plate or plates. Riveting as a method of joining possessed some advantages in this respect because such a crack, if it occurred, was usually confined to that plate and did not cross the riveted joint to enter the adjacent plate.

Increasing the carbon content of the steel or weld metal increases the risk of forming a brittle deposit and similarly, other alloying elements which may be added to steel for the purpose of increasing strength may behave adversely in the same way. If welding conditions can be favourably developed and maintained then it is possible to weld satisfactorily higher carbon or alloy steels. Preheat and post-heat, which delay and reduce the rate of cooling so as to prevent the formation of brittle martensite, are therefore requisites. Low-hydrogen electrodes also assist under given conditions and these two features enable a steel with a certain maximum level of carbon (or its equivalent in alloy content) to be welded. While preheating the edges to be welded and the application of post-heat to the final weld is possible, practical difficulties and extra cost involved may impose limitations. During the manual welding of a complex structure, it may not be possible to preheat at all. Even if this is practicable in the sheltered conditions of a construction shop, it is not possible to preheat beyond a certain temperature since working conditions for the operator may become physically unbearable. It is impossible for a man to seam weld inside a boiler drum 4 or 5 ft in diameter if the preheat necessary is of the order of 300° C.

In practice over the years, various formulae have been evolved for the desirable composition limits of a steel which can be welded without risk of cracking and without preheat with normal craftsmanship. One such formula was established by Dearden and O'Neill[2] who stated that if the C + Mn/6 was equal to or less than 0·43 then no cracks were formed when using an ordinary cellulose-coated electrode of matching mechanical properties. The formula is known as the 'carbon equivalent formula' in which 0·01% C and 0·06% Mn are considered to be interchangeable. The original formula has undergone modifications in the light of experience and Lloyd's Register of Shipping at present applies the following form for higher tensile steels.

Carbon Equivalent (C.E.)

$$= C + \frac{Mn}{6} + \frac{Cr + Mo + V}{5} + \frac{Ni + Cu}{15} \leqslant 0.43.$$

This empirical formula is more comprehensive since it takes into account elements which may be present as residuals in modern mass-produced steels and which are regarded as detrimental to weldability in their cumulative effect.*

It is not customary to take into account small quantities of sulphur and phosphorus which are present in all steels since the maximum permissible level of these is dictated by the original specification for the steel and at these maximum values they do not exert any deleterious effect. Most steels are now made to a maximum of 0·045% each of sulphur and phosphorus and in practice are often considerably under these values. Other alloying elements which exert considerable effects on either the properties or heat-treatment characteristics are far more important. Elements which can conceivably affect mechanical properties and weld characteristics (even in small quantities below 0·1%) and not yet taken into account in any formula are boron, titanium, nitrogen, niobium, tantalum, etc. The effects of these elements are not known. They are, however, only used in very small concentrations.

In any C.E. formula it would be absurd to suggest that the maximum value,

* The formula is primarily intended to cover C–Mn–Si steels only and not high- or low-alloy steels although it is often quoted in connection with the latter.

0·43, is fixed and unalterable. The quality of individual workmanship can determine whether it is too high or whether it can be increased. This maximum can be increased in order to enable the composition of the steel to be altered towards higher tensile strengths if low-hydrogen electrodes are used.

For alloy steels containing purposeful additions of nickel, chromium, molybdenum and vanadium in appreciable quantities, the carbon equivalent can only be kept as low as possible if the carbon content itself is as low as is consistent with the achievement of the required mechanical properties. In low-alloy structural steels, however, 0·43 is unavoidably exceeded and hence preheat and/or post-heat should be used, together with low-hydrogen electrodes to achieve the most satisfactory results. Such steels have c.e. values of 0·58–0·65 approximately and they are in good practice welded with low-hydrogen electrodes. The necessary preheat may vary between 80° C and 150° C depending upon the thickness of the plates—thicker plates requiring higher preheat temperatures within this range.

Practical Example of the Justification of the Weldability Formula

Lloyd's Register has for some time permitted the use of higher tensile steels for ship construction. A condition of their use is that the higher the tensile strength then the higher must be the energy absorption in a Charpy test at a stipulated temperature. This is a wise provision to ensure that strength is not secured at the expense of toughness.

An example of the justification for the use of a c.e. formula in connection with higher tensile steels for shipbuilding is provided by practical welding tests carried out (under shipyard conditions) on a series of higher strength steels produced by different makers. These were supplemented by Reeve tests for welding cracks. It is this latter test which is more discriminating between different steels since welding conditions and parameters can be standardized more precisely.

The Reeve test is illustrated in Fig. 28. It was slightly modified from the original form in order to provide more specimens for examination. Essentially it is a test of a fillet weld, the top plate being firmly bolted to the base plate prior to welding in order to introduce stresses consequent on cooling when the welding is complete. Microsections taken through the fillet weld from the positions shown are carefully polished, etched and examined for microcracks and a hardness survey of the heat-affected zone is made.

Since all plates cannot, in practice, be produced to one precise chosen composition, it is of interest to compare the properties arranged in ascending order of the carbon equivalents for each of the compositions tested. Table 12 gives the results which show that using no preheat, evidence of microcracking appears at a carbon equivalent of about 0·45 when using the formula which includes 'residuals'. When 100° C preheat is used cracking is almost com-

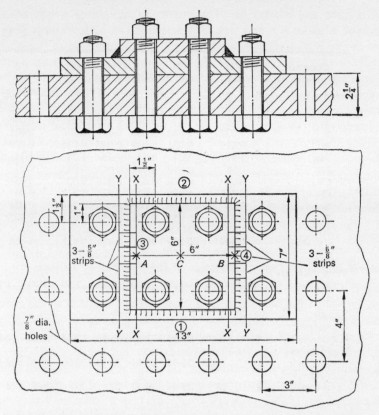

FIG. 28. Modified Reeve cracking test equipment. ¾ in. bolts in ⅞ in. holes.

pletely eliminated up to a carbon equivalent of about 0·49/0·50. The hardness of the heat-affected zone is seen to be a rough measure of the liability to encounter cracks. If the hardness exceeds approximately 390 D.P.N. cracks are likely to be present. Experience of many tests confirms this dangerous hardness level which is equivalent to a tensile strength of 80/85 tons/in². The properties of the high-silicon steel (Code Nos. 7–9) are worthy of note in view of the C.E. value of 0·43/0·44.

Significance of the Formula in Relation to Steels

So long as welding practices remain as they are at present there appears to be no immediate possibility of developing any new balanced or semi-killed steel (for economy in production) which can be produced in the normal hot-rolled condition for all thicknesses. Such a steel would have to possess a yield stress appreciably in excess of 23 tons/in² while still keeping below the advisable maximum of 0·43/0·45 for the carbon equivalent. The author has tried the

Table 12. *Increase*

Code no. / Deoxidation	(1) Bal.	(2) G.C.*	(3) Bal.	(4) Si.K.†	(5) Bal.	(5) Bal.	(6) Bal.	(6) Bal.	(7) Si.K.	(7) Si.K.
C	0·175	0·18	0·19	0·18	0·20		0·185		0·19	
Si	0·05	0·22	0·040	0·195	0·035		0·046		0·45	
S	0·022	0·032	0·035	0·037	0·040		0·021		0·017	
P	0·016	0·031	0·029	0·030	0·030		0·026		0·022	
Mn	1·27	1·31	1·27	1·38	1·28		1·35		1·31	
Ni	0·08	0·048	0·045	0·040	0·045		0·04		0·08	
Cr	0·04	0·024	0·02	0·016	0·02		0·034		0·05	
Cu	0·065	0·028	0·028	0·027	0·028		0·065		0·11	
Sn	0·01	0·006	0·006	0·006	0·006		0·024		0·022	
Nb	0·040	0·055	0·039	0·054	0·043		0·023		0·048	
Al	—	N.D.	—	—	—		—		N.D.	
C.E. value‡	0·404	0·409	0·411	0·418	0·422		0·426		0·430	
Plate thickness (in.)	0·63	1·16	0·875	1·00	1·25	1·50	1·00	1·50	0·62	
Tensile strength (tons/in²)	30·05	29·70	33·55	32·90	33·80	32·65	33·20	34·40	36·15	3
Yield stress (tons/in²)	20·15	19·80	23·95	23·35	23·70	22·90	21·40	22·15	26·80	2
Elongation % on 8 in.	25	28	25·5	25·50	21	25	26·5	24	23·5	2
Weld test. H.A.Z. hardness D.P.N.										
(a) No preheat — Average D.P.N.	218	217	303	300	340	288	—	—	—	
Max. D.P.N.	247	268	330	330	383	309	—	363	—	
Cracks	Nil	Nil	Nil	Nil	Nil	Nil	—	Nil	—	
(b) 100° C preheat — Average D.P.N.	—	—	—	—	—	—	—	—	—	
Max. D.P.N.	—	—	—	—	—	—	—	330	—	
Cracks	—	—	—	—	—	—	—	Nil	—	

* G.C. signifies grain controlled by addition of aluminium.

† Si.K. signifies silicon-killed steel.

$$\ddagger \text{ c.e.} = C + \frac{Mn}{6} + \frac{Cr + Mo + V}{5} + \frac{Ni + Cu}{15}.$$

A.Z. cracking with increasing C.E. *value*

(8) Si.K.	(9) Si.K.	(10) Bal.	(11) Bal.	(12) G.C.	(13) Bal.	(14) Bal.	(15) Bal.
·205	0·20	0·19	0·18	0·19	0·19	0·225	0·205
·44	0·47	0·05	0·04	0·32	0·08	0·06	0·07
·023	0·020	0·031	0·030	0·035	0·046	0·038	0·042
·025	0·024	0·027	0·024	0·025	0·032	0·029	0·036
·28	1·32	1·44	1·48	1·43	1·54	1·46	1·54
·15	0·08	0·10	0·044	0·077	0·13	0·11	0·14
·06	0·035	0·05	0·15	0·16	0·10	0·06	0·09
·09	0·09	0·13	0·045	0·045	0·23	0·13	0·23
·02	0·02	0·016	—	—	0·032	0·017	0·032
·043	0·050	0·017	0·028	0·052	0·030	0·022	0·028
N.D.	N.D.	—	—	0·04	—	—	—
·436	0·438	0·455	0·453	0·469	0·492	0·497	0·504
1·00	0·63	1·00, 1·50	1·00, 1·50	1·00, 1·50	1·00	1·00	1·50
38·25	35·50	36·40, 35·10	34·25, 32·20	35·10, 35·35	36·15	37·40	36·05
27·95	28·30	26·95, 24·55	24·70, 22·55	24·60, 24·55	25·80	26·15	25·10
25·5	23	24·5, 27·5 5×D.§	25, 24·5	24, 24·5	27 5×D.	25 5×D.	28 5×D.
312	—	—, 336	311, 296	368, 358	377	363	386
409	—	—, 360	383, 366	425, 413	449	400	429
Nil	—	—, 3/12¶	2/12, Nil	3/12, 1/12	6/12	12/12	9/12
—	—	—, 322	275, 275	311, 330	327	315	355
—	—	—, 360	327, 325	376, 363	355	357	418
—	—	—, Nil	Nil, Nil	Nil, 2/12	3/12	Nil	Nil

5×D. = Gauge length.

3/12 = 3 cracks observed in 12 surfaces examined.

introduction of small amounts of titanium, nitrogen, copper and chromium into experimental heats of steel of purposely low carbon and manganese levels, both singly and in various combinations and so far has not succeeded in defeating a carbon equivalent value of 0·43/0·45 by producing mechanical properties radically superior to those already obtainable by using higher carbon and manganese contents. This does not imply that a solution to the problem is impossible but it does appear that the solution involves a more costly steel through (*a*) having to produce a fully-killed steel with its lower yield of saleable material per ton of ingot, or (*b*) using more costly elements as substitutes for carbon and manganese, assuming that the resulting compositions would be weldable, or (*c*) quenching and tempering balanced steel of existing compositions.

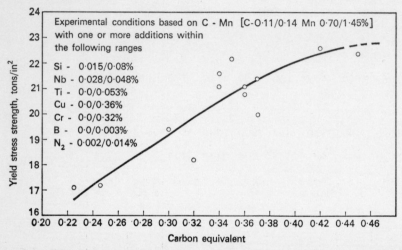

FIG. 29. Yield stress of balanced C–Mn steels with various additions—normalized.

Experimental steels of various compositions, made in a small, high-frequency furnace and cast into ingots (weighing 22 lb) were forged into plates $\frac{5}{8}$ in. thick. These were normalized in order to 'standardize' all structures. The plates were then suitably cut to provide both tensile and Charpy specimens. The results obtained are given in Fig. 29 from which it is seen that when the steels are arranged in order of increasing carbon equivalent value, the yield stress and ultimate strength values increase also. It is to be noted that a yield stress of approximately 22·5/23 tons/in² corresponds to the accepted maximum desirable carbon equivalent of about 0·43.

The Effect of Plate Thickness

It will be readily appreciated that the thickness of plates to be welded is important. Difficulties in welding increase as thickness increases because it is

PLATE 11

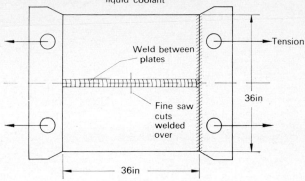

Insulated plate cooled to desired temperature
by crushed solid CO_2 or pumped
liquid coolant

→ Tension

Weld between
plates

36in

Fine saw
cuts
welded
over

36in

Uniform stress exerted by hydraulic jacks

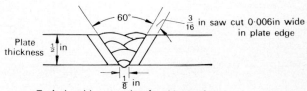

60°

$\frac{3}{16}$ in saw cut 0·006in wide
in plate edge

Plate
thickness $\frac{1}{2}$ in

$\frac{1}{8}$ in

Typical weld preparation for thinner plate
Thicker plates require a "Double V" preparation

Principle of the 'wide plate' test with introduced notch defect in a welded joint. (*Courtesy of British Welding Research Association.*)

PLATE 12

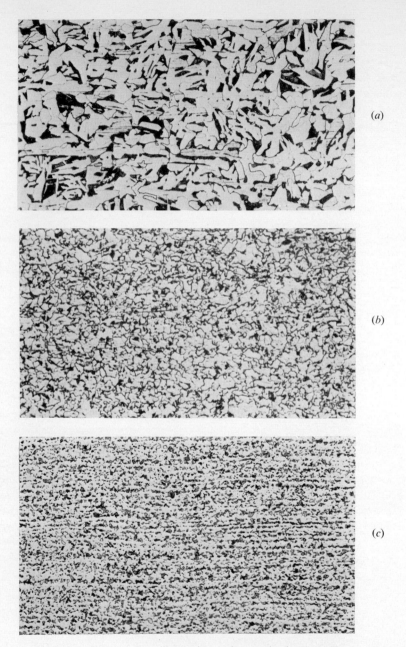

(a)

(b)

(c)

Ferrite–pearlite structures illustrating various grain-sizes. × 100.

impossible to use a heat energy input which is directly proportional in all cases to the thickness by using a single electrode. A satisfactory rate of energy input for a thin plate joint is more easily achieved, and the heat conduction away from the weld by the parent metal on either side is not excessive. As joint thickness increases, thereby necessitating multi-runs to complete the weld, so does cooling between passes. The chilling effect thus produced may develop a greater degree of hardness in the heat-affected zone. This increases the risk of reaching the 'cracking level', viz. 390/400 D.P.N. Preheat therefore becomes more important as the plate thickness increases for any particular composition and recommendations in this and other aspects of welding are given in B.S. 1856 ('Welding of Mild Steel') and B.S. 2642: 1964 ('Welding of Higher Tensile Steel'). A plate of a given thickness and of a suitable composition with a low C.E. value may need no preheat if an ordinary rutile or cellulose base coated rod is used. If the thickness of the plate (of the same composition) is increased a degree of preheat becomes necessary when using the same electrode. Similarly, a particular thickness necessitating preheat when using an ordinary electrode may need none if a low-hydrogen electrode is used instead.

The Effect of Gas-cutting and Shearing to Dimensions

It is customary when supplying plates to provide these with mill-sheared edges up to say $1\frac{1}{2}$ in. thick in mild steel or steel of B.S. 968 quality. Plates over this thickness are usually gas cut because the necessary shears would become too expensive. There is also a tendency in the mild steels when cold-sheared to be distorted and slightly torn at the edges, especially if there is appreciable wear on the blade guides and edges. The harder the steel, the more 'square' are the sheared edges but the less is the maximum thickness which can be sheared by any equipment.

Both cold-shearing and gas-cutting involve certain risks with respect to brittle fracture at low temperatures because of the severe degree of cold work imposed by shearing, and the risk of producing an excessive skin hardness on the gas-cut edge. By gas-cutting even a mild steel can be severely hardened as a result of carbon penetration from a badly adjusted gas torch. The edge, in effect, becomes 'case-hardened'. When gas-cutting steel to B.S. 968 or the higher tensile steels, the rate at which the freshly cut edge cools can produce a brittle skin. The subsequent shaping by cold-bending of plates with such hardened edges, either sheared or gas cut, is therefore accompanied by a risk of brittle fracture unless the hardened surface is just removed by grinding or machining in the vicinity of the intended bend.

For welding purposes, however, plates necessitate bevelling of the edges in order to develop the required V- or double V-joints to be filled in by the weld metal. In order to guard against incipient cracks which may be present, it is

K

customary to insist that metal to a depth of $\frac{1}{4}$ in. be machined from the flame-cut edges before welding higher yield point steels such as B.S. 968. That this amount is entirely unnecessary is shown by the following experiments.

Tests on $\frac{1}{2}$ in., 1 in., $1\frac{1}{2}$ in., 2 in., and $2\frac{1}{2}$ in. thick plates of B.S. 968 of the analyses shown in Table 13 were conducted by cutting samples with an oxy-propane torch at controlled speeds. Inclined sections were taken through the flame-cut edges by careful grinding at an angle of 3° to the flame-cut surface. This procedure in effect lengthened the section through the hardened area, so enabling hardness measurements to be made at small increments in depth below the gas-cut surface.

Table 13. *Effect of gas-cutting on edge hardness of B.S. 968 steel**

Plate thickness (in.)	C	Mn	Si	S	P	Nb
0·5	0·22	1·54	0·010	0·022	0·030	0·025
1·0	0·24	1·56	0·019	0·032	0·024	0·032
1·5	0·22	1·54	0·023	0·038	0·021	0·026
2·0	0·24	1·56	0·042	0·030	0·025	0·032
2·5	0·22	1·54	0·190	0·030	0·017	0·032
Plate thickness (in.)	0·5	1·0	1·5	2·0	2·5	
Max. hardness D.P.N.	320	400	375	435	390	
Depth below surface with D.P.N.	in.	in.	in.	in.	in.	
above 350	0·005	0·005	0·010	0·020	0·027	
300	0·010	0·016	0·017	0·025	0·030	
250	0·015	0·028	0·029	0·032	0·048	

* Results supplied by Mr E. L. Goult (Dorman Long (Steel) Ltd).

It will be noted from Table 13 that, with the exception of the thinnest plate, surface hardnesses are produced which correspond with those which may be encountered in the heat-affected zone of a weld itself and at which levels cracking is liable to occur. Bending a plate with a gas-cut edge is therefore likely to result in the development of cracking as shown in Plate 10. It is very probable that the extreme outer surface of the gas-cut edge is carburized to a minute depth and therefore the true skin hardness is actually considerably higher than indicated by the values in Table 13. Microscopic examination of a section through the gas-cut surface confirms this.

It does appear, however, from Table 13 that it is not necessary to machine to a depth of $\frac{1}{4}$ in. in order to remove the hardened material. From the values given, $\frac{1}{16}$ in. to $\frac{1}{8}$ in. appears to be adequate.

From the descriptions of some of the characteristics of welding and cutting given, it is seen that bad workmanship or incorrect conditions can lead to the presence of microcracks at joints in the parent metal itself. Obviously two consequences may ensue: (a) microcracks, even assuming they do not propagate in a catastrophic manner in service, can contribute to a lower effective fatigue strength of the structure; and (b) occasionally, depending on their position and the concentration of stress in their vicinity, they may lead to catastrophic failure under ambient or low-temperature conditions. The greatest care in construction is therefore essential in structures such as pressure vessels and it is customary to examine all weld runs by X-ray methods. If defective patches are found, these are chipped out completely and remade satisfactorily before proceeding to subsequent runs. In this way perfect joints can be produced and complete confidence assured as to satisfactory service. Pressure vessel construction to Lloyd's Class A.1 standards necessitates the employment of 'approved' welders who are required to produce 'test welds' periodically during the course of construction.

It would be absurd to claim that ordinary structural welding is perfect in every part, but the design factors adopted ensure that, apart from exceptional circumstances, there is today little likelihood of failure in service when welding is carried out by reputable companies. Woodley, Burdekin and Wells[3] have investigated the effect of plate thickness on brittle fracture by testing welded wide plates containing a notch in the weld (to represent an imperfection). Tests were carried out down to $-100°$ C using steels to specifications B.S. 1501-151 and -161, L.T. 50. The plate thicknesses ranged from $\frac{1}{4}$ in. to 2 in. Both 'as-welded' and 'stress-relieved' conditions were used. As a criterion of a reasonable margin of safety, 0.5% plastic extension before failure was adopted in the tests. The tests were designed to cover a range of fracture types, varying from those occurring at low stress with negligible ductility to those produced under high stress conditions with appreciable plastic deformation.

The test plates were 36 in. square welded from two halves. In order to concentrate the applied tensile stress, a saw-cut notch 0.006 in. wide and 0.2 in. deep was first cut into one prepared edge of each half plate at the centre of its length. These edges were then welded manually in the downhand position. For the 2 in. thick plates a double V-edge preparation was used and for the $1\frac{1}{2}$ in., $\frac{3}{4}$ in. and $\frac{3}{8}$ in. a single V-edge preparation (60°) was used. The number of weld runs required to fill the 2 in. welds were 30/40, for the $1\frac{1}{2}$ in., 24 runs, while the $\frac{1}{4}$, $\frac{1}{2}$, and $\frac{3}{8}$ in. plates necessitated only 3/5 passes including the backing run. Various electrodes including the low-hydrogen types were used. The 2 in. and $1\frac{1}{2}$ in. welds were made with 6 or 8 s.w.G. electrodes and the $\frac{1}{4}$ in. with 8 or 10 s.w.G. electrodes.

The faces of the test squares when mounted in the testing machine (2000 tons capacity for the 2 in. plate) were cooled down by crushed solid CO_2

placed in boxes attached to the plates. Liquid nitrogen (−196° C) was pumped through sintered-nickel pads in contact with the plate surface in the region of the predicted crack path which was a line drawn vertically through the location of the artificially introduced notch. Plate 11 illustrates schematically the principle of the wide plate test and Plate 16(*b*) shows the apparatus used.

When a tensile stress was applied to the two ends of the welded composite plate the overall extension of the whole specimen was measured by proving rings having strain gauges attached. Local extension was measured by gauge marks attached on each side of the predicted path of fracture. As a result of

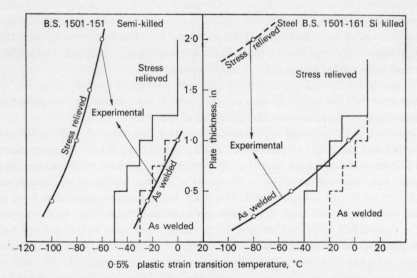

FIG. 30. Experimental *vs.* permissible stresses from B.S. 1500, Appendix C, for plate. (C. C. Woodley, F. M. Burdekin and A. A. Wells[3].)

these experiments the following information became available. For a chosen test temperature, the yield stress and the fracture stress were obtained while an automatic device recorded the test load applied and the resulting overall extension. The plastic strain resulting from the application of a test load was taken as the average of all 5-in. gauge lengths in the vicinity of the crack and the notch itself. From these results it was possible to predict a certain temperature at which fracture would just take place when 0·5% plastic strain had been reached, even in cases where the plastic strain (in extension) exceeded the 0·5% criterion without fracture. These temperatures are plotted in Fig. 30 on which the accepted design criteria taken from specification B.S. 1500 (Appendix C) are superimposed.

The results of these experiments indicate that existing design factors are conservative under some conditions and suggest that the following conclusions can be drawn with reference to the types of steel examined.

Factors of Safety in Design

(*a*) *Steel to B.S. 1501-151.* The experimental results fit the B.S. 1500 design criteria reasonably well in the 'as-welded' condition. If stress-relieving of the welded structure is carried out, the experimental results are appreciably superior, that is, higher stresses than those permitted can be imposed safely on the structure.

(*b*) *Steel to B.S. 1501-161—L.T. 50.* For this class of steel, intended for use in pressure vessels operating under low-temperature service conditions, the experimental results proved (in both the 'as-rolled' and 'stress-relieved' states) to be much superior to the standard criteria, for equivalent plate thicknesses. This implies that the present standard requirements are very conservative. The steel would, in practice, withstand lower temperatures without developing a brittle fracture when 0·5% plastic strain is encountered.

(*c*) *General Remarks.* The results also showed that the thinner the plate the lower is the 0·5% plastic strain transition temperature.

Provided that materials to be used in construction are truly representative of those normally obtainable, work such as described serves to establish a confidence in advancing beyond the limits of previous empiricism and experience. The authors[3] in a discussion of their results, point out that specification B.S. 1515 now permits design stresses up to two-thirds of the yield point of the material. A pressure vessel is required to undergo a hydrostatic pressure test before approval for insurance purposes. In such a test we have the following conditions:

(*a*) Design stress = two-thirds of the yield stress.
(*b*) An excess pressure, applied over a short time, equal to 1·3 times the design pressure.
(*c*) An accepted elastic stress concentration factor of 2·5 which may occur, for instance, at a nozzle cap in the vessel. Under such an excessive stress condition, localized yielding of metal will occur and it is not likely that the subsequent service working pressure would cause any further yielding. A lower ductility limit of 0·5% as adopted in the tests on wide plates previously described thus gives a safety factor of about 2·5 even in the presence of a sizable crack (such as the notch used in the tests) and which, in the tests, was unfavourably orientated at the position of maximum strain.

The authors also state that for cryogenic service it is not usual to carry out hydrostatic tests at the lower service temperatures under which the vessel will operate. There is an extremely large and still growing body of evidence to show that a structure is protected from fracture at low temperature when it has been proof loaded with the same loading pattern, sign and magnitude at a higher temperature.

General conclusions are that plate thickness and the defect size exert a marked effect on the temperature at which 0·5% strain occurs with fracture. Stress-relieving shifts the 0·5% plastic strain transition temperature towards lower temperatures. Conventional Charpy tests carried out on the materials used showed that a safe working temperature could be used which was lower than that deduced from the transition curve. It is important to bear in mind, however, that in the work carried out only static loading is considered.

REFERENCES

1. R. D. Stout and W. D'O. Doty. *Weldability of Steels* (Welding Res. Council (New York), 1953), p. 194.
2. J. Dearden and H. O'Neill. *Trans. Inst. Weld.*, 3 (1940), 203.
3. C. C. Woodley, F. M. Burdekin and A. A. Wells. *Brit. Weld. J.*, 11, no. 3 (1964), 123.

PART IV

THE PROPERTIES OF WROUGHT STEELS

CHAPTER 10

THE CHARACTERISTICS OF VARIOUS MILD STEELS

Since by far the greatest tonnage of steel used for structural purposes is the ubiquitous 'mild steel', this material may be considered as 'basic' with respect to its properties at ambient and low temperatures. It has been shown to possess relatively poor impact properties and, in terms of the temperature range considered in this book, a high transition temperature range.

From the engineer's point of view, therefore, while it is perfectly adequate for many applications, the trend towards more severe service demands has prompted efforts to improve its properties particularly with respect to notch toughness. This has been apparent over the past 10–15 years with respect to steels for ship construction, and considerable progress has been made, so that catastrophic failures, particularly in ships, are becoming very much rarer, when measured in terms of frequency of occurrence over a number of 'ship years in service'.

In seeking an improvement in the properties of the basic material (mild steel), there are several aspects to be considered. One may be satisfied with the existing property levels such as tensile strength, yield stress and elongation because the two former values are fundamental requirements for design purposes. Accepting this, some improvement is achieved if we develop a lower transition temperature at the same tensile strength level. Additionally, it can be considered desirable to increase the energy absorption values at any chosen temperature as a further safeguard against the initiation of a crack in service. A high absorption of energy to initiate a crack is however distinct from the energy required to propagate the once initiated crack. These improvements cannot be used in design if the criterion by which they are assessed is that of the notched-bar test because the value measured, that is, energy absorption, is without an absolute meaning. Its importance, however, is very significant since it leads to an ability to classify steels in a relative order of merit. This can be the means of rejecting an inferior material which otherwise possesses satisfactory tensile properties. The acceptance and maintenance of the mild

137

steel strength values coupled with a generally improved standard of notch toughness (combining lower transition temperatures and enhanced energy absorption values) was the first aim in developing an improved quality, and formed the basis of the classification of the 'notch ductile' steels standardized in Specification B.S. 2762 : 1964. Similar steels have been developed to satisfy Lloyd's requirements for shipbuilding.

Another line of improvement could be to develop steels which have enhanced mechanical properties with an equivalent degree of resistance to brittleness possessed by ordinary mild steels. This objective, while providing an alternative, is obviously not worth pursuing since equivalent toughness to that of ordinary mild steel is now considered inadequate. The most important objective is to develop steels with both enhanced mechanical properties and still further increased resistance to brittleness. This is the most difficult problem because an empirical approach must be made. While fundamental principles may be used, that is, silicon killing and grain refinement, these are limited in effect. Resort must be made therefore to the use of alloy additions and to more complicated forms of heat-treatment.

An overruling requirement accompanies these aims. Any steel so developed must be capable of fabrication by welding with reasonable ease otherwise it is of little interest to the designer. Riveting is no longer adequate. Some indication of the difficulties encountered in welding when the carbon equivalent exceeds about 0·43/0·45 (especially if no preheat is to be applied and ordinary rutile electrodes are used) is given in chapter 7. It is obvious that if specific alloy additions are to be made to achieve the objective previously mentioned the carbon equivalent of 0·43/0·45 is likely to be exceeded even if the carbon content is reduced to an unusually low level. It then becomes necessary to use some degree of preheat and special electrodes. The primary aim in producing an alloy steel with all properties improved is to reduce the carbon content to as low a level as possible.

The Importance of Higher-strength Steels

The desire for higher strength and greater toughness than the general levels procurable in mild steel are understandable in terms of modern trends in design. There is a movement towards reducing dead weight. In a structure such as a bridge this may not be important but it must be borne in mind that if thinner but equally 'strong' plates and sections can be used—the consumption of electrodes and time involved in welding are reduced, thereby contributing appreciably towards lower overall costs. In many structures the reduction of dead weight is of very considerable importance. Thus in the case of large oil tankers a saving in dead weight will permit an appreciable increase in payload while enabling the same speed to be developed for the expenditure of the same horse-power. Alternatively, higher speeds may be achieved as a result of weight saving or for the same cruising speed the saving may take the form of a lower power consumption.

These arguments apply particularly to all moving structures. Much importance is attached to the use of high-tensile notch-tough steels in modern earth-moving equipment since an increase in handling capacity per unit is an obvious result. The use of steels in plate form having a tensile strength of 50/60 tons/in² is now common practice in the latter application.

Their Application to Ship Construction

Until recently the standard material used in ship construction was exclusively mild steel (tensile strength 26/33 tons/in²). Appreciable quantities of steels of the same strength level but with improved notch toughness have also been incorporated. This implied the use of design factors based on the above tensile strength. Early in 1962 Lloyd's Register laid down conditions which permit the use of higher tensile steels so that some reduction in scantlings could be effected in order to save weight and possibly improve the competitive position of builders. These conditions, while not specifying a tensile range numerically, stipulated that any new steel used should satisfy certain requirements with respect to notch toughness. After the development and use over the past 10–15 years of improved notch-tough steels it was obvious that to achieve enhanced tensile strength at the expense of notch toughness could not be permitted. A factor K was therefore introduced, which is derived as follows:

$$K = \frac{45}{U + Y},$$

where U is ultimate strength (in tons/in²) of a higher tensile steel and is to be taken as one-third of the guaranteed range above the minimum. (NOTE: This was subsequently modified to one-half of the guaranteed strength range above the minimum, 'Extract from Rules for the Construction and Classification of Steel Ships—No. 8–1964'). The term Y is the specified minimum yield stress or 0.5% proof stress or $0.7 \times U$, whichever is the lowest.

It will be noted in the above formula that if normal values are substituted for ordinary mild steel (26/32 tons/in²), the value of K is 1·00, based on a minimum yield stress of 16 tons/in².

$$K = \frac{45}{29 + 16} = 1 \cdot 00.$$

If, however, steels having a higher tensile strength and yield stress are used then K becomes less than 1·00. If we substitute a steel of 32/38 tons/in² ultimate strength and a minimum yield stress of 23 tons/in², then

$$K = \frac{45}{35 + 23} = \frac{45}{58} = 0 \cdot 77.$$

In order therefore to ensure an adequate degree of notch toughness the existing minimum Charpy impact values for each of the various grades of ordinary mild steel (26/32 tons/in^2 tensile strength) must be increased by a factor of $1/\sqrt{K}$. Therefore in the higher tensile steel quoted when $K = 0.77$, the minimum Charpy impact values required must be increased by a factor of 1·14.

Obviously there is a practical low limit to the value of K. While steels of 50/60 tons/in^2 are procurable and which have Charpy impact values satisfying the requirement, the problem of reducing scantlings is bound up with the modulus of rigidity. To maintain adequate rigidity while diminishing plate thickness beyond a certain minimum would necessitate more frequent stiffeners. The cost of incorporating them into the structure might destroy any economic advantage otherwise securable. There is also a practical limit to which Charpy impact values can be improved as the tensile strength increases. A useful compromise is therefore achievable by using the steel (32–38 tons/in^2 ultimate tensile strength) quoted as an example above. In this steel the gain in yield stress over ordinary mild steel is some 40/50%, that is, from 16·0 tons/in^2 to 23 tons/in^2. Steelmakers are now supplying such a steel.

As an example of the saving in weight possible in tanker construction, the following estimate is given. A 65,000 tons deadweight tanker requires approximately 12,000 tons of ordinary mild steel. Design is based on a minimum tensile strength of 26 tons/in^2 and a yield stress of 16 tons/in^2. It would be possible to substitute mild steel by a steel of, say, 22 tons/in^2 yield stress by redesign to the following extent:

Bilge and sheerstrake plating	1% =	120 tons
Deck and bottom plating	10% =	1200 tons
Deck and bottom longitudinals (flat bar)	10% =	1200 tons
Deck and bottom longitudinal girders and longitudinal bulkheads—top and bottom strakes	6% =	720 tons
	Total	3240 tons

The incorporation of this weight of the higher tensile steel could therefore substitute a weight of mild steel in proportion to the ratio between the two yield stresses, i.e. $\frac{22}{16} \times 3240$ tons = 4455 tons, by the decreased thicknesses. The saving in total weight of steel would be of the order of 1200 tons, or 10% approximately. This is a very appreciable margin.

The Improved Mild Steels

As a material available in bulk, mild steel dates from Bessemer's successful experiments in 1856. He produced for the first time a liquid metal on a relatively large scale by blowing air through molten pig iron low in phosphorus. This was followed by deoxidation carried out by means of ferro-manganese. The steel was cast into ingots and subsequently hot worked. The final product, when cold, possessed a reasonably high strength. It was malleable and could be produced with fairly consistent properties.

Bessemer steel was supplemented in 1868/70 by open-hearth furnace steel originating from the experiments of Siemens. In his furnace, the melting and refining of crude pig iron together with scrap, which was then becoming available in increasing quantities, could be accomplished. This operation resulted in a material similar to Bessemer's product. The open-hearth process introduced the possibilities of larger individual batches of uniform composition because furnace capacities soon became greater than those of the Bessemer converters.

The ability to remove phosphorus came subsequently and resulted from the work of Gilchrist and Thomas who substituted a 'basic' lining (dolomite, magnesite) in the converter, for the previously used 'acid' (i.e. silica) lining. The basic lining enabled slags containing lime to be used, the lime being essential for the removal of phosphorus.

The more recent changes which have been introduced to provide a material adequate for modern demands may now be considered. What processing facilities are available to enable the steelmaker to effect these changes? It must be borne in mind that in spite of a much greater degree of control over composition than was possible in the early days, there are still processing limitations if cost is to be kept to reasonable levels. The following statements summarize the courses available.

(1) Composition may be changed to alter properties but not indiscriminately since the required design properties must be maintained.
(2) A 'killed steel' may be produced, but since this entails a lower yield of finished material some increase in cost is involved.
(3) An improvement in notch toughness will result from normalizing by refining the original 'as-rolled' grain-size. Such a heat-treatment has an added advantage in that it gives a product with more uniform properties over a larger range of thicknesses than that derived from the hot rolling operation alone. Additional heat-treatment also involves increased cost.
(4) Grain refining of the austenite may be effected by producing a 'killed' steel and adding aluminium as an inoculating medium. If this is followed by a normalizing treatment, the finest possible grain-size is obtained and with it the lowest transition temperature and maximum degree of notch toughness for a particular steel composition.

It was first realized that increasing the manganese increased the toughness of mild steel. While an early request by Lloyd's Register that mild steel should have a minimum manganese/carbon ratio of 2·5/1 was already satisfied in this country, this state of affairs did not apply universally. The author encountered during the Second World War foreign steels containing 0·30% C and 0·25% Mn which were brittle. The next step in improvement was to increase the Mn/C ratio up to 8 to 1 or 10 to 1. In order to preserve the tensile strength within the range of 26/32 tons/in^2 this necessitated lowering the carbon content to a degree corresponding roughly to the strength formula given on p. 78. Instead of a steel with, say, 0·22% C + 0·55% Mn (in which the Mn/C ratio is 2·5/1), the steel now becomes a 0·14% C steel containing 0·14% C + 0·55% Mn + 8 (0·08 C) Mn = 0·55% Mn + 0·64% Mn = 1·2% Mn. Hence a steel of equivalent strength now contains 0·14% C + 1·2% Mn.

Such a steel represented a considerable advance in notch toughness even in the 'balanced' condition and it was found to be capable of further improvement by normalizing. In the 'as-rolled' condition it became established as 'steel to Lloyd's P403' rule in 1950. In 1956, as a result of collaborative research work by various British steel companies, who produced plates, the N.D. (notch ductile) series of mild steels designated in Specification B.S. 2762 were introduced and of these steels the N.D. IV grade constitutes the toughest mild steel it is possible to obtain from simple Fe–C–Mn alloys without having recourse to quenching and tempering. This specification was the first comprehensive one issued throughout the world and foreign specification bodies have since introduced their equivalents.

Mild steels now available in the commonly used tensile range of 26/32 tons/in^2 may be summarized as follows:

(1) *Ordinary Mild Steel Semi-killed* (0·15/0·26% C; 0·55/0·65% Mn; 0·02/0·06% Si)

The steel is a 'balanced' product. It should give a Charpy impact value in the 'as-rolled' condition of about 15/20 ft-lb at 0° C and it is therefore just 'borderline' with respect to the arbitrary basis adopted by Williams[1] who examined casualty material from numerous brittle fractures encountered in ships. He found that all plates which had failed possessed Charpy V-notch values below 15 ft-lb. Hodgson and Boyd[2] also collected and examined casualty data. Their arrangement for examination of these data differed from that of Williams. They plotted the results for both energy absorption and percent crystallinity in the fracture at the 'casualty' temperature. With few exceptions, all plates which failed in a brittle manner were found to be clustered in an area defined by a range of 3–35 ft-lb Charpy energy absorption, and 70–100% crystallinity in the fracture. It could be concluded, therefore, that a minimum energy value of 35 ft-lb together with a crystallinity value not exceeding 60 or 70% is necessary if brittle failure under certain conditions is to be avoided.

Ordinary mild steel is supplied in the 'as-rolled' condition. It can be normalized to refine the grain. This treatment results in some increase in the yield stress value and notch toughness. For stringent requirements under conditions of high stress and low temperature it should not be used unless supplemented by steels of higher notch toughness located in the more critical portions of the structure. Its grain-size on the A.S.T.M. scale is 2–3. The steel can be 'silicon killed' but the improvement in notch toughness which results is not compatible with the increase in cost which arises from a lower ingot to plate yield of saleable material. Ordinary mild steel is not at present sold with any guaranteed minimum impact value.

(2) Low Carbon–High Manganese Steels (N.D. I)

This steel is the originally modified mild steel, the improved notch toughness being achieved by a lower carbon and higher manganese content. It is produced in the 'balanced' condition and supplied 'as rolled'. It is the lowest grade of the four notch-tough steels listed in Specification B.S. 2762 : 1964, 'Steel for Bridges and General Building Construction', and also satisfies Lloyd's Grade B quality. It must possess a minimum Charpy impact value of 20 ft-lb at 0° C in the direction of rolling, this value being an average of three tests. No individual test of the three must be less than 15 ft-lb. It is produced in two tensile strength ranges, viz. (a) 26/31 tons/in^2 and (b) 28/33 tons/in^2. Like ordinary mild steel it is coarse grain.

(3) N.D. II Steel

This grade is identical with N.D. I in composition but is improved further by normalizing after rolling. The effect of this is to lower the transition temperature considerably so that a minimum Charpy value of 20 ft-lb at −15° C is specified.

(4) N.D. III Steel

By silicon killing steel of the composition of N.D. I and N.D. II, viz. 0·12%/0·18% C and 0·9%/1·5% Mn another grade becomes available for which a minimum impact value of 20 ft-lb at −30° C must be achieved. This grade is not used to the extent of the other two. It is sometimes necessary to normalize it in addition to silicon killing in order to achieve the specified minimum Charpy value. Because of the high Mn/C ratio it is much superior however to an ordinary mild steel which may be killed with silicon.

(5) N.D. IV Steel

In this grade the same high Mn/C ratio is used and like N.D. III the steel is also silicon killed. A fine grain structure is achieved by the addition of aluminium to the ladle when tapping (usually 3 lb Al/ton steel) followed by normalizing after rolling. This grade therefore represents the ultimate in toughness properties which can be achieved by normal processing facilities from a simple C/Mn steel. Its ductile to brittle transition range of temperature is the lowest which can be attained in this series of steels and this is due to its fine grain-size (6–8 on the A.S.T.M. scale). For plates the minimum individual Charpy impact values specified are as follows:

−10° C	45 ft-lb
−20° C	40 ft-lb
−30° C	35 ft-lb
−40° C	25 ft-lb
−50° C	20 ft-lb

For sections the Charpy impact values are relaxed somewhat. The reason for this is that sections if normalized, may warp and twist badly. This involves expensive cold straightening afterwards. The impact values given below can be achieved in the 'as-rolled' condition.

−10° C	30 ft-lb
−20° C	25 ft-lb
−30° C	20 ft-lb

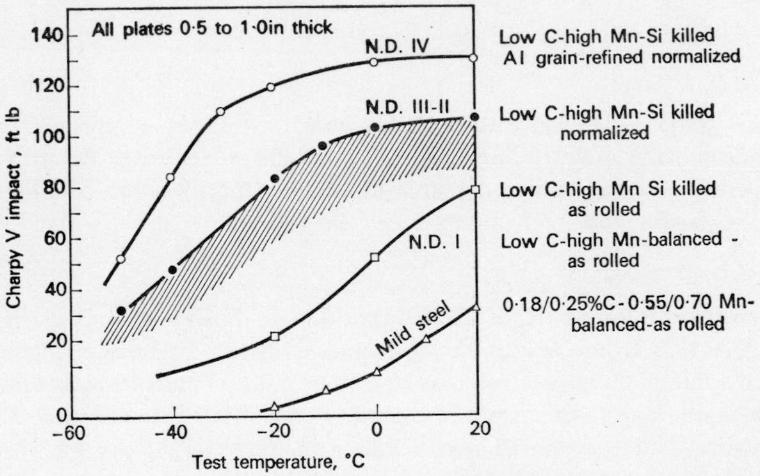

FIG. 31. Average impact values (longit.) for plates, 1956–58. (Author.)

Fig. 31 shows typical transition curves for the N.D. series and ordinary mild steel. It is to be noted that while minimum values for Charpy impact tests are specified, these are in the majority of cases exceeded generously in practice. The N.D. series forms an excellent example of the grading of notch toughness characteristics in an effective and reliable manner to enable the cheapest material to be purchased for a specific purpose.

While, in the description of the development of the notch-tough mild steels the basic example given was 0·14% C, 1·2% Mn, it must be remembered that plate or section thickness requires some adjustment of these levels as is the case for ordinary mild steels—in order to maintain tensile properties. Actual compositions may vary therefore outside these values and the carbon content in the specification may be up to 0·20% maximum with 1·50% Mn maximum for N.D. I and N.D. II, but N.D. III and N.D. IV are limited to 0·17% C and 1·50% Mn maximum. Steelmakers endeavour to produce material below these levels because of the presence of unavoidable small quantities of residual elements, which add slightly to the tensile strength. The essential requirement to ensure the best Charpy values under all heat-treatment conditions in all grades is the highest Mn/C ratio possible, which is consistent with satisfactory tensile properties in the thicknesses required.

REFERENCES

1. M. L. Williams. *Weld. J.*, **37** (1958), 445-S (*Weld. Res. Suppl.*).
2. J. Hodgson and G. M. Boyd. *Trans. Instn. nav. Archit.*, **100** (1958), 141.

L

CHAPTER 11

THE HIGHER TENSILE STEELS

As seen from Fig. 15, which shows the relationship between carbon content, tensile strength and Charpy impact values for straight carbon steels, an increase in tensile strength achieved by increasing the carbon content results in a lesser degree of notch toughness at least in the 'as-rolled' or normalized condition.

It is obviously desirable, however, that the designer and engineer should have available steels of higher tensile strength than mild steel, possessing at the same time an adequate or increased degree of toughness for some desired low-temperature service conditions. The requirements of welding as discussed in a previous chapter indicate the necessity for a low level of carbon and therefore increased strength must be achieved by other elements. Alternatively it is possible by a heat-treatment such as quenching and tempering to secure a micro-structure which possesses considerably improved properties over those obtainable from material in the more usual 'as-rolled' or normalized state. The first step towards this extension of the property levels of mild steel is provided by a grade of steel produced in accord with Specification B.S. 968 : 1962. Description of this steel in some detail is warranted on account of the mechanism by which increased strength is achieved.

Steel to B.S. 968: 1962

The specification was originally introduced under wartime conditions in 1941 to provide what was considered at that time a 'high yield stress steel' suitable for fusion welding. When it was introduced the property of notch toughness and the suitability of the steel for low-temperature applications were not considered, since brittle fracture as a problem had not achieved the prominence it was to assume a few years later as a result of the Liberty ship failures.

Experience, however, showed that the alloy content necessary to attain the specified mechanical properties placed the steel on the borderline of good weldability, particularly in thick plates. A further disadvantage of the original steel was that the mechanical properties fell off rapidly as the thicknessi ncreased. While a yield stress of 23 tons/in² could be achieved in thin material, for example, 0·5 in. at a 'weldable' carbon and manganese level $(C + \dfrac{Mn}{6} \leqslant 0.45)$, the value fell to 19 tons/in² in thick plates (1½ to 2 in.) or sections.

Effect of Niobium

In 1939 patents were granted in America covering the addition of niobium to mild steel in order to raise its yield and tensile strength. Commercial production did not start until about 1958. The addition of small quantities of niobium to a C–Mn steel has enabled the production of a material with a minimum yield stress of 23 tons/in² for all thicknesses up to 2 in. This has in turn permitted the maximum carbon and manganese levels of the original B.S. 968 to be reduced somewhat, resulting in some improvement in weldability. Reasonable precautions in welding are still required, however, particularly for thick material, and recommendations are given in Specification B.S. 2642, 'General Requirements for the Metal Arc-Welding of Medium Tensile Weldable Structural Steels to B.S. 968'.

Niobium is extremely powerful in its effect when added to steel and very small quantities only are necessary, viz. 0·02/0·04% to increase the yield stress by 4/7 tons/in² and the tensile strength by 3·5/5·5 tons/in². As the niobium is increased beyond 0·04% its effect rapidly falls off. It is to be noted that the effect on the yield stress is greater than that on the ultimate tensile strength. Hence niobium steels have a greater 'yield stress to ultimate strength' ratio than ordinary mild steels. For hot rolled and normalized mild steels the yield stress is usually 0·55/0·58 times the tensile strength—depending on thickness. In niobium-treated steels the ratio is 0·58/0·65.

The addition of vanadium can give similar effects but a greater amount is required. Because the cost of these elements per 1 lb is roughly the same the cheaper steel obviously results from the use of niobium. Niobium, like vanadium, is a carbide-forming element but is not a powerful deoxidizer. It is possible therefore to add the element to a balanced steel which does not 'pipe' extensively. The yield of usable material is thereby greater, and enhanced mechanical properties are securable at a reasonable cost when compared with killed mild steel.

Not only is niobium a carbide-forming element, but additionally (like vanadium) it can produce steel with a finer grain than that of a balanced mild steel. The general characteristics of niobium-treated steels are as follows:

(1) The ductile/brittle transition temperature of heavy plates or sections, if these are finish rolled at a high temperature, is considerably raised in the 'as-rolled' condition. This is disadvantageous.

(2) If thin plates or sections are finished at 830/860° C the transition temperature is lowered as compared with (1) above. Hence the rolling temperature range is important. This decreased transition temperature in the 'as-rolled' condition may still be higher than that of steels which do not contain niobium.

(3) The yield stress and tensile strength are reduced slightly by normalizing, but excellent notch ductility then results. It is therefore advantageous if niobium-bearing steels are normalized. The transition temperatures referred to above are based arbitrarily on an energy absorption of 25 ft-lb by Charpy impact test.

Much work has been done on niobium-bearing steels to elucidate the precise way in which the element exercises its effectiveness. De Kazinczy,

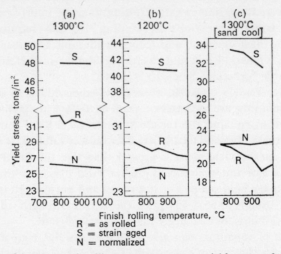

Fig. 32. Effect of heating and rolling temperatures on yield stress of C–Mn–Nb steel.

Axnäs and Pachleitner[1] examined both laboratory and commercially produced steels. A series of laboratory ingots, the compositions of which ranged from 0·06 to 0·15% C, 0·9/1·8% Mn and 0·03/0·05% Nb, were treated under three different conditions.

Group (a) heated to 1300° C before rolling and air cooled after rolling.
Group (b) heated to 1200° C before rolling and air cooled after rolling.
Group (c) heated to 1300° C before rolling and slow cooled in sand.

Properties were then ascertained in the as-rolled, strain-aged and normalized conditions. Strain-ageing was carried out by prestraining to 4% and then ageing at room temperature, 60° C and 100° C for different times up to one month before retesting. A general effect of this treatment was found to be that niobium delayed the incubation time for the maximum effect of strain-ageing in both the as-rolled and normalized conditions. This treatment also slowed down the increase in the yield stress obtained after the longest ageing period. The authors suggest that part of the nitrogen in the steel is precipitated as niobium nitride—thus decreasing the amount of interstitial

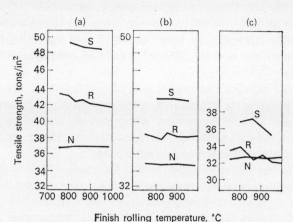

FIG. 33. Effect of heating and rolling temperatures on tensile strength of C–Mn–Nb steel.

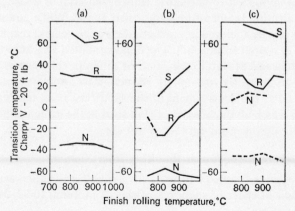

FIG. 34. Effect of heating and rolling temperatures on 20 ft-lb transition temperatures of C–Mn–Nb steel.

nitrogen. The nitrogen atoms during ageing have to travel over large distances before their concentration at dislocations is built up sufficiently to cause 'locking'.

The results of the experiments are best shown diagrammatically and Figs. 32–34 summarize the behaviour of tensile strength, yield stress and the Charpy V-notch 20 ft-lb transition temperatures respectively. The heat-treatment given to group (c) involving slow cooling in sand is of less practical interest than the heat-treatments given to groups (a) and (b). An examination of these two groups shows the effect of normalizing in the lowering of both yield stress and tensile strength values obtained in the as-rolled condition. Both these properties are superior, however, to those of mild steel similarly heat-treated. The arbitrary Charpy transition temperature ($+30°$ C) is high in the 'as-rolled' condition for group (a). While group (b) shows somewhat lower yield and tensile strengths for both 'as-rolled' and normalized conditions, this group shows the best (i.e. lowest) transition temperature, i.e. $-60°$ C approximately.

The increased strength and poorer (i.e. higher) transition temperature encountered in group (a) is attributable to the precipitation of niobium carbide as fine particles. Coarse precipitates which remain undissolved by heating only to $1200°$ C do not confer this increased strength. Hence the lower values for yield stress and tensile strength in group (b).

Referring to the Charpy impact values for group (b), it is seen that the lower finishing temperature, resulting from a lower temperature prior to rolling, has a pronounced effect on the transition characteristics. The transition temperature rises rapidly as the finish rolling temperature increases. In practice, thicker plates are finished at higher temperatures than thin plates. It is therefore important to normalize thicker material as a safeguard against the higher transition temperature mentioned above. While control of rolling temperatures can be achieved in practice, their achievement results in a much-reduced rate of output from a mill. The delays entailed are caused by reducing different thicknesses of slab to the same or different thicknesses of plate and the necessity to assess the amount of reduction to apply at each pass as the temperature falls. The achievement of the same 'last pass' temperature under conditions in which all thicknesses of slab start at the same temperature from the slab or bloom reheating furnace is not easy.

The Mechanism of Improvement Resulting from Niobium

Morrison[2], in a summary of work by himself and other workers, states that the beneficial effect of small quantities of niobium ($0.02–0.03\%$) is due to two main effects:

(a) Grain refinement, and
(b) precipitation hardening.

The latter effect is the more important of the two if the steels have been heated to above $1100°$ C (note that the property differences obtained by Kazinczy et al.[1] were obtained by heating to $1200°$ C and $1300°$ C respectively). At the higher temperatures niobium can go into solution in the austenite and is then precipitated during the γ to α transformation as small particles of niobium carbide (or possibly niobium carbo-nitride). This gives the pronounced hardening effect. If the steel is subsequently normalized, these previously precipitated particles are not again wholly taken back into solution but act as nuclei causing grain refinement on passing again through the γ to α transformation while air cooling.

The mechanism of grain refinement in niobium steels therefore differs somewhat from that achieved by the addition of aluminium to liquid steel. In the latter case a fine grain results from the initial presence of Al_2O_3 and AlN particles during the change from liquid to solid, whereas in niobium steels the necessary nuclei are formed in the solid state during the γ to α transformation. A second conversion of the structure to austenite has to take place in order to secure grain refinement. Where aluminium has been used a fine grain can be achieved directly from the initial hot working temperature if the finishing temperature corresponds to the normalizing temperature. Nuclei of alumina when once formed in the liquid do not go into and out of solution subsequently.

The evidence of Kazinczy et al.[1], which shows that strain-ageing is delayed by the addition of niobium, seems to support the concept that a carbo-nitride or a nitride is indeed formed. If this is so then the amount of interstitial nitrogen is thereby reduced to some extent and consequently the remaining nitrogen atoms have to diffuse over larger distances. This explains the delay before the ageing effects reach a maximum.

Practical Considerations

It is important to remember that niobium is only a weak deoxidizing agent. This is fortunate since it can be added to semi-killed steels without producing excessive shrinkage. Additions of ferro-niobium are made to the ladle during tapping. While mould additions are possible the relatively high melting point of the alloy (about 1650° C) makes this practice undesirable. Great care is required to secure uniformity of distribution if mould additions are made.

Care is also necessary if ladle additions are made because in the case of B.S. 968 large additions of ferro-manganese are also necessary (up to 1·5% Mn is required). If the distribution of the alloys throughout the ladle is not uniform then objectionable concentrations of manganese can result. This effect may be particularly apparent in the last ingot poured from the ladle. If the alloys are added to the ladle too soon, the metal at the bottom of the ladle may be richer in manganese and niobium than the remainder of the steel. This metal is sluggish, relatively cold, and it does not leave the ladle first when the stopper is opened because of the natural circulation by convection of the hotter liquid above. Consequently, it may enter the last mould (or moulds) to be filled and even within the mould is capable of sinking towards the bottom depending on its amount and temperature. Its density is higher, and objectionable concentrations of manganese and carbon (because ferro-manganese also contains carbon) may result.

The specification B.S. 968 states that plates below 0·5 in. thick need not necessarily be normalized before delivery (provided the required minimum properties are obtained on testing). The reason is that such thicknesses finish at or very near the normalizing temperature in standard mill practice. Thicker plates, because of higher finishing temperatures, tend to fit in group (a) of Kazinczy et al.[1] where maximum grain refinement has not resulted, and consequently while higher strengths are obtained the Charpy impact values are poor. Grain refinement by normalizing—making use of the already precipitated nuclei (previously mentioned)—immediately results in a drastic lowering of the transition temperature as assessed by an arbitrary Charpy impact value.

The Impact Strength of Rolled Sections in B.S. 968 Steel

For general structural purposes, forms of product other than plate are necessary and the notch toughness of joists and various sections is extremely important. Sections such as H-beams, and particularly the modern broad flange beams behave differently during rolling than does a plate. It is obvious

Table 14. *Charpy impact tests on angles and plates in B.S. 968 steel*

Form	Thickness (in.)	Composition			Charpy Impact (long.)	
		C%	Mn%	Nb%	Temp °C for 20 ft-lb	Ft-lb at 0° C
12 in. × 12 in. angle	1·16	0·18	1·32	0·013	+10	10
,,	1·19	0·18	1·40	0·012	−15	35
,,	1·25	0·18	1·32	0·011	−20	35
,,	1·06	0·19	1·42	0·010	−30	37
,,	0·97	0·21	1·44	0·012	+5	10
,,	1·0	0·18	1·35	0·015	−5	25
,,	1·0	0·20	1·37	0·005	−15	29
,,	1·0	0·20	1·35	0·016	−25	40
,,	1·0	0·18	1·36	0·010	0	21
,,	1·16	0·20	1·38	0·012	−20	35
,,	1·06	0·17	1·30	0·010	−20	32
,,	0·87	0·17	1·40	0·012	−40	72
Plate	0·50	0·16	1·24	0·02/0·03	−33	49
,,	0·62	0·17	1·32	0·02/0·03	Below −50	108
,,	0·87	0·19	1·36	0·02/0·03	Below −50	88
,,	1·12	0·20	1·45	0·02/0·03	Below −50	91

NOTE: All plates were normalized except one, viz. 0·50 in. thick. All angles tested in the 'as-rolled' condition.

that a flat plate will cool more uniformly after emerging from the rolls. The fact that the development of a beam section during rolling involves several passes through differently shaped openings in the rolls implies different rates of cooling in various portions of the cross-section as rolling proceeds. Generally the web of an H-section cools faster than the flanges. The latter may also be thicker than the web in certain types of sections. Hence, both in ordinary steels and the higher tensile varieties, differential properties result. Normalizing as a remedy for brittleness is not so easily applicable to sections as to plates. Subsequent cold straightening in three dimensions is necessary. Very heavy sections which are symmetrical can be normalized somewhat more easily with less warping, but even then differential rates of cooling from the normalizing temperature may affect the ultimate properties.

In view of these inherent manufacturing difficulties it is necessary therefore to reduce the specification requirements for notch toughness of sections as compared with those of plate material. Table 14 gives some typical Charpy values obtained on heavy angles in the 'as-rolled' condition and on some normalized plates. While the majority of tests on the angles satisfy the criterion of 20 ft-lb at −15° C they are inferior to the results for plates with respect to the temperature at which an arbitrary value of 20 ft-lb is obtained and the level of energy absorption at 0° C.

Large thick sections in this steel should therefore be very thoroughly tested for impact properties if normalizing has not been carried out. It is possible that the building up by welding of heavy sections from plate which has been normalized is a better guarantee of adequate notch toughness.

Silicon-killed Steels Treated with Niobium

The foregoing has dealt with the strengthening effects of niobium on a C–Mn steel. These effects are achieved by its grain-refining influence when in the normalized condition and the precipitation hardening which takes place. By virtue of the fine grain, good Charpy impact values at sub-zero temperatures can be secured.

It is well known that elements such as chromium and molybdenum which affect the hardenability of steel can be additive in their effect. The author considered therefore that the effect of grain refining by the addition of both niobium and aluminium was worth investigating from the point of view of impact strength at low temperatures. It was conceivable that the effect of the two elements together would be superior to the sum of the two individual effects. An opportunity to investigate this possibility arose in 1962 when the author was requested to develop a steel for a specific application. The specification laid down was that the steel should possess a minimum yield stress of 26 tons/in² and a minimum Charpy impact value of 40 ft-lb at −10° C. No minimum tensile strength was stated, since it was the intention of the designer to base the design on the yield strength. There was no existing standard constructional steel specification which covered these requirements. The steel was required in the form of large plates $\frac{7}{8}$ in. and $1\frac{1}{4}$ in. thick and these were to be cold rolled into cylinders and joined end to end by welding to produce tubes 70–90 ft long. These were to be drilled into the sea bed, to form supports for a pier for the mooring of large tankers. Weldability with reasonable ease to facilitate fabrication was a necessity and consequently the maximum carbon and manganese contents were limited.

A steel which is grain-refined by aluminium requires to be silicon killed and in view of the existence of a continental specification (D.I.N. 17155 Grade 19Mn5) which permits a maximum silicon content of 0·5% instead of the more usual 0·10% to 0·20% the author decided to use this as a base. The higher silicon content exerts a strengthening effect by forming a silico-ferrite. The lower levels of silicon normally used to deoxidize the steel do not add appreciably to the strength. It may be noted that the formula (see p. 78) giving the relationship between strength and composition shows that the effect of silicon on strength is not as great as that of phosphorus, but phosphorus is only permissible in small amounts. The silicon levels on which the formula is based are those normally used for deoxidizing only.

A further advantage of using a higher silicon content to obtain strength is that this element does not interfere seriously with welding, provided low H_2 rods are used. Silicon is, however, a grain-coarsening element and this effect is made use of in high silicon steels (2–4% Si) intended for electrical equipment, for example, sheet steels for transformer cores and armature stampings. The coarse grain securable by suitable heat-treatment improves magnetic permeability and so increases electrical efficiency.

Grain refinement was therefore a prime necessity and it was visualized that the effect of two separate grain-refining additions (aluminium and niobium) might be still more effective when added to a steel which could, without them, develop a coarser grain-size than that associated with a killed steel having a normal silicon level.

On these considerations, therefore, a basic specification was decided upon as follows:

C %	Mn %	Si %
0·22 max.	1·50 max.	0·40/0·55 max.

The steel was to be grain-refined by the addition of 3 lb Al/ton to the ladle and ferro-niobium added to give 0·02/0·04% Nb. The first experimental cast of 80 tons was made in February 1962 and was unfortunately slightly higher in silicon and manganese than intended, viz.

C %	Mn %	Si %	Nb %
0·22	1·65	0·59	0·036

Trial plates were however rolled and tested. The results obtained are given in Table 15 for 2 in. thick material. Test plates were purposely rolled thicker than required in order to prejudice test results unfavourably.

Table 15. *Properties of a high silicon steel treated with aluminium and niobium*

Heat-treatment	Tensile strength (tons/in²)	Yield stress (tons/in²)	Elonga-tion % on $4\sqrt{A}$	Reduc-tion of area (%)	Charpy V-notch ft-lb (long.) at $-°$ C				
					+20°	0°	−10°	−30°	−50°
Commercially norm. 880° C	41·9	31·3	29·5	56·8	78	77	51	41	19
Commercially norm. 880 + SR*	38·4	28·3	29·5	53·8	80	75	53	29	18

* SR = Stress relieved. 2 hr at 625° C.

These preliminary results showed that the required specification values could be met and tended to support the hypothesis concerning the combined effects of the additions. As a result, production of this steel was commenced and more detailed work was carried out on samples from different casts. This enabled a clearer picture of the potentialities of the steel as a high strength notch-tough material suitable for use at sub-zero temperatures to be established. The results given in Table 15 were confirmed, and indeed in most tests much higher impact values were secured. With respect to notch toughness properties, any specification must nominate a minimum value which is achievable on an economic basis. The normal expectation is that steel to any specification will yield values which exceed the minimum generously.

Effect of Various Heat-treatments

A fully killed and grain-refined steel develops the best combined properties when correctly heat-treated. The N.D. IV grade of notch-tough mild steel is an example. Hence, properties of such a steel in the 'as-rolled' condition are of secondary importance. The work described was carried out to study the response of the steel to various heat-treatments.

(*a*) *Normalizing and stress relieving*. The general effect of 'stress-relieving' such as might be necessary for a fabricated pressure vessel is to lower the tensile and yield strengths, to reduce impact strength and to raise the ductile/brittle transition temperature—the effects arising from precipitation of nitrides. This is shown in Table 15.

(*b*) *Effect of double normalizing and strain-ageing.* Table 16 compares results from another cast which was rolled into $\frac{3}{8}$ in. thick plates. Test coupons were heat-treated in the laboratory. The analysis of this cast was:

C %	Mn %	Si %
0·23	1·42	0·45

Table 16. *Effect of double normalizing on a high silicon steel treated with aluminium and niobium*

Heat-treatment	Tensile strength (tons/in²)	Yield stress (tons/in²)	Elonga-tion % on 4√A	Reduc-tion of area (%)	Charpy V-notch ft-lb (long.) at −° C				
					+20°	0°	−10°	−30°	−50°
Norm. 910° C	41·4	30·8	34	57	85	82	62	50	38
Norm. 910° C + norm. 880° C	41·6	29·6	36	59	90	88	83	58	44

The effect of double normalizing, while reducing slightly the yield stress values, improves the Charpy impact values.

Table 17 gives a fuller survey of properties obtainable from the original cast made (see Table 15). Results were ascertained on 2 in. thick plate coupons, each 8 in. × 18 in. which were heat-treated in the laboratory. The D.V.M. notch was used to enable a comparison to be made with certain continental steels.

The results suggest that 880° C as a normalizing temperature for this steel is very slightly superior to 900° C. While this is not so apparent from the results for the non-aged impact values it is more apparent in the specimens which have been strain-aged. In spite of the fact that the steel is fully silicon killed and aluminium grain refined there is a deterioration in the impact properties after 2% straining followed by ageing at 250° C. This deterioration is however very slight and the steel can be classified as 'non-ageing' from a practical aspect. Precipitation effects occur in all steels under such conditions and 'ageing' is a relative term. The deterioration would have been very much increased had the steel not been silicon killed and aluminium grain refined and, additionally, the strength properties would not have been achieved.

In Table 17 values for 'percent crystallinity' are recorded. These show that, while energy absorption levels are high at quite low temperatures (−40° and −70° C), there is a sharp change in % crystallinity with respect to

Table 17. *Effect of normalizing temperature, stress-relieving and strain-ageing on a high silicon steel treated with aluminium and niobium*

	Code no.	Heat-treatment	Tensile strength (tons/in²)	Yield stress (tons/in²)	Elongation % on $5\cdot65\sqrt{A}$	Reduction of area (%)	Yield-tensile ratio	D.P.N.
Trans.	HC1	N 880° C	40·3	29·7	18·5	33·3	0·74	192
	HC2	N 880° + SR 625° Cs	38·4	28·8	21·0	36·8	0·75	185
	HC3	N 900° C	40·3	29·0	18·5	29·7	0·72	191
	HC4	N 900° + SR 625° C	38·4	28·2	20·5	34·0	0·74	184
Longit.	HC1	As above	41·9	31·3	26·0	56·8	0·75	—
	HC2		38·4	28·3	26·0	53·8	0·74	—
	HC3		40·2	29·3	25·0	49·8	0·73	—
	HC4		38·4	27·5	26·5	55·2	0·72	—

		Non-aged				Strain-aged 30 min at 250° C					
			D.V.M. notch at −°C				D.V.M. notch at −°C				
		Charpy V-notch* at −10°C					2% Strain + ageing					10% Strain + ageing
			+20°	0°	−40°	−70°	+20°	0°	−10°	−30°	−50°	+20°
ft-lb/cm²	HC1	57	118	112	67	59	102	104	84	76	44	85
	HC2	54	121	109	74	63	102	85	73	60	45	72
	HC3	56	125	101	76	57	106	97	79	43	43	70
	HC4	53	119	107	69	52	112	98	82	62	41	70
% Crystallinity	HC1	65	0	20	93	98	0	33	50	85	100	15
	HC2	80	6	60	90	93	6	60	82	85	90	13
	HC3	78	2	63	93	97	0	20	56	97	90	20
	HC4	75	0	37	90	97	3	32	65	97	95	35

* Both Charpy and D.V.M. notch values are expressed in ft-lb/cm² in accord with continental practice. U-notch is 3 mm deep. All impact specimens longitudinal.

temperature. This would indicate a well-defined tough/brittle transition temperature between 0° and −40° C.

(c) *Effect of quenching and tempering.* Since the steel is extremely 'fine grain' and contains no elements inducing depth hardenability it is to be expected that given a quenching and tempering treatment the properties obtained will vary with plate thickness. That this is so, is revealed by the results obtained from laboratory quenching and tempering coupon plates of two thicknesses. Table 18 gives the results.

The appreciable deterioration in the impact values of the thicker plate is to be noted and the effect of the reduced ability to harden in depth is reflected also in the respective yield stress values. Plate 12 shows the somewhat coarser structure obtained in the thicker plate.

The values in Table 19 were obtained from a different cast and confirm the high order of both strength and low-temperature impact values which can be obtained from the steel.

Table 18. *Effect of plate thickness on depth hardenability of a high silicon steel treated with aluminium and niobium*

Code	Thick-ness (in.)	Heat-treatment at ° C	Tensile strength (tons/in²)	Yield stress (tons/in²)	Elonga-tion % on 5·65√A	Charpy V ft-lb at −10° C	Crystal-linity (%)
75	⅝	Q 890° + T 650°C* (2 hr)	41·3	34·7	25	79	0
85	1	Q 890° + T 650° C (2 hr)	39·8	32·6	27	51	0
77	⅝	Q 890° + T 670° C (2 hr)	39·3	33·0	32·5	83	0
87	1	Q 890° + T 670° C (2 hr)	40·2	32·0	31·0	52	0

* Q = Quench; T = Temper

Analysis:

C%	Mn %	S %	P %	Si %	Nb %
0·205	1·46	0·026	0·012	0·49	0·038

Table 19. *Typical properties (for various heat-treatments)—⅝ in. plate of a high silicon steel treated with aluminium and niobium*

Code	Heat-treatment (temperature and time)		Hard-ness D.P.N.	Tensile strength (tons/in²)	Yield stress (tons/in²)	Elonga-tion % on 5·65√A
	° C	Hours				
S1	N 910	(¾)	190	41·4	30·8	30
S2	N 910	(¾) + N 880 (¾)	189	41·6	29·6	30
S3	N 910	(¾) + T 750 (1)	192	42·7	29·7	29
S4	Q 910	(¾) + T 750 (1)	229	48·4	36·8	27
S5	Q 910	(¾) + T 680 (¾)	213	44·1	36·0	25

Charpy V-notch ft-lb and crystallinity—at ° C (longitudinal)

Code	+20°	0°	−10°	−30°	−50°
S1	85 (0)	82 (20)	62 (80)	50 (90)	38 (90)
S2	90 (0)	88 (20)	83 (70)	58 (80)	44 (90)
S3	94 (0)	82 (32)	67 (85)	52 (90)	41 (90)
S4	85 (0)	83 (0)	75 (65)	54 (77)	43 (90)
S5	97 (0)	96 (0)	92 (50)	90 (55)	60 (67)

Analysis:

C%	Mn%	S%	P%	Si%	Nb%
0·23	1·43	0·019	0·013	0·45	0·032

It can be seen from the above results that the effect of double normalizing stated on p. 156 is confirmed. Plate 12(c) illustrates the unusually fine grain structure which can be achieved by double normalizing. This fineness is also partially due to the modified form of the pearlite resulting from the relatively high level of manganese and may be contrasted with (a) and (b) of the same Plate—which are respectively N.D. IV single normalized and mild steel 'as-rolled'.

The transformation range of this steel has been calculated from the formula given by Grange[3], the result being Ac_3 817° C; Ac_1 708° C.

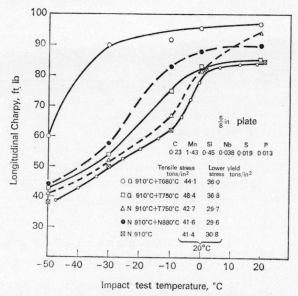

Fig. 35. Effect of various heat-treatments on the impact properties of a high silicon structural steel.

The tempering of coupons S3 and S4 has been carried out in the middle of this range and, while this is unconventional, the impact and tensile properties of S3 are similar to those of the normalized steel. S4, however, which was initially quenched, develops a much higher tensile and yield strength for a similar degree of notch toughness.

Quenching, followed by the conventional sub-critical, tempering treatment gives both the highest yield stress and by far the best degree of notch toughness at all testing temperatures used.

The comparative degrees of notch toughness developed by the steel as a result of different heat-treatments are shown in Fig. 35 and the relative positions of the impact energy curves illustrate the way in which the notch toughness of any steel may be varied in order of magnitude. The marked superiority of quenching and tempering is obvious, but it must be borne in mind that in choosing any steel for a specific purpose cost is of prime importance. Consequently, no hard and fast principle can be laid down as to whether it is better to choose a specific composition range with (*a*) no heat-treatment, i.e. as-rolled, or (*b*) a simple heat-treatment such as normalizing,

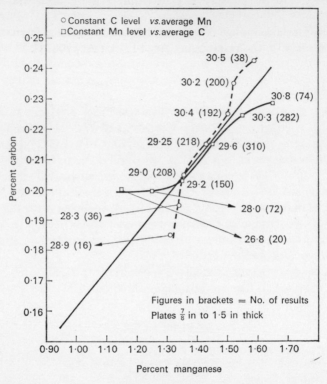

FIG. 36. Yield stress values for a niobium-treated aluminium grain-refined steel in double normalized condition.

or (*c*) a cheaper composition accompanied by a more complex and expensive heat-treatment.

It has been mentioned that the steel described was designed by the author to fulfil a particular specification laid down by an engineer. In a contract of any size, many casts are necessary, and with respect to composition it is quite impossible to reproduce identical analyses in every cast. Consequently, reasonable ranges of both composition and properties must be acceptable provided certain minimum requirements are achieved.

Fig. 36 gives a survey of the yield stresses obtained for (*a*) constant carbon levels at 'average' manganese values, and (*b*) constant manganese levels at 'average' carbon values in 45 different casts. From these curves it is seen that the limits of carbon and manganese achieved were $0\cdot18/0\cdot235\%$ and $1\cdot25/1\cdot6\%$ respectively. The silicon range was $0\cdot45/0\cdot55\%$. In all cases the minimum yield stress of $26\cdot0$ tons/in^2 was attained or exceeded. From the results also it was apparent that a variation in the carbon level between the limits achieved had a lesser effect than a variation in the manganese level—the average Charpy values being constant at 70/75 ft-lb. This illustrates the beneficial effect of a higher Mn/C ratio on the impact properties. At the lower manganese levels the average impact values for each group of tests are lower. Here the manganese/average carbon ratio is the lowest. At the highest manganese levels the converse is true and average impact values are considerably higher.

Generally, the results show, in the thickness range produced (viz. $\frac{5}{8}$ in. to $1\frac{1}{4}$ in.) that it is possible to obtain a yield stress of $27\cdot0/28\cdot0$ tons/in^2 from a steel containing $0\cdot20/0\cdot22\%$ C, $1\cdot30/1\cdot45\%$ Mn, $0\cdot45/0\cdot55\%$ Si, annd inthe double normalized condition such a steel will have a Charpy impact of 60 ft-lb at -10° C. These enhanced properties arise from (a) the use of niobium as a means of increasing the yield stress/tensile strength ratio, (b) the use of aluminium as a grain-refining agent (coupled with the effect of niobium), (c) the double normalizing treatment which results in an exceptionally uniform fine grain structure, and (d) the strengthening effect of tne high silicon content on the ferrite.

Such a steel obviously has extensive applications in highly stressed welded structures intended to operate at temperatures down to $-25^\circ/-30^\circ$ C.

REFERENCES

1. F. De Kazinczy, A. Axnäs and P. Pachleitner. *Jern. Ann.*, **147**, no. 4 (1963), 408.
2. W. B. Morrison. *Iron Steel, Lond.*, **37**, no. 9 (1964), 390.
3. R. A. Grange. *Metal Prog.*, **79** (April 1961), 73.

M

CHAPTER 12

THE PRODUCTION OF QUENCHED AND TEMPERED STEEL PLATES

Improved notch toughness and a lower ductile/brittle transition temperature combined with high strength can be obtained by quenching a steel and subsequently tempering it to produce a tempered martensite or tempered bainite structure. This is a generalization applicable to the plain carbon-manganese steels as well as the more special low-alloy steels.

Unfortunately, until plant capacity increases significantly, the increased cost involved in the production of quenched and tempered steels tends to outweigh, to the designer, the value of the improved properties. This statement is true at present. Obviously the provision of adequate plant to ensure large through-put tonnages would reduce considerably the costs, and undoubtedly developments will take place in this direction. Quenched and tempered plate steels of comparatively simple composition can offer a solution to some of the weldability problems associated with the present higher strength steels.

Improvement in Properties Obtained

There are many arguments which suggest that the commercial price of a steel should in some way bear a logical relationship to a combination of physical properties, but this is very difficult to achieve. In different grades of steel one or more properties (e.g. toughness or weldability) may differ considerably. This gives rise to some difficulty in evaluating correctly each individual property in a way which is equitable, especially when methods and costs of manufacture are taken into account. The cost of manufacture, which must dominate, is not necessarily reflected in the combination of engineering properties secured.

An example of the improvement in properties of an ordinary low carbon–high manganese steel by quenching and tempering is demonstrated by the following experiment. The steel chosen was ship plate produced to fulfil the requirements of Lloyd's P403 Rule, i.e. the Mn/C ratio is in excess of 2·5 to 1. From the analysis given below the Mn/C ratio is nearly 7 to 1, this being favourable towards a lower ductile/brittle transition temperature. As indicated by the silicon content the steel was produced in the balanced condition: 0·155% C; 1·01% Mn; 0·030% Si; 0·035% S; 0·032% P.

Plates from this cast were supplied to the purchaser in the 'as-rolled' condition.

A sample plate was first tested in this condition. The remainder of the sample from which the testpiece was cut was then heated and held at 980° C

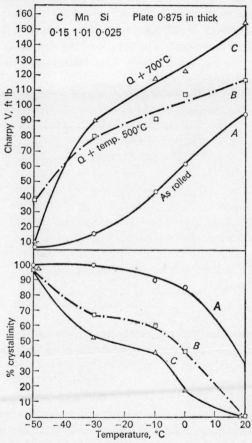

Fig. 37. Impact values for a low carbon–high manganese steel. Lloyd's P403 (balanced).

for one hour and water quenched. Microscopic examination showed the plate to possess a homogeneous structure, consisting of dilute bainite. After cutting, pieces were tempered for one hour at successively higher temperatures ranging from 450° C to 700° C. The samples tempered at 500° C and 700° C were used for the determination of Charpy impact values over a range of temperatures and specimens tempered at all temperatures were tested for tensile strength at room temperature. Results for hardness and tensile strength are given in Table 20 below, and Fig. 37 shows the transition curves as defined by the Charpy tests and fracture appearance.

Tempering at 700° C (just below the Ac_1 temperature) has produced no marked change in the yield stress and ultimate strength but there was a very marked improvement in the impact values. Tempering at 500° C has lowered the temperature at which a 70% crystalline fracture occurs by about 40° C and has produced an increase in impact strength at all test temperatures. It is at the lower tempering temperature also that a distinct increase in yield and ultimate strengths has resulted. The degree of improvement of the properties obtained is not constant for all steels. The experiment recorded was one of

Table 20. *Tensile properties of quenched and tempered low carbon–high manganese steel plate 0·875 in. thick*

Condition	B.H.N. 3000 kg load	0·2% proof stress (tons/in²)	Tensile strength (tons/in²)	% Elongation on 2 in.
'As rolled' Water quenched 980° C and tempered at:	143	19·8	27·8	36
450° C	179	22·0	31·0	20
500° C	178	21·6	30·8	23
600° C	168	21·1	30·0	27
650° C	156	20·5	29·4	33
680° C	156	20·4	29·1	34
700° C	143	20·0	28·8	38

the author's earliest and the effects obtained are still more marked on plain C–Mn steels having a somewhat higher carbon content, and also on low-alloy steels.

Problems Involved in Quenching and Tempering

The quenching of plates of considerable area presents a specific problem by reason of the relative dimensions of the three axes. It can be visualized that the quenching of small articles in the form of cylinders or discs or some combination of the two is relatively simple. Even if quenched in batches, the access of the quenching medium to all portions of the surfaces is extremely rapid and thorough because the quenching medium is large in relation to the mass being quenched. Also the time of transfer from furnace to quenching medium is small, thus avoiding loss of temperature during transfer. For larger masses, however, difficulties arise because time of transfer cannot be so rapid, and moreover, immediate simultaneous immersion of the whole mass cannot be achieved. For instance, plates, weighing say 10 tons or more, cannot simply be dropped into a quenching tank. Large masses, however, do not lose temperature as rapidly as small masses and consequently temperature losses over the time-interval between removal from the furnace and quenching are not serious. It follows that if the object to be quenched (such as a large rotor shaft for a turbine, or a hollow cylindrical forging) has a major axis of symmetry, it should be immersed along this axis. If this operation is rapid and circulation of the coolant by pumps is adequate, then serious distortion is prevented. Distortion or even cracking can arise from non-uniform and sequential cooling of different areas or volumes of the object.

Let us consider a flat steel plate of large dimensions, for example, 8–10 ft wide and 30–40 ft long. While this could be considered to have a major axis of symmetry (e.g. along the centre of the length) to immerse it vertically as in the case of a large shaft would introduce distortion. The reason for it is that dimensions in a plane at right-angles to the major axis are so unequal (viz. the thickness of the plate versus its width). The ratio between the two is too high to avoid buckling caused by quenching stresses. Subsequent flattening in the tempered condition would be necessary, and this is extremely difficult and expensive. Additionally, plates are produced in a horizontal plane and moved by means of roller tracks. They must also be heated horizontally to the quenching temperature since in any other position they would distort under their own weight because of their relative softness at the normalizing temperature. It is not easy to pick up a plate weighing say 8–12 tons quickly by its edge when at an elevated temperature.

The Quenching Press

A limited amount of tank quenching of relatively thick plates has been done, but the more effective method is by spray quenching both surfaces of the plate simultaneously while in the horizontal position. This is now achieved in a specially designed quenching press which was developed during the last war. Such a press is limited to the use of water as a quenching medium since the use of oil is prohibitive on account of the large volume necessary. Since water quenching is used, the plates must be relatively low in carbon to avoid quenching cracks. This low level of carbon is additionally necessary because the plates are usually intended for welded constructions.

A relatively small press which the author used during the war was capable of quenching 8 ft × 6 ft plates. These plates were intended for use as light bullet-proof armour around the bridges and decks of small coastal vessels. The plates were $\frac{1}{4}$ and $\frac{5}{16}$ in. thick and satisfactory toughness was assessed by their ability to withstand an armour-piercing 0·303 bullet (driven by a special charge) at a distance of 150 yards and striking normal to the surface. Slight bulging only was permitted in firing trials. Each plate was tested for hardness after tempering, and a range of 255–302 B.H.N. was found to give satisfactory results. The steel used was a simple low carbon–high manganese type containing 0·20/0·23% C and 1·3/1·5% Mn. Plates were quenched from 920° to 930° C and subsequently tempered for $2\frac{1}{2}$ hr approx. at 450° C.

The top and bottom platens of the quenching press for clamping the plates were hollow cast-iron boxes with half inch high studs 'cast on' at intervals of 2 in. Each stud was $\frac{3}{4}$ in. diameter. Between the studs holes $\frac{3}{16}$ in. diameter were drilled so that in flooding the box platens by a quick-release valve thin plate was effectively quenched simultaneously on both sides by the high-pressure sprays emerging between the studs. The press exerted a total pressure of some 600 tons over a 60 ft² area. The heating furnace, situated in front of the press, was charged by means of a special machine equipped with two arms which ran on heat-resisting rails resting in two slots in the hearth. The charging arms could be raised or lowered at any length of insertion into the furnace. It was therefore possible to place a cold plate on to these arms at the ingoing end of the furnace and then insert the arms below all plates already in the furnace. Hence these arms could be used to lift and push out the end plate nearest the quenching press, thereby moving all other plates along one position towards the discharge end. Arms were then lowered and withdrawn leaving the cold, freshly charged plate as the last in the series. The end plate was discharged on to a short roller track which moved it on to the bottom platen of the press. The top platen was then lowered to clamp the plate and water admitted to the spray nozzles. This operation took some 15/20 sec to accomplish from the time the heated plate emerged from the furnace.

Much more complicated equipment is needed to handle larger plates of different sizes. Owing to their length they cannot be skidded into position— hence controllable rollers must be used to locate them under the press. This is accomplished in modern large presses by eliminating the box platens and using a vertically retractable roller track to keep the plate clear of any clamping device while being located suitably in the press. Fig. 38 shows this schematically. In position (a) the roller gear itself is raised by hydraulic rams with respect to the bottom platen and the rollers are then level with the conveyor rollers leaving the furnace. When the plate is located correctly the press rollers are lowered on to the bottom platen leaving the clamping claws free to grip the plate. Simultaneously the top platen moves down, thus leaving the plate gripped between the claws. The three flat machined surfaces of the claws each contain V grooves to allow water to flow through. The claw areas in actual contact with the plate are each 2 in. × 1 in., and hence 12 in² per 144 in² of plate are used each side for clamping. In the press shown in Plate 13 plates 45 ft long × 10 ft wide can be quenched. Any thickness from $\frac{3}{16}$ in. to 4 in. can be accommodated and the degree of overall flatness obtained is limited only by the accuracy of the two planes through the surfaces of the claws. The total pressure exerted amounts to 800 tons for 450 ft² of plate, the pressure being applied by means of twenty-eight 8 in. diameter hydraulic cylinders.

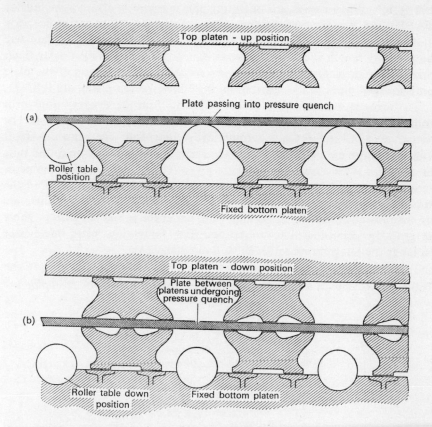

FIG. 38. Diagram showing action of quenching press: (a) top platen up, roller table up carrying plate above bottom platen; (b) top platen down, roller table down and plate clamped between top and bottom platens.

There are three pressure zones for different plate lengths to avoid the necessity for using maximum energy. Oil pressure in the cylinders is 1250 lb/in².

The water is delivered to the nozzles by over one hundred spray pipes located between both upper and lower platen claws. These spray pipes are drilled to give jets at three angles for maximum coverage. The spray pipes are fed from a 36 in. main into a system of intermediate headers designed to give a very even distribution of the water to the spray pipes which contain in all some 30,000 jets. The amount of water required for a press which is continuously occupied in quenching is very considerable. The equipment shown in Plate 13 is supplied from a 200,000 gal reservoir, and pumping is done by 3×520 h.p. 7000 gal/min. pumps—the water being supplied at a pressure of 100 lb/in². When sprays are operating the pressure in the system falls to 40–50 lb/in². It is extremely important to ensure that water reaches both top and bottom surfaces of the plate simultaneously, otherwise the plate will bow in both length and breadth directions. This is achieved by a delay timer operating a valve which prevents water reaching the underside of the plate until the feed pipes to the distribution system of the top platen are full.

The press is situated at a distance of 10 ft from the delivery door of a roller hearth furnace in which the plates are heated prior to the quench. The temperature of the furnace is automatically controlled. The hearth is 180 ft long and plates are oscillated within the furnace continuously up to the time of discharge. This movement results in an extremely uniform plate temperature prior to discharge. After quenching is complete and the water to the sprays is shut off the remaining film of water is blown off the top of the plate by compressed air during its passage from under the raised top platen. Table 21 gives the quenching times found necessary for various plate thicknesses to lower the temperature to 25/30° C from 900/920° C.

Table 21. *Recommended minimum quenching times for low-alloy steel plates—press quenched*

Plate thickness (in.)	Quench time (mins)	Plate thickness (in.)	Quench time (mins)
$\frac{1}{4}$	2	2	11
$\frac{1}{2}$	4	$2\frac{1}{2}$	15
$\frac{3}{4}$	5	3	19
1	6	$3\frac{1}{2}$	22
$1\frac{1}{2}$	9	4	25

NOTE: Relationship between thickness and the recommended minimum time is not linear.

The contact of the claws with the plate surface prevents somewhat less than one-twelfth of each square foot of plate area from receiving direct contact with the water. The relative smallness of these evenly spaced and shielded areas, however, is compensated by the heat conductivity of the steel and this is sufficient to ensure the requisite rate of heat abstraction necessary to produce the martensitic or bainitic condition. The claws do not indent the surface of the plate since the pressure per square inch of contact is not sufficient, but the positions occupied by them can be seen as a pattern on the thin surface scale after the plate has dried out.

Commercial Tempering of Quenched Plates

Since the properties obtainable by tempering a quenched steel are both time and temperature dependent it is obviously of the greatest importance that heating up to the required tempering temperature should be as uniform as possible with respect to various portions of the total mass. In the case of large plates, non-uniformly heated areas may cause warping due to irregular release of stresses set up by quenching. Further, slower heating of some areas of the plate compared with others, may lead to a significant increase in the

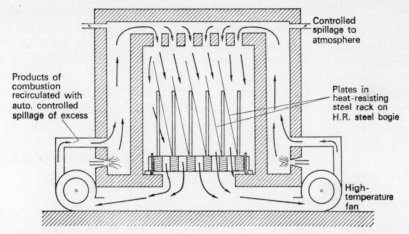

FIG. 39. Principle of forced circulation bogie furnace for tempering plates in vertical position.

intended time at the tempering temperature of other areas which achieve the correct tempering temperature more quickly. In consequence, irregular properties may occur with respect to different areas of the plate. The deviation of these from the permitted specification range can be much more serious than variations occurring in an ordinary 'hot-rolled' plate subsequently air cooled.

For the tempering operation, therefore, special furnaces are required. Since heat transmission by radiation depends on the difference between the fourth powers of the absolute temperatures of the source of heat and the mass to be heated, heat transfer is not very effective in the comparatively low temperature range (viz. 450° C to 690° C) required for tempering. The heating method adopted at these lower temperatures is not by radiation from flames, but by convection, that is, by the circulation at a high velocity, of the furnace gases. The temperature of these is thermostatically controlled and they are so directed that all areas are uniformly swept by them. This is done in special furnaces of the type shown schematically in Figs. 39 and 40.

In Fig. 39 a series of plates can be stacked vertically as in a 'toast rack', the base—a bogie—being slotted so that the hot gases can circulate between the plates uniformly. The hot gases are admitted through a hollow grid roof from a combustion chamber and withdrawn similarly through the bottom of the furnace by a high-temperature fan. It is customary in such furnaces to recirculate the maximum volume of products of combustion and admit just a

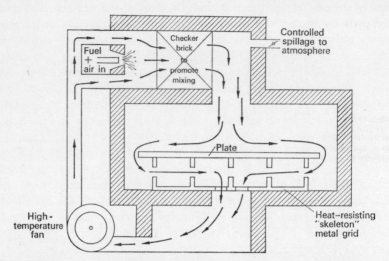

FIG. 40. Principle of fixed hearth forced circulation furnace for tempering large heavy plates in a horizontal position.

sufficient amount of air to the circulating gases. This air will maintain combustion of an amount of fuel which will, in turn, maintain the required temperature. The relatively small excess volume of products of combustion is continuously discharged to atmosphere. This type of furnace was used for the production of standard size pieces of light armour plate described on page 165.

In Fig. 40 the furnace is designed for large plates which cannot conveniently be handled 'on edge', the circulating gases taking the path indicated and being admitted and withdrawn from the chamber through central slots in roof and bed so that both surfaces of the whole plate are uniformly swept by the hot gases. In this type of furnace it is useless to insert one plate superimposed on another even if 'spacers' are used since the shielding of the lower plate by the upper prevents the achievement of the correct tempering temperature in the bottom plate within the same time. This may result in different properties of the two plates. To temper more than one plate in the horizontal position would require the gases to be circulated horizontally instead of vertically.

While it has been stated that furnaces in which the charge is heated by radiation are not efficient at commonly used tempering temperatures it is possible to use such a furnace provided it is heated by a very large number of small burners. If sufficiently numerous they can maintain a uniform temperature provided temperature control is adequate, and the charge to be heated is small in relation to the mass of the furnace. As in the forced circulation furnace (Fig. 40) any attempt to secure economy by increasing the number of layers to be heated results in non-uniformity of properties and is ultimately more costly by necessitating re-treatment which may involve re-quenching. Under-tempering, resulting in too brittle or hard a material, can be rectified by further tempering, but it is not easy to carry this out with certainty every time, because of doubt as to the further time and precise temperature required. Allowance must be made for the time taken for the second heating up to the chosen tempering temperature and this allowance can only be roughly estimated. Preferred fuels for tempering furnaces are gaseous, for example, town's gas, clean producer gas or coke oven (+ blast furnace) gas. Light oils may be used but are far from ideal due to the sooting up of burners and the relative crudity of the temperature control. Electric muffle furnaces can be used for small repetition articles. A new heating method in the course of development is by means of a fluidized bed in which the article to be tempered is immersed. Refractory granules are both heated and fluidized by hot gases, and heat transfer as well as the attainment of the required temperature is extremely rapid. Uniformity of temperature is excellent, but the process is at present confined to temperatures lower than those required by steel. With care and good automatic control devices a large forced circulation furnace is capable of heating up a 45 ft × 10 ft plate uniformly to within $\pm 6°$ C over the whole surface. This should result in properties well within the accepted limits of a specification if the chosen mean tempering temperature is correct.

Ideally it is preferable to quench after tempering in order to avoid temper brittleness. This is not, however, usually done for large plates on withdrawal from the furnace. Air cooling (as in normalizing) on skeleton stands under which air can freely circulate is usually found to be adequate.

From the foregoing it will be seen that the economics of tempering vary considerably. A fully loaded furnace is one in which the maximum permissible amount of hearth space is taken up—the thickness then determining the length of time required to attain the necessary temperature by virtue of the varying total weight of charge. Unfortunately, no other economy is possible because, to develop maximum toughness very often a longer time at a lower temperature is preferable to a shorter time at a higher temperature. Reference may be made to the curves shown in Fig. 19 where equal hardnesses and hence tensile strengths are obtainable by the application of different combinations of times and temperatures. Necessary minimum times depend on the type of steel. A plain C–Mn steel can be tempered for a shorter time at a lower temperature than a low-alloy steel. If vanadium is present in the latter, the best impact properties are only securable if the tempering time is sufficient to ensure that the secondary hardness peak has been developed and passed. This peak results from the precipitation of vanadium carbide in a finely dispersed form.

CHAPTER 13

THE QUENCHED AND TEMPERED HIGH-STRENGTH STEELS

Introduction

Preceding chapters have dealt with steels in an ascending order of tensile strength, viz. 26/33, 33/39 and 38/43 tons/in² and with minimum yield stress of 14/16, 21/23 and 26/28 tons/in² respectively. Some indication of the notch-toughness properties at ambient and low temperatures has been given. This notch-toughness can be secured by using the simplest compositions involving carbon, manganese and silicon and by producing either balanced, silicon killed or killed and grain-refined steel subjected to a relatively simple heat-treatment such as normalizing only.

It is true to say that a practical limit to the combined properties has been reached with such simple steels which are considered weldable without undue inconvenience. The N.D. series of B.S. 2762 confirm this.

The addition of an element such as niobium which exercises a strengthening effect by virtue of precipitation increases the level of the properties achievable. If the degree of fineness of this precipitate and its distribution can be closely controlled within narrow limits by special rolling techniques, there is little doubt that further improvements in properties could be effected for any chosen level of carbon, manganese and silicon. Controlled rolling, in the sense of distributing the amount of deformation as the temperature of the material falls, is not easy. Its disadvantage is that it reduces the rate of output otherwise achievable.

To achieve still higher strength properties, the more conventional approach is to use additional alloying elements. These 'low alloy' steels can be further improved by quenching and tempering and this operation can also improve the simpler C–Mn–Si steels. Greater care is necessary in welding the low-alloy steels because their carbon equivalent values are higher than those of the simpler steels.

173

Principles Involved

It is essential that higher strength shall be accompanied by enhanced notch toughness, and it has been shown that quenching and tempering at some 'optimum' temperature in general results in both (*a*) an increased energy absorption level in the impact test, and (*b*) a tendency to eliminate any sudden change from the ductile to the brittle state. It is obvious, therefore, that this heat-treatment is essential. There are now available presses which enable the

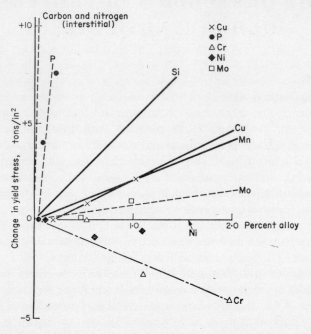

FIG. 41. Effect of various elements in solution in ferrite on the yield stress. (F. B. Pickering and T. Gladman, B.I.S.R.A. Carbon Steels Comm. Harrogate Conf. May 1963.)

quenching operation to be carried out without distortion of the material. Both plates and sections so treated can meet most structural material requirements.

The problem of alloy additions to achieve the required properties is more complex. Tempered martensite as a microstructure gives the best degree of toughness. This is followed by 'tempered' bainite. If the tempering temperature is too low, then extremely high tensile properties can be secured but toughness is reduced. A fairly high tempering temperature is desirable on the other hand in order to secure maximum structural stability should fabrication or service conditions involve subsequent heating. Such heating has to be limited to a temperature safely below that of the tempering temperature, otherwise the originally certified minimum properties would be altered.

The normal alloying elements which can be considered are nickel, chromium, molybdenum, vanadium, boron, niobium, copper. The effect of some of these on the yield stress of iron is shown in Fig. 41. This does not imply, as confirmed in steels for other purposes, that the simple addition of one element is necessarily sufficient to achieve an end. Combinations of two, three or even four in varying proportions are found in practice to be superior. Possible exceptions to this rule are the simple nickel steels containing $1\frac{1}{2}\%$, $2\frac{1}{2}\%$, $3\frac{1}{2}\%$ and 5% Ni. These possess an increasing degree of toughness in the normalized condition. Apart from 5% Ni they are not used in the quenched and tempered condition for large structural applications. However, the special grade containing 9/10% Ni is indeed quenched and tempered. This steel is described elsewhere.

The choice of a number of elements automatically implies that, while the combinations of these elements in different quantities have been applied, there is not necessarily any one specific composition which is unique with respect to all others. There is considerable flexibility with respect to chosen combinations, since properties are a function of the microstructure. To ensure reproducibility of the properties, any combination of elements must obviously be kept within close limits of composition.

A primary requirement of any low-alloy steel intended for quenching and tempering is that the carbon content shall be kept low in order to favour weldability, which is also adversely affected by the presence of the alloying elements added. A low carbon content automatically prohibits the formation of too hard a martensite, which would be formed in the heat-affected zone of a weld—and would lead to cracking on cooling, if above about 390 D.P.N. Too high a carbon content would also give rise to cracking during the quenching operation.

For structural material quenching must be carried out with water. The cost of oil would be prohibitive, although the latter is used for forgings and specialized individual items, such as machined components. If oil is used, its lesser rate of heat abstraction permits the use of steels containing higher carbon contents without a risk of cracking, but this is not in accordance with the primary requirement.

The ultimate properties achievable at present for structural materials in bulk are those associated with a martensitic-bainitic structure which, in the 'as-quenched' condition, possesses a D.P.N. of 380/450. Since this corresponds to a tensile strength of 75/80 tons/in^2 it is possible to develop a considerable degree of resistance to impact at low temperatures if this tensile strength is reduced by tempering to a level of 55/65 tons/in^2.

A guiding principle in formulating the composition of a low-alloy steel is that alloying elements may be divided into two classes, those which form carbides and those which enter into solid solution in the iron. The majority of the former raise the transformation temperature and therefore generally increase the tempering temperature necessary to produce a chosen level of hardness (or strength). Examples are chromium, molybdenum and vanadium. The action of the latter is exceptional in that vanadium carbide is precipitated on tempering producing a peak in the hardness curve. This is evident when hardness is plotted against time for a particular tempering temperature. Fig. 19 shows this for a complex low-alloy steel, and while excellent properties do accrue from the use of small additions of this element (0·07% to 0·10%), a steel containing vanadium entails an extended tempering time which is necessary to lower this secondary hardness peak to a satisfactory and stable level. One can object to the use of vanadium because of this feature, which results in increased costs arising from a considerably lower production rate from the tempering furnace.

The solid solution elements such as nickel and copper, particularly the former, lower the transformation range and consequently tend to lower the tempering temperature necessary to achieve a specific hardness or strength after quenching. In combinations therefore with carbide-forming elements an empirical balance between the two types is necessary if a particular steel is to satisfy the notch-toughness requirements accompanying a specific tensile strength range.

Depth hardenability is obviously important. This property may limit the thickness of a useful section it is possible to produce. If hardenability is insufficient, then both strength and toughness properties may be very much inferior in the centre of the section as compared with the outside. The property of depth hardenability may be achieved by the addition of minute quantities of boron, usually of the order of 0·002%/0·006%. This element possesses a very small atomic radius (as does N_2 and carbon). It can occupy interstitial positions in the ferrite and it exercises a remarkable effect in stiffening the crystal lattice. In the 'as-rolled' or normalized condition, steels containing small quantities of boron may be remarkably strong but this strength is usually accompanied by relatively poor impact properties. In the quenched and tempered condition, however, the tendency to embrittle is very much reduced and consequently the addition of boron to secure depth hardenability is less objectionable. It has been found that the effect of boron on hardenability is considerably enhanced in the presence of molybdenum.

The Characteristics of Some Commercial Low-alloy Steels in Plate Form

Matsuda[1] describes a variety of low-alloy steels of high strength. Table 22 lists those which have a minimum yield stress of 29·0 tons/in². The

Table 22. Quenched and tempered low alloy–high strength steels (Matsuda[1])

Grade	\multicolumn{9}{Nominal composition (%)}									Yield stress min (tons/in²)	Tensile stress (tons/in²)	Elongation % min. on 2 in.	Charpy V-notch (longit.) min ft-lb at 0°C
	C	Mn	Si	Cu	Ni	Cr	Mo	V	B				
FTW58	0.18 max.	1.50 max.	0.55 max.	—	—	—	—	—	—	29.0	36.6-43.2	16	46
Welcon-2H	0.18 max.	1.35 max.	0.55 max.	—	—	—	—	—	—	29.0	36.6-43.2	16	46
Welten-60	0.16 max.	1.30 max.	0.55 max.	—	0.60 max.	0.40 max.	0.25 max.	0.15 max.	—	29.0	37.9 min.	16	Not stated
Q.T. 60B	0.12 max.	1.10/1.50	0.35/0.55	0.30 max.	—	—	—	—	—	29.0	37.9 min.	16	35
Q.T. 60A	0.12 max.	0.60/1.00	0.15/0.35	0.40 max.	0.40/0.70	0.40/0.70	0.20 max.	0.03/0.06	—	30.0	37.9 min.	16	46
2H Super	0.08/0.16	0.60/1.00	0.55 max.	0.15/0.50	1.0 max.	0.50/0.80	0.40 max.	0.03/0.10	—	40.1	49.2-50.9	22	Not stated
Hi-Z	0.10/0.18	0.60/1.00	0.15/0.35	0.15/0.50	0.70/1.0	0.40/0.80	0.40/0.60	0.10 max.	0.002/0.006	44.6	50.9-60.2	20	15
2H Ultra	0.08/0.16	0.60/1.20	0.55 max.	0.15/0.50	1.5 max.	0.80/0.80	1.70 max.	—	0.006	44.6	50.9-60.2	20	Not stated
K-O	0.10/0.20	0.60/1.00	0.15/0.35	0.15/0.50	0.70/1.0	0.40/0.80	0.40/0.60	0.03/0.10	0.002/0.006	44.6	50.9-60.2	18	35

NOTE: Up to 0.25% Mo is added to FTW58 in thicknesses over 1.0in. to secure adequate depth hardenability. Sulphur and phosphorus maxima are in most cases 0.040% each. The term 'yield stress' also implies 0.2% proof stress for those steels which do not show a distinctive 'yield point' when tested.

N

Table 23. *Quenched and tempered low-alloy steels of high-notch toughness*

Code	Designation	Origin	Composition (%)									
			C	Mn	Si	Ni	Cr	Mo	V	Ti	B	Cu
A	T. 1	U.S.A.	0·10/0·20	0·6/1·00	0·15/0·35	0·7/1·00	0·4/0·80	0·4/0·60	0·03/0·10	—	0·002/0·006	0·15/0·50
B	T. 1A	U.S.A.	0·12/0·21	0·7/1·00	0·2/0·35	—	0·4/0·65	0·15/0·25	0·03/0·08	0·01/0·03	0·002/0·005	—
C	Loycon	G.B.	0·15 max.	1·2 max.	0·25 max.	1·6 max.	0·85 max.	0·35 max.	0·10 max†	—	—	—
D	Super Elso70	France	0·18 max.	1·10 max.	0·30 max.	1·0/2·50*	1·0 max.	0·40 max.	0·10 max.	—	—	—
E	Q.T. 35	G.B.	0·15 max.	1·2 max.	0·20 max.	1·2 max.	1·0 max.	0·50 max.	0·12 max.	—	—	—

Code	Carbon equiv.	Yield stress min. (tons/in²)	Tensile strength (tons/in²)	Elonga-tion % min. on 2 in.	Charpy V-notch (longit.) min. ft-lb at —°C
A	0·64	44·6	50–60	18	30 at −12° C
B	0·48/0·50	44·6	50–60	16/18	15 at −45° C
C	0·62	42–48	47–56	18	60 at −10° C
D	0·68	44·6	51–60	18	35 at −10° C
E	0·65	38 min.	—	—	40 at −40° C

* Nickel content depends on thickness.

† The vanadium may be omitted and the steel 'grain refined' by the addition of aluminium.

NOTES: (1) Minimum elongation on T. 1A steel depends on thickness. 16% for over ¾ in.

(2) Loycon is characterized by an impact energy curve which shows little change of energy down to the region of −50°/−70° C. The 'Nil Ductility Temperature' (N.D.T.) is in the range −85° to −95° C.

(3) The C.E. values are for typical compositions which are known to satisfy the particular specification. None of these low-alloy steels are made with the maximum proportions of each element in the same cast. If this occurred considerably higher C.E. values would result.

Charpy impact values at 0° C are given where available. All these steels entail water quenching and tempering. There is, however, little information given with respect to the sub-zero temperature impact properties. As indicated by the varying Charpy impact values at 0° C, they must differ considerably in this respect.

Table 23 gives some properties of quenched and tempered steels extensively used in plate form for general structural purposes. Steel *C* is one which was developed in the author's laboratories to provide an equivalent material to that of steels *A* and *B*. Steel *E*, with slightly lower mechanical properties, has been used in naval construction. Both British steels have been in production for several years and are established for specific applications in spite of the absence of a British Standard covering the quenched and tempered steels. It is not easy, however, to produce such a specification since both composition and heat-treatment may be varied widely to provide almost any desired range of properties up to a practical maximum of 50 tons/in² yield stress. This practical maximum is limited by welding considerations and is governed by the maximum hardness achievable without cracking in the quenched and tempered condition. It becomes necessary to reduce this hardness and strength by subsequent tempering to secure adequate ductility and toughness, coupled with a yield/tensile strength ratio of the order of 0·85/0·90.

The evolution of these steels is empirical. Beyond the basic principles which have already been enumerated the development of combinations and relative amounts of elements added is a matter of trial and error. All steels listed in Table 23 have been developed independently. A specific interest is attached to steel *C* since it was developed originally for use as a pressure vessel steel in the normalized condition. Experimental quenching and tempering revealed its potentialities as a high-strength material, and details of its development for use in the normalized condition are given by Pearson and de Lippa[2].

To secure the properties shown, water quenching from 910/920° C followed by tempering within the range 620–680° C is necessary, the precise tempering temperature depending on the individual cast analysis.

Less data is available for the foreign steels and it is difficult to compare detailed toughness properties at various sub-zero temperatures. The author makes this statement on the basis that a true assessment of their suitability for use at any specific low temperature can only be founded on a statistical examination of the results from hundreds of results covering large tonnages rolled from many casts.

It may be stated, however, that the stipulated minima for impact values are generously exceeded in practice. One difficulty in comparing steels arises when two types of impact testpiece are used, for example, the keyhole notch and the V-notch. There is no constant correlation between the results at all test temperatures. Fig. 42 shows impact energy values for the steels in Table 23 based on published data and in the case of steels C and E on actual tests. The marked superiority of steel E with respect to impact values at sub-zero

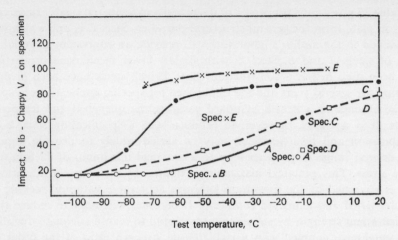

FIG. 42. Impact curves for four steels of Table 23 showing minimum values specified.

temperatures is associated with the ratio between the nickel and chromium contents. It appears that a lower carbon content and a somewhat lower nickel content would be beneficial in steel D.

General Characteristics of the Quenched and Tempered Steels

Table 23 reveals a distinct difference between the American steels and the European steels. In the former, importance is attached to the extremely powerful effect of boron in small quantities in securing depth hardenability whereas in the latter the more conventional combinations of nickel, chromium, molybdenum and vanadium are used. There is obviously a designed attempt in the American steels to secure an effective combination of alloying elements based on the use of smaller quantities with a view to economy. This is desirable provided the combined properties achieved are equal in all respects to those of the other steels for all applications. It is, however, difficult to nominate any one steel as being superior to the others because of their complexity and the varying service conditions which may be encountered in their application.

The cost of production is also influenced by the length of time necessary for complete heat-treatment. While heating and quenching times are practically the same for all steels their behaviour during tempering differs considerably. As previously stated (p. 176), steels containing vanadium have disadvantages in that tempering times of the order of 5/5½ hr at the required temperature are necessary. Recent work has, however, resulted in the elimination of vanadium and its substitution by aluminium as a grain-refining agent in steel C with complete success as to the properties achievable and a reduction in tempering time to the order of 1¼ hr. The use of aluminium to refine the grain-size, while reducing slightly the depth hardenability, has not proved disadvantageous. It is, however, axiomatic that the optimum properties achievable from any tempered steel are more likely to be secured by longer tempering times at lower temperatures than by shorter times at higher temperatures—due to the much finer and more uniform distribution of precipitates. For all steels in Table 23 the properties listed as minima are obtainable in plates up to and including 3 in. thick. Above this thickness certain concessions with respect to properties are required because of the inability to achieve complete hardening. Except for very special applications, however (as in some naval constructions), the tendency is to apply such steels in lower thickness ranges. Obviously they are used to save weight.

Applications

High strength quenched and tempered steels are being incorporated in rapidly increasing quantities in earth-moving and mining equipment where conditions of service involve high stresses. Earth-moving equipment is often required to operate at low ambient temperatures particularly in northern regions. Weight saving in the dead weight of earth-moving equipment can mean increased payloads. Penstocks and exposed pipelines for hydro-electric schemes provide another application and at high altitudes low temperatures are encountered during winter. Spherical vessels for gas storage under pressure and road tankers for the transport of liquids in bulk, provide yet other examples of savings in welding costs and dead weight made possible by the use of thinner plates.

Welding and Fabrication

When compared with the simpler C–Mn steels on the basis of a carqon equivalent formula all these steels exceed the 0·45 index considerably (see Table 23). Low-hydrogen electrodes are therefore essential for welding and while in the simpler applications of thin plate to general construction work preheat may not be essential, thicker material and tank and pressure vessel applications do necessitate preheat additionally, for example for steel E the following preheat temperatures are used: for 1¼ in. plate 120° C, ¾ in. 80° C and ¼/½ in. 40° C. The electrodes are baked at 300° C just prior to use. Plates may be gas cut or sheared, depending on thickness. Gas cutting produces a hardened skin on the edge. The steels will harden appreciably if air cooled from the normalizing temperature. Temperatures in excess of this are developed locally at gas-cut edges. To machine a gas-cut edge may therefore necessitate some degree of softening by heating to a temperature somewhat below that at which the original plate was tempered. It is unwise to gas cut the steel in the 'as-rolled' condition since this is obviously in the air hardened condition and cracking may occur.

All the steels may be bent or formed cold, provided adequate radii are used. It is recommended that for plates up to 1 in. thick the minimum radius of bend should be twice the thickness. From 1 in. to 2 in. thick the minimum radius should be three times the plate thickness. Bending should preferably be made at right-angles to the direction of rolling. If made parallel to the direction of rolling some fracturing may occur due to the presence of elongated inclusions. In cold forming some 'spring back' occurs and must be compensated for either in die design or by further pressing. The design of structures to be built of these low-alloy steels presents some problems. There are obviously limitations, depending on the structure, as to the weight saving which can be achieved. If the modulus of rigidity is taken into account, then no structure can be made lighter in weight, to the point where adequate rigidity is impaired. The problem is, however, simplified by the fact that while certain standard structural sections are produced and used in these qualities, by far the major tonnage is produced and applied as plates, and consequently adequate rigidity can be achieved by means of gussets and stiffening ribs added to the plate itself. The familiar dumper truck is an excellent example.

In the early stages of the application of these steels some suspicions arose as to the increased possibility of fatigue failures under certain conditions. In these steels it will be noted that the 'proof ratio', that is, the ratio of yield stress or 0.2% proof stress to tensile strength is high as compared with that of ordinary steels (viz. 0.80–0.90 for the former and 0.55–0.65 for the latter). The relatively small plastic range above the yield (or proof) stress would increase risks should a fatigue crack develop under conditions of high stress. It has however been established that, in relation to commonly used and accepted steels (such as the ordinary C–Mn steels killed with silicon and the Mn–Mo pressure vessel steels, both of considerably lower tensile strengths), the fatigue strength of the quenched and tempered steels is much greater (viz. 22–26 tons/in^2). This level is somewhat lower than would be expected from the tensile strength range of the quenched and tempered steels but is superior to that of the lower tensile steels for the same number of stress reversals. Fatigue failure of structures fabricated from quenched and tempered steels are therefore more likely to arise from the presence of weld cracks than from fatigue cracks in the parent metal. Plate 5 shows the type of martensitic (untempered) and lower bainitic structure which characterizes these steels.

Stress-relieving of welded structures can be carried out provided the temperature employed does not exceed that of the tempering temperature used to produce the plate. As in the case of all low-alloy steels the stress relaxation effected is not so complete as for simple C–Mn steels, but the lowering of peak stresses on a structure is achieved to a satisfactory practical level.

Low-temperature Limitations of Quenched and Tempered Steels

Some of the steels described are suitable for use at ambient or low temperatures of the order of −30° to −40° C. The author has been consulted many times as to whether the N.D.IV grade which has a guaranteed minimum

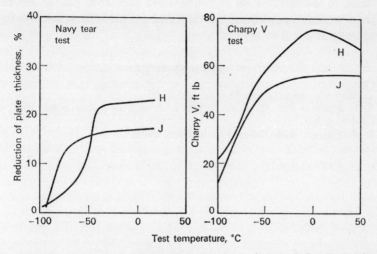

FIG. 43. Transition curves for two quenched and tempered steels. (After R. E. Lismer[3].)

Charpy impact value of 20 ft-lb at −50° C is suitable for use at this temperature. The suitability of this steel for use at −50° C depends much upon the type of structure and stress conditions. While a minimum value of 20 ft-lb can be generously exceeded in production plates, to use the steel at this low temperature is regarded as being on the borderline of safety and caution is advisable. The quenched and tempered steels, however, constitute a much safer material at −50° C provided welding is competently executed and they are therefore to be recommended in preference to the simple C–Mn steels.

While a simple Charpy energy absorption value does not constitute a complete assessment of the resistance to brittle fracture at a chosen low temperature it is sufficiently discriminating between various types of steels, provided the ascertained differences between the steels are not marginal. Moreover, it is not always easy to define the precise temperature at which the transition from the ductile to the brittle state occurs, particularly in quenched and tempered steels. The 'percentage crystallinity' in the fracture is often difficult to determine owing to the fineness of the structure. The degree of distortion of the specimens is a better visual guide if the test is conducted at a series of diminishing temperatures.

An excellent experimental survey of various commercial plate steels including quenched and tempered steels has been made by Lismer[3]. Both Charpy impact and Navy tear tests were conducted on a series of C–Mn and low-alloy steels and weld metal deposits. Fig. 43 illustrates his results, from which it will be seen that the quenched and tempered steels do not show the same order of merit in the two types of test with respect to the change from the ductile to the brittle state as temperature decreases. On the evidence of both tests, however, confidence is established to enable these steels to be used at temperatures down to $-70°$ C.

REFERENCES

1. T. Matsuda. *Metal Prog.* **81** (Jan. 1962), 68.
2. T. F. Pearson and M. Z. de Lippa. Iron and Steel Inst. Spec. Rep. no. 69 (1961), p. 463.
3. R. E. Lismer. *Weld. Metal Fabric.* (Feb. 1962).

CHAPTER 14

THE CRYOGENIC STEELS

Increasing Application

Cryogenic is derived from the Greek word 'Krúos' meaning icy-cold, frost —hence it implies a refrigerant or freezing mixture. In modern terminology it has acquired a specific meaning in that cryogenic steels are those best suited for use at extremely low temperatures.

The need for such materials has arisen over the past ten to fifteen years because of the development of space projects which demand the safe and economic handling of liquefied gases. The development of the bulk transport of liquid methane from gas fields discovered in various parts of the world is an additional and growing industry. All industrial gases can be liquefied and their transport in this form followed by subsequent evaporation, and distribution renders possible the economic transfer of fuel gases over large distances which would otherwise be impossible. Since the boiling points of many industrial gases are low and since each gas has a 'critical' temperature and pressure in the liquid condition, the development of materials capable of remaining tough and resistant to shock or impact at these low temperatures is obviously of the greatest importance.

Some idea of the temperatures associated with various gases in the liquid condition has been given in Table 1 (p. 4).

The gases He, H_2, O_2 and N_2 have boiling points which approach absolute zero ($-273°$ C) and it has become customary therefore in most cases to assess the notch toughness of cryogenic materials at $-196°$ C, the temperature at which liquid nitrogen boils under atmospheric pressure. Liquid nitrogen is convenient. It is easy to obtain for test purposes, and is inert and relatively easily stored and handled.

Apart from certain aluminium alloys and metallic copper—which possess face-centred cubic crystal structures, there are only two types of ferrous alloy which are suitable for use at these extremely low temperatures. These are the austenitic stainless steels and the more recently developed low-carbon steel containing 9/10% nickel.

Stainless Steels in Plate Form

As in the case of many quenched and tempered steels of lower total alloy content, the Charpy impact/temperature curves for the stainless steels show no distinct transition from the tough to the brittle state. As the temperature falls the energy absorbed to fracture the specimen decreases gradually. In Table 24 steels suitable for use at very low temperatures are listed together with typical Charpy impact values. In common with all metals and alloys the tensile strength and hardness increase while the percentage elongation falls very appreciably as the temperature is lowered.

All these steels are electric furnace products. The high chromium contents cannot be achieved in the highly oxidizing conditions of the open-hearth furnace. The steels are characterized by low carbon contents while the sulphur levels are much lower than normally encountered in open-hearth steels. Water quenching preserves the austenitic state. Niobium and titanium are added to 'stabilize' the carbides, thus preventing their precipitation at the grain boundaries and so avoiding embrittling effects.

The extraordinary toughness of steel a can be attributed partially to the low carbon level. There is evidence by Mayer and Balajiva[2] that a low carbon content is also advantageous with respect to impact properties in the cast stainless steels. The achievement of very low carbon contents is, however, expensive in the electric furnace. This constitutes a disadvantage of these steels for general application involving bulk tonnages. The very high alloy content also makes them costly. Low-carbon ferro-chrome, which is necessary to achieve low levels of carbon, is extremely expensive. All complex stainless steels involve great care in processing. Ingots are usually chipped and ground before reheating for rolling. Further dressing of the surfaces of the slabs before final rolling is also necessary.

Table 24 also lists the mechanical properties of the steels at two selected low temperatures. As temperatures are lowered, the tensile strengths of the austenitic stainless steels increase considerably. These increases are greater than those encountered in ferritic steels. This marked improvement is in part explained by the breakdown of austenite into the harder martensite as deformation takes place during the test. This explanation is also accepted as the reason for the superior abrasion resistance of 14% Mn steel (Hadfield's manganese steel). It is significant that in the case of steel d containing 22% Ni, with 24% Cr, the austenite is more stable. Hence lower temperatures produce a lesser degree of hardening and stiffness and consequently elongation remains higher than those of the other steels. It is to be noted that none of the stainless steels possesses very high yield strengths at room temperature, when compared with the quenched and tempered martensitic steels.

While the remarkable sub-zero temperature properties of these alloys are

Table 24. *Properties of some 'stainless steels' for use at sub-zero temperatures*[1]

Steel	Heat-treatment. Water quenched from	Composition (%)							0·2% proof stress (tons/in²)	Tensile strength (tons/in²)	Elongation % on 4√A	Charpy V-notch (longit.) ft-lb at −°C					
		C	Si	Mn	Ni	Cr	Mo	Nb				−200°	−150°	−100°	−50°	0°	50°
a	1050° C	0·06	0·47	0·95	9·7	18·1	0·04	0·92	14·9	38·2	62	145	155	162	170	176	185
b	1050° C	0·08	0·56	0·84	7·9	18·0	0·09	—	17·1	41·6	69	70	105	125	145	160	175
c	1050° C	0·05	0·57	0·88	8·6	19·3	3·07	(Ti) 0·36	22·4	40·5	59	25	70	95	115	125	138
d	1050° C	0·10	1·58	0·87	21·7	23·4	0·04	—	20·6	42·6	50	45	60	75	95	115	138

Mechanical properties at −° C

Steel	−78° C			−196° C		
	0·2% proof stress (tons/in²)	Tensile strength (tons/in²).	Elongation % 4√A	0·2% proof stress (tons/in²)	Tensile strength (tons/in²)	Elongation % 4√A
a	13·3	66·6	51	12·3	97·1	46
b	18·3	83·5	48	19·8	114·2	41
c	25·3	62·3	56	35·4	93·3	46
d	25·8	55·1	68	42·4	78·7	59

All results obtained on ½ in. plate thickness.

unique in the wrought form, problems arise during subsequent fabrication by welding. Generally, if welded with electrodes of similar composition to the parent metal, the impact properties of both the deposited metal and the joint are inferior to those of the parent metal, the steel c containing 3% Mo being particularly poor in this respect. This reduction in the degree of notch toughness is attributed to the cast structure of the deposit. Suitable electrodes, different in composition from the steels have, however, been developed and these are capable of producing weld metal possessing impact properties compatible with those of the parent metal even at the lowest temperatures. A high Ni–Cr–Fe alloy (71–15–8%) Inco-Weld A can be used. The electrode is available both bare and flux coated. The former is used in the inert gas shielded or Argonarc process while the latter electrodes are used for manual welding. The mechanical properties of the weld—yield stress and tensile strength also equal or exceed those of the parent metal.

Welding of the 'stainless' materials is usually carried out by a specialist fabricator who has developed specific techniques and controls. Testing and inspection of welds during the fabrication of pressure vessels and chemical plant is extremely involved and costly. Operations of this type are not usually attempted by the average constructional shop.

9% Nickel Steel

While the austenitic stainless steels display remarkable properties of toughness at extremely low temperatures their high cost and relatively low tensile properties constitute a disadvantage. The fact that such steels are produced in the electric furnace and cast into relatively small ingots to obtain a superior product is less economical than the use of very large ingots.

To select a suitable structural material for low-temperature duties is a complex operation. It is not simply a matter of choosing a material which possesses satisfactory properties at the intended service temperature. Cost must always be an important consideration and this limitation is not confined to the initial raw material necessary, but must also involve the mode of fabrication, inspection and, in many instances, the design itself and the special skills required.

It was natural therefore that materials cheaper than the austenitic stainless steels would have been sought. Research commenced in 1944 by the International Nickel Company indicated that increasing percentages of nickel, when added to a low-carbon steel, progressively lowered the ductile/brittle transition temperature. At 13% Ni the impact energy absorption curve was almost flat from room to near the lowest-attainable temperature and no transition range was apparent.

While the cost of the 13% Ni alloy is also very high, more detailed work subsequently revealed that a satisfactory compromise between economy in cost and satisfactory properties could be achieved at a nickel level of 9%.

In 1952 the first tentative A.S.T.M. Specification covering 9% Ni steel was issued. This became an accepted standard in 1956 as A.S.T.M. A353. In 1959 a higher strength—Grade B—was adopted. When the original specification was formulated the criterion for satisfactory performance at service temperatures was a minimum of 15 ft-lb impact energy absorption at $-196°$ C using the Charpy 'keyhole' specimen.

This criterion is reminiscent of the general findings on the brittle failures of ship's plates which had been investigated previously. Plates which had failed under known low-temperature conditions were found to have an energy absorption lower than 15 ft-lb at those temperatures. This arbitrary value gave rise to considerable speculation and since then there have been issued two Code Cases No. 1308 (9 March 1962) and No. 1308–4 (1 May 1963). In these documents the Charpy V-notch test is specified. Code Case 1308 (1962) requires a 10×10 mm Charpy V-notch specimen to give 30 ft-lb minimum (average of three tests) for material in the quenched and tempered condition and 25 ft-lb minimum in the double normalized and tempered condition. In the quenched and tempered condition no single test out of three must fall below 23 ft-lb while in the normalized and tempered condition 19 ft-lb is a minimum permitted. This constituted a significant increase in the stringency of the test requirements as compared with a level previously considered adequate.

In the later modifications of Code Case No. 1308 the following Charpy V-notch values are now specified and these apply to both heat-treatments.

Table 25. *Impact value requirements (Charpy V-notch longit.) for 9% Ni steel*

Size of specimen	Min. Charpy V-notch impact value required for acceptance (ft-lb at $-196°$ C)	Min. Charpy V-notch impact value permitting retest (one specimen only of a set) (ft-lb)
10×10 mm standard	25	20
$10 \times 7·5$ sub-standard	21	17
$10 \times 5·0$ sub-standard	17	14
$10 \times 2·5$ sub-standard	8	6

The sub-standard testpieces are an obvious necessity for plates thinner than 0·5 in. There is at present no British Standard in existence for 9% Ni steel and the latest A.S.T.M. Code Case 1308–5 is almost universally accepted.

Much valuable and costly work to test the steel on a large scale has been done by the U.S. Steel Corporation in conjunction with the International Nickel Company and the Chicago Bridge Company. In 1960 a series of rectangular tanks and cylindrical vessels were constructed in 9% Ni steel by welding. These were filled with refrigerants, for example, liquid nitrogen at $-196°$ C and then ruptured either by increasing internal pressure or by impact while under pressure. Separate vessels were also constructed of material in the quenched and tempered condition. Some were tested in the 'as-welded' condition and a number were stress-relieved after fabrication. Some idea of the scale on which these experiments were conducted is given by the fact that the cylindrical vessels used (six in number) were 13 ft long and 4 ft diameter having hemispherical ends. Plates used were $\frac{3}{8}$ in. thick. The vessels were designed for pressures of 350/370 lb/in² but the actual bursting pressures at the temperature of liquid N_2 were 1550/2300 lb/in². These impressive experiments indicated that stress-relieving might be safely omitted after construction since all fractures were ductile, that is, they were produced by tearing and no evidence of shattering was encountered.

Up to 1960 some 200 vessels constructed from 9% Ni steel had been put into service. These were shop fabricated and stress-relieved. The first vessel erected on site was built in France in 1960—being a storage tank 28 ft diam. by 28 ft high. This vessel could not be stress-relieved.

Composition and Mechanical Properties

The material under consideration is essentially a low carbon–low manganese steel, silicon-killed and grain-refined by the addition of aluminium. The original A.S.T.M. Specification A353 nominated two grades, viz.

	Grade A	Grade B
C %	0·13 max.	0·13 max.
Mn %	0·80 max.	0·90 max.
P %	0·035 max.	0·035 max.
S %	0·040 max.	0·040 max.
Si %	0·15/0·30	0·15/0·30
Ni %	8·5/9·5	8·5/9·5
Tensile strength, tons/in²	40·2 min.	42·4 min.
Yield stress, tons/in² (or 0·2% proof stress)	26·8 min.	33·4 min.
Elongation % on 2 in.	22 min.	20 min.

The differences in properties between these two grades are so small that, with rapidly growing experience, it was found possible in both Code Case No. 1308 and No. 1308–4 to nominate Grade B only with higher mechanical properties,

Tensile strength, 44·6 to 53·5 ton/in²
Yield stress (or 0·2% proof stress), 33·4 tons/in² min.
Elongation % on 2 in., 22 min.

The steel has high tensile and yield strengths which can lead to economies in weight saving by reducing the thickness of material. In this respect 9% Ni steel is superior to the stainless steels, a factor which must be taken into account when assessing the relative merits of the two materials from the points of view of cost. On account of the simple composition of 9% Ni steel, its manufacture is not necessarily confined to the electric furnace process. Perfectly satisfactory steel can be made in the basic open-hearth furnace and the oxygen converter.

Metallurgical Features

The specification for this steel stipulates minimum toughness properties for two different but optional heat-treatments, viz. (*a*) double normalizing followed by tempering, or (*b*) water quenching and tempering.

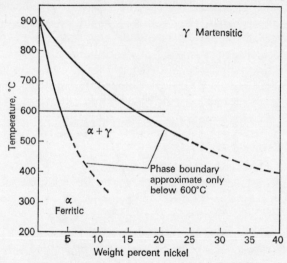

FIG. 44. Phase diagram of iron-nickel alloys.

According to Code Case No. 1308-4 which supplements the original A.S.T.M. Specification No. A353 the minimum Charpy V-notch impact values required are identical in either heat-treatment condition. It has, however, been stated that the effect of quenching and tempering on many steels is to lower the tough/brittle transition temperature range when compared with the same steel in the normalized condition. At the same time the energy absorption values at low temperatures are markedly improved.

Similarly quenching and tempering improves the low temperature impact properties of 9% Ni steel but the mechanism whereby this is achieved is not the same as for other steels since this material exhibits unusual transformation characteristics on which the mechanical behaviour depends. As part of the development work carried out by the International Nickel Company, Brophy and Miller[3] studied in detail a range of iron–nickel alloys containing 8–10% Ni—all having a low carbon content, i.e. below 0·10%. Dilatometric measurements during controlled rates of heating and cooling established that, when samples were heated at the rate of 120° C/hr a change point (as measured by the rate of expansion falling to zero) occurred at about 550° C.

A further increase of temperature caused a contraction until 730° C was reached. Temperatures above this again caused expansion. This latter change point corresponds to the Ac_3 point in ordinary steels and is revealed as a phase boundary in the Fe–Ni constitution diagram above which the steel exists as the γ solid solution, that is, a homogeneous solid solution of nickel

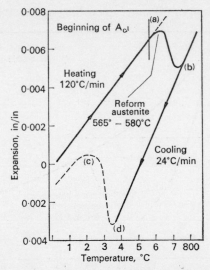

FIG. 45. Dilatation curves of 9% Ni steel. (G. R. Brophy and A. J. Miller[3].)

and carbon in iron (see Fig. 44). The first change point at 530° C encountered on heating up results from crossing the boundary between the α-iron phase field and the α + γ phase field shown in Fig. 44. Since equilibrium is not established in simple heating up the change occurs at a higher temperature than indicated in the diagram.

If the specimen is now cooled after entering the single phase field which exists above 730° C (a cooling rate of 40° C/min was chosen as being representative of the cooling rates of plates of moderate thicknesses in air), then it was found that a continuous uniform shrinkage took place down to approximately 340° C. Still further cooling down to 315° C resulted in a subsequent expansion. This was followed by final shrinkage on cooling down to room temperature—the change from expansion to shrinkage taking place

PLATE 13

View of exit end of plate-quenching press. Top platen raised, showing clamps and water spray tubes.

PLATE 14

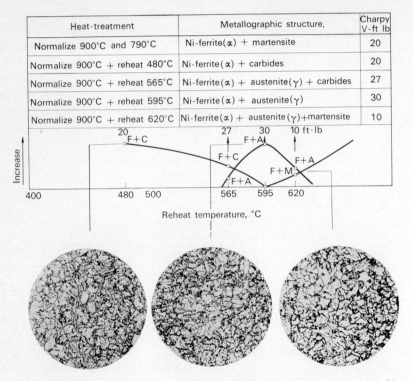

Heat-treatment	Metallographic structure,	Charpy V-ft lb
Normalize 900°C and 790°C	Ni-ferrite(α) + martensite	20
Normalize 900°C + reheat 480°C	Ni-ferrite(α) + carbides	20
Normalize 900°C + reheat 565°C	Ni-ferrite(α) + austenite(γ) + carbides	27
Normalize 900°C + reheat 595°C	Ni-ferrite(α) + austenite(γ)	30
Normalize 900°C + reheat 620°C	Ni-ferrite(α) + austenite(γ)+martensite	10

Diagrammatic form of changes in 9% Ni steel (Table 26) and representative structures obtained.

over the range 260°/200° C.* Representative heating and cooling curves for
8·5% Ni are shown in Fig. 45. It will be observed from a comparison of
Fig. 44 with Fig. 45 that the change point temperatures occur as in Fig. 46.

From a consideration of these temperatures it is apparent that an iron
alloy containing 8·5–9·5% Ni is composed of the α + γ phases down to
about 200° C (lowest change point in Fig. 45). It must be borne in mind that
in the Brophy and Miller experiments the temperatures of changes occurring
on heating and cooling will not correspond to those of the equilibrium diagram since true equilibrium is not achieved at these relatively fast rates. There

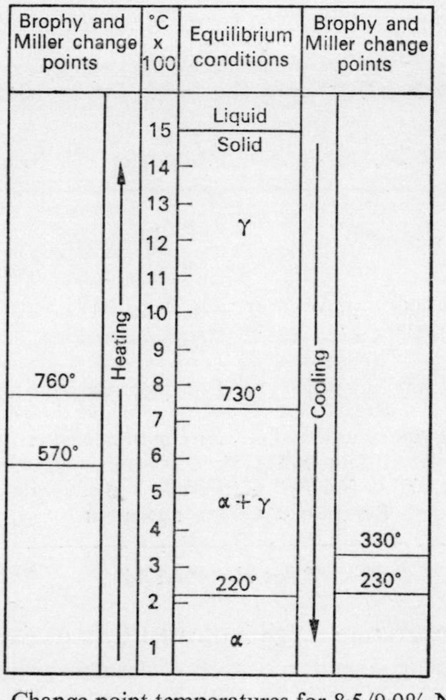

Brophy and Miller change points	°C x 100	Equilibrium conditions	Brophy and Miller change points
	15	Liquid	
	14	Solid	
	13		
	12	γ	
	11		
	10		
	9		
760°	8	730°	
	7		
570°	6		
	5	α + γ	
	4		330°
	3		
	2	220°	230°
	1	α	

(Heating / Cooling)

FIG. 46. Change point temperatures for 8·5/9·0% Ni steel.

exists experimental evidence to show that true equilibrium between 315° and
370° C is not obtained even if specimens are held for several years within this
temperature range. For this reason the definition of the boundary between
the α and γ field down to room temperature has never been completed. It
is only at temperatures above this range that the atomic diffusion rates
are sufficiently rapid to enable equilibrium conditions to be achieved in
reasonable experimental times.

Referring to the Brophy and Miller dilatometric curves, the contraction

* It was also observed that between 260°/200° C the overall rate of shrinkage slowed
down.

o

occurring between 'a' and 'b' in Fig. 45 indicates the accepted critical range in which the γ solution of Ni + C in Fe (austenite) forms continuously at relatively high rates during heating. The temperature interval indicates the absorption of pre-existing α-iron to form the uniform solid solution which produces the contraction.

Conversely the lag of the temperature/volume change shown in the cooling curve indicates the persistence of the γ solid solution from 'b' to 'd' (uniform contraction). This solid solution is modified between 'd' and 'c' to martensite, followed by a final shrinkage to room temperature which is accompanied by the precipitation of some ferrite and carbide at 200° C and below.

These dilatation curves were used to measure the coefficient of contraction of the austenite (γ solution) and the coefficient of expansion of the ferrite—the former being $11 \cdot 5 \times 10^{-6}$ and the latter $6 \cdot 6 \times 10^{-6}$. If, then, austenite

Table 26. *Structural changes in 9% Ni steel**

Heat-treatment	Structure	Charpy (ft-lb)
'a' Normalize at 900° C and 788° C	Martensite + ferrite	20
'b' Normalize at 900° C and 788° C Reheat 480° C	Ferrite + carbide	20
'c' Normalize at 900° C and 788° C Reheat 565° C	Ferrite + austenite	27
'd' Normalize at 900°C and 788° C Reheat 595° C	Ferrite + austenite	30
'e' Normalize at 900° C and 799° C Reheat 620° C	Ferrite + martensite (+ austenite)	10

* See also Plate 14.

forms within the temperature range indicated by a deviation from the expansion line on heating up, then the degree of deviation should be a measure of the amount of austenite formed. Having formed, its effect will be to increase the coefficient of contraction on cooling before final transformation to ferrite and carbide takes place. This point was investigated by heating very slowly cooled (annealed) specimens in the dilatometer to a series of temperatures between 530° and 790° C covering the range of the deviation in Fig. 45 and holding at temperature for 2 hr. It was found on heating to 530° and 550° C that there was no measurable contraction at these temperatures. Hence little or no austenite was formed. At 580° and 600° C a small contraction occurred with time and on heating to 665° C the contraction increased to a sharp maximum. Above this temperature the total contraction was now reduced by the large contraction which occurred previously during heating through the lower temperatures of the initial range, that is, subsequent to the peak at 'a' in

Fig. 45, the critical range being finally passed at 'b' in heating. Still higher reheating temperatures yielded higher coefficients of contraction, until that of austenite ($11·5 \times 10^{-6}$) was reached.

Work by Marshall, Heheman and Troiano[4] has added further knowledge of the unusual transformation characteristics of 9% Ni steel. When the steel is quenched from the austenitic field the structure consists almost entirely

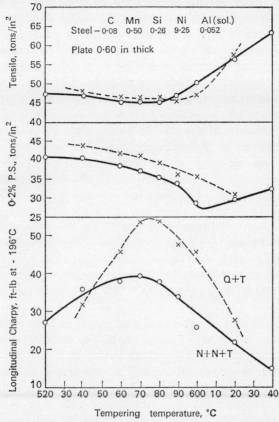

FIG. 47. Effect of tempering temperature on the properties of 9% Ni steel.

of martensite. (This behaviour is similar to that of ordinary steels where the austenite breaks down to martensite on rapid cooling.) If, however, the steel is air cooled then the structure consists of ferrite + martensite + a little austenite. This structure can be brought to equilibrium conditions by tempering at about 480° C (just below 'a' in Fig. 45) which results in a complete decomposition of the martensite, yielding a nickel-ferrite structure together with carbides. Such a structure does not possess optimum toughness properties at low temperatures.

If the steel is normalized and then reheated (tempered) to between 550° and 580° C (i.e. just beyond 'a' in Fig. 45), the result is the formation of some austenite. The quantity and stability of this phase depends on the tempering time and a precise temperature. The amount of austenite retained while cooling back to room temperature passes through a maximum. This austenite is formed by abstracting carbon from the ferrite matrix, and because it is richer in carbon thereby than the uniform austenite formed above 790° C it is consequently more stable on cooling down. Its stability is remarkable in that it is retained on cooling to temperatures as low as −200° C.

It is this fact which confers the remarkable low-temperature toughness on the material. This reformed austenite occupies normally some 12–15% of the steel by volume, the remainder being a nickel-ferrite.

An increase of the tempering temperature to above 580° C now leads to an increase in the amount of austenite formed by absorption of the existing ferrite. This results in a dilution of the carbon content of the austenite and its stability decreases in consequence. Hence, on cooling from the higher tempering temperature to room temperature this austenite decomposes to martensite—the presence of which now reduces notch toughness at low temperatures. The effect of various tempering temperatures is shown in Fig. 47.

In Fig. 47 two sets of curves are given. These show the effect of various tempering temperatures on the properties of material from a large cast of 9% Ni steel made in the basic open-hearth furnace. One set shows the effect of water quenching and tempering at various temperatures, and the other the effect of double normalizing (900°–790° C) and tempering at various temperatures.

It is to be noted that the quenched and tempered steel is superior to the double normalized and tempered material—particularly with regard to yield stress values and Charpy impact values at −196° C. The two different heat-treatments have little effect on the tensile strength up to the optimum tempering temperature of 570° C. It can be concluded that the quenched and tempered steel contains more stable high carbon austenite resulting from tempering than the double normalized and tempered material.

The explanation of this phenomenon lies in the fact that quenching has prevented the separation of any ferrite and carbides down to room temperature. Consequently the formation of austenite either richer in carbon on tempering or somewhat greater in amount has been facilitated by the lack of the necessity to reabsorb carbides, which are present as a result of normalizing. Marshall et al.[4] have, however, proved that if the tempering operation after normalizing is carried out for very extended times, then the optimum Charpy values at −196° C can be obtained as a result.

The reason for the inferiority of the double normalized and tempered steel (as compared with the quenched and tempered material) is therefore a function of the tempering time. To achieve the maximum toughness at $-196°$ C from the normalized condition would require economically impracticable tempering times.

From the specification the steel may be defined nominally as a 'low-carbon medium manganese steel containing 8·5/9·5% Ni'. In spite of the carbon and manganese limitations and the relatively small range of the nickel content, considerable variations in properties arise in commercial material from different sources.

Brophy and Miller[3] state that low-temperature impact properties are improved with decreasing carbon. This may imply either (a) a reduced amount of austenite, or (b) an austenite having a lower carbon concentration. If true, this would indicate that the nickel-ferrite is tougher than the stable nickel-austenite. They also state that reheating to form stable austenite

Table 27. 9% Ni steel from various sources. Properties in the quenched and tempered condition

Code	Tempering temperature (° C)	Plate thickness (in.)	Charpy V-impact at $-196°$ C (ft-lb)	Yield or 0·2% proof stress (tons/in²)	Ultimate tensile strength (tons/in²)	Composition %						
						C	Mn	Si	Ni	S	P	Al (total)
B	580	1½	69	44·2	48·0	0·075	0·37	0·28	8·90	0·007	0·009	0·024
F	570	0·6	40	41·6	46·2	0·08	0·50	0·26	9·25	0·033	0·009	0·053
D	580	⅜	54	48·1	52·6	0·11	0·65	0·27	9·24	0·007	0·013	0·036
E	570	⅜	41	44·8	48·2	0·07	0·42	0·17	9·36	0·028	0·013	0·009
A	607	⅜	32	36·3	43·3	0·04	0·35	0·19	8·50	0·025	0·016	0·007
C	570	⅜	30	47·4	50·2	0·06	0·50	0·21	9·70	0·015	0·018	0·048

becomes less important the lower is the carbon content, but the necessity for reheating does not disappear even at the lowest practical carbon levels, i.e. 0·04/0·05%. The author does not accept this hypothesis, but considers that impurities such as sulphur and phosphorus exercise a strong influence. The results shown in Table 27 have been obtained from specimens both from commercial casts made by the author and material from other sources. All results were obtained from quenched and tempered specimens. The analyses given are those of the specimens tested.

If we arrange the results in order of merit with respect to Charpy impact values at $-196°$ C, the analyses of the various specimens show no specific order with respect to level of carbon.

From Table 27 it is seen that, as might be expected, the highest and lowest tensile strength values coincide with the highest and lowest carbon values respectively. Also as might be expected, as the carbon content increases the greater the possibility of reforming an austenite richer in this element when tempering. This results in better Charpy impact properties at $-196°$ C. Steel A, in which the nickel content is only 8·50%, is an exception.

If we consider steels B, F and D as a group it appears that, in the quenched and tempered condition, a carbon level of 0·08/0·10% is preferable from the point of view of impact strength. The evidence is, however, by no means certain, since other factors which have been proved by experience also influence the results. An undoubted requirement for the best impact level is that efficient grain refining by aluminium must be achieved and an addition of 3–5 lb Al/ton of steel is necessary in basic open-hearth practice depending on the state of oxidation of the bath. In this respect steels E and A—the first made by the author—are deficient in the total aluminium content. Consequently the impact values at $-196°$ C are not as high as is desirable (although they satisfy the specification requirements).

An additional influencing factor is the nitrogen content of 9% Ni steel. Steels B and D are electric furnace products as shown by the extremely low levels of sulphur. In the electric furnace, the N_2 in the steel is generally higher than that of the open hearth. The high level of aluminium may therefore be necessary also to tie up the N_2 as aluminium-nitride in order to prevent brittleness. Conceivably some of this aluminium-nitride may be precipitated favourably on tempering with beneficial effects on the strength values and without (or with very little) detriment to the impact values at low temperatures. The view is also advanced that very low levels of sulphur and phosphorus are desirable (well below the maxima permitted by the specification) from the point of view of both impact levels and welding. With respect to impact values only it is to be expected that the level of the phosphorus is more significant than that of sulphur. It is this interplay of factors which presents problems in the production of first-quality material—and which constitutes both a fascination and challenge to achieve not only properties which merely satisfy permissible minima—but those which are generously in excess.

Temper Brittleness

While complete analyses with respect to residual elements were not available in all steels listed in Table 27 Marshall *et al.*[4] have shown that 9% Ni steels do indeed exhibit temper brittleness which is attributed to a deterioration of the ferrite phase by reason of the movement of interstitial atoms. These have a faster diffusion rate and may therefore cluster around existing dislocations and at grain boundaries. 'Trace' elements may therefore play a part. Steven and Balajiva[5] compared super purity steels with their commercial equivalents. Susceptibility to temper brittleness was absent in the super purity materials, but reappeared on the addition of traces of various elements such as phosphorus, arsenic, antimony and tin.

Marshall *et al.*[4] indicate that this form of brittleness occurs on tempering at 300/350° C (which is near the temperature used to produce 'ageing' effects in steels). As a result Charpy impact values at −196° C are much lower. If, however, the embrittled steel is tested at room temperatures, the fall in the impact value is not so serious. Testing at increasingly higher temperatures, however, reveals the occurrence of a minimum impact value at 300/350° C. The statement by the authors, that loss of notch toughness when 9% Ni steel is tempered below 530° C is not associated with the decomposition of austenite (reformed by tempering at higher temperatures), conflicts with the findings of Brophy and Miller[3]. The latter from their dilatation curves in Fig. 45 show that reheating to 483° C does indeed result in decomposition of the austenite to yield a nickel–ferrite plus carbide structure.

Welding of 9% Nickel Steel

It might at first be imagined that, because of the relatively simple composition of 9% Ni steel, the provision of a welding rod which matched the composition would enable the mechanical properties of the parent metal to be achieved easily in the weld deposit and joint. Unfortunately this is not so, and at present the steel is welded with complex alloy rods which develop essentially an austenitic type of structure of ample toughness at low temperatures but with somewhat lower strength than that of the parent metal.

Continuous machine welding is not at present entirely satisfactory although this will be achieved. To some extent therefore the economic advantages securable from the use of the steel as a substitute for the more expensive stainless steels are partially offset since the latter can be satisfactorily welded by the submerged arc process.

In spite of this, however, the steel is being increasingly used, the welding being done manually. For this purpose low carbon content of the steel is desirable (below 0·10%). A definite advantage from the welding aspect is that the material is not susceptible to excessive hardening in the heat-affected zone and consequently underbead cracking does not appear to occur. This latter feature often presents difficulties in the welding of low-alloy steels containing higher levels of carbon. A further favourable feature, as demonstrated by many practical tests involving destruction of vessels by excessive pressures at −196° C, is that post-weld or stress-relieving treatments do not appear to be necessary. Indeed, the latest Code Case 1308-5 only specifies some form of stress-relieving after fabrication if the cold work imposed during forming exceeds 3% strain. Cold deformation of the fully heat-treated material does reduce notch toughness as is shown in Table 28.

Stress-relieving at 565° C after cold working can restore the notch toughness at low temperatures as shown by Armstrong, Gross and Brien[6]. This is equivalent to re-tempering.

Table 28. *Effect of cold straining on impact value at −196° C of ⅜ in. plate—9% Ni steel*

Cast no. F 7432	C %	Mn %	Si %	S %	P %	Ni %
	0·045	0·35	0·19	0·025	0·016	8·50

Heat-treatment—Water quenched from 790° C tempered 1¾ hr at 580° C

Condition	0·2% proof stress (tons/in²)	Tensile strength (tons/in²)	Elonga-tion % on 2 in.	Reduction of area (%)	Charpy V-impact value at −196° C (ft-lb)
Quenched and tempered	35·9	43·0	28	59	36
Cold strain 2%	—	—	—	—	25
4%	—	—	—	—	22·6
6%	—	—	—	—	17

A difficulty sometimes encountered in welding 9% Ni steel is the phenomenon of 'arc blow' when using flux-coated electrodes and direct current. This takes the form of an erratic or unstable arc and is usually attributed to residual magnetism in the steel. Requests are often made to steel producers to avoid lifting this steel with magnets while transferring cold during processing in the mills. It is obviously extremely difficult to achieve this absence of a magnetic field especially when other ferrous material is in the vicinity. Remedies lie therefore with the fabricator during his handling of the material. Welding 'earths' can be relocated or alternating current coils can be moved along each side of the joint during welding.

Electrodes Used

The nominal compositions of three types of electrode suitable for manual welding are given by Thorneycroft and Heath[7] in Table 29 together with some weld properties.

These values show that, while notch-toughness requirements are fully met, the tensile strength of the weld metal is lower than that of the parent plate. This feature is probably, in practice, of less importance than at first apparent. As already stated, tensile and yield strength values increase very appreciably at low temperatures. Hence, under actual working conditions (say −196° C), the room temperature tensile properties of the plate are exceeded very substantially. In the case of the 25 Cr–20 Ni alloy the tensile and yield strengths rise to twice their room temperature values when the material is cooled to $-196°$ C. At first sight, therefore, there appears little disadvantage in the slightly lower joint strengths at room temperature, especially when design is based on room temperature strength properties of the parent metal (which likewise undergoes an increase in strength at lower temperatures).

Table 29. *Properties of a welded butt joint in $\frac{1}{2}$ in. plate of 9% Ni steel*

Type of electrode— nominal composition (%)	0·2% proof stress (tons/in²)	Tensile strength (tons/in²)	Fracture	Weld metal Charpy V- impact at $-196°$C (ft-lb)
25 Cr-20 Ni-Fe	22	38	In weld metal	35–55
50 Ni-16 Cr-Fe	27	40	In weld metal	50–55
75 Ni-15 Cr-Fe	35	47	In weld metal	50–60
Parent plate	44	50	—	25 min.

However, the A.S.M.E. Boiler and Pressure Vessel Code permits a working stress of 22,500 lb/in² for 9% Ni steel for service at temperatures below 315° C. Hence, if the 25 Cr–20 Ni electrode in Table 29 is used, there is legally a restriction in that the specified minimum strength value of the plate cannot be used in design. A lower value must be used because of the safety factor. This may therefore prevent the use of the thinnest gauge plate which would otherwise be possible, a disadvantage from a weight-saving point of view. The general trend therefore is to use, for both the metal-arc and the shielded arc process ('Argonarc'), the complex high nickel alloys of the Inconel-base type. It has been found that purposeful additions of manganese, niobium, and molybdenum or manganese and titanium exercise a beneficial effect. Table 30 gives some weld deposit compositions from the Inconel-base types of electrode.

It is claimed that the Inconel-182 possesses certain advantages over the Inco-weld A, namely there is a greater freedom from porosity when welding in the overhead position. Fillet welds involving severe restraint are also less prone to cracking.

In view of the complex nature of these deposited alloys, their extremely high cost can be surmised—hence the high cost of welding mentioned earlier. Endeavours are being made, however, to reduce the cost of welding. Instead of using a core wire of the compositions shown—which are characterized by a high electrical resistance, the 'Nyloid' electrode uses a pure nickel core wire with the required alloys added to the flux coating. A weld metal deposit lower in chromium and somewhat higher in iron (13% Cr and 10% Fe) and containing manganese, niobium and molybdenum is obtained.

Both mechanical strength and impact properties are adequate. A tensile strength of 46–53 tons/in² and Charpy V-impact values in the range 40–60 ft-lb can be obtained.

The chief claim for this electrode is that faster deposition rates are possible. Increase in speed up to 25% results from the ability to carry a 50% heavier

Table 30. 9% *Ni weld metal deposits*

Type of electrode	Weld deposit—typical composition (%)								
	C	Si	Mn	Cr	Fe	Ni	Mo	Nb	Ti
Inco-weld A flux-coated	0·04	0·20	1·6	15·2	8·2	71·5	1·0	2·2	—
Inconel-92 (base 'Argonarc')	0·03	0·10	2·4	16·8	6·9	Bal.	—	—	3·4
Inconel-182	0·04	0·10	7·3	14·6	7·5	Bal.	—	1·8	0·6

current than for other electrodes. This benefit arises from the better electrical conductivity of the pure nickel core. Additionally, since there is less over-heating of the electrode, wastage is kept to a minimum. Because of the increase in speed, labour costs are appreciably reduced.

Preparation for Welding

During the actual production of 9% Ni steel a very tough adherent scale forms on the plate. This is a characteristic of all nickel steels but becomes increasingly obvious as the nickel content increases. Nickel is less easily oxidized than iron with the result that during reheating operations for processing (ingot to slab or bloom; and slab or bloom to plate or billet) the surface is oxidized to form an iron-oxide scale. This scale contains minute particles of unoxidized nickel. As a result the scale is 'reinforced' by metal and it is extremely adherent to the steel surface. The brittleness characteristic of nickel-free mill scale is absent. This adherent scale will actually develop a metallic appearance if polished. While a plate may appear to possess a smooth blue-black surface, the removal of the scale by grit-blasting may reveal patches of the true plate surface which resembles 'morocco leather'. In these areas the scale has been particularly tenacious and has not rolled out to a uniform thickness.

Such a feature is not only objectionable from an aesthetic point of view, but it may, if extremely coarse in texture, cause local reduction of the intended plate thickness. This in turn may result in rejection of the whole plate. Practical expedients to eliminate this undesirable feature consist in throwing material such as birch twigs, heather or brushwood—or common salt on to the surface of the plate during rolling. These materials 'explode' at the angle of contact between roll and plate thus exercising a shattering effect on the scale. The author has introduced the use of 'soda ash' for the purpose. While this also detonates like salt it also has a solvent action on the scale. The underside of a plate is usually less prone to surface defects because scale can drop away during rolling. High-pressure water sprays (1500 lb/in²) may be used additionally while the plate is moving between the rolls. While sprays only are adequate for mild steels, they are ineffective for 9% Ni steel. Electric heating prior to rolling is preferable to heating in oil- or gas-fired furnaces. The sulphur content of the gases in the latter accelerates appreciably the rate of scale formation prior to rolling. Very rapid heating to the rolling temperature is desirable to produce the thinnest possible layer of scale.

Preparation for welding therefore involves the removal of this tough scale. Plates may be grit-blasted and oiled before despatch. If they are oiled then degreasing with the usual industrial solvents is necessary before welding. Grinding on both sides of the plate to produce a $\frac{1}{2}$ to $\frac{3}{4}$ in. scale-free band inwards from the edge is usually done. If the surface of the plate is very good the thin uniform layer of scale may sometimes be removed by a multi-jet gas torch which disrupts the scale by sudden expansion. Movement of the descaling torch must be rapid enough to prevent the plate edge from reaching a temperature harmful to the properties. Thorneycroft and Heath[7] quote the use of an oxy-acetylene descaler using 10 lb/in² gas pressure and 80 ft³/hr. This can descale approximately 4 ft²/min. and a $\frac{5}{8}$ in. plate becomes only handwarm after this treatment. A plate $\frac{1}{8}$ in. thick may reach 200° C with the same treatment.

In the preparation of actual edges for welding, gas cutting can be used both for sizing the plate and bevelling, provided light grinding is employed prior to welding to remove the thin film of scale produced. Gas cutting does result in some hardening of the edge. While the initial hardness of the material in the heat-treated condition is approximately 200/230 D.P.N. this hardness may rise to 380 D.P.N. approximately in a zone about $\frac{1}{2}$ to $1\frac{1}{2}$ mm thick inwards—the extreme outside face being de-carburized. Such edges do not show loss of ductility on cold bending and the thermal effect of welding superimposed on such gas-cut edges produces no harmful effects.

With respect to the actual weld, the heat-affected zone is characterized, as in all welds, by an appreciable increase in hardness—the values being of the order of 360/380 D.P.N. The maximum hardness occurs at about 2 mm from the fusion line.

'Argonarc' Welding

In addition to manual welding by using the normal flux-coated electrode the argon shielded arc method is currently being developed and used. Certain advantages are claimed, namely that by using a fine wire (only 0·03 in. diam. —usually Inconel-92), the welding heat input is relatively small and consequently the process can be operated in the vertical and overhead position in addition to the normal downhand position. While, in a fabrication shop, the latter position is the most common, site erection may involve other positions. Successful welding has been achieved in vertical and overhead positions, using the Argonarc fine-wire technique for joints in $\frac{1}{4}$ in. and $\frac{3}{8}$ in. thick material. The low rate of heat input reduces excessive surface oxidation of the deposited liquid metal and there is less risk of slag becoming entrapped in the weld metal when changing the welding position.

9% Nickel Steel in Forms other than Plate

While by far the largest outlay for 9% Ni steel is in the form of plates, small forgings of 2–3 in. across the section are successfully produced. The author has obtained excellent properties from 3 in. billets. An advantage of small forgings is that they can be conveniently and efficiently quenched after tempering—which tends to improve the impact properties by avoiding temper brittleness.

Castings have been successfully made to satisfy Code Case 1308 requirements. Jackson and Ridal[8] and Hardwick[9] state, however, that there is a danger of 'flaking' due to hydrogen. The former authors state that test bars were removed from the mould at 1000° C and held at 650° C for 21 hr to reduce the hydrogen content. To the author this is a *sine qua non*, and even for plate material the practice outlined in chapter 5 for low-alloy steels is rigorously adopted for material produced in the open-hearth and oxygen converter furnaces. The solubility of hydrogen in steel appears to increase as the nickel content increases—although no fundamental data are available to show the extent to which this happens. In the case of castings, which, unlike forgings or plate material, undergo no hot deformation, precautions against the persistence of hydrogen are absolutely essential. A reduction of the hydrogen content below that of the threshold value is the objective.

It is necessary to note that the properties of 9% Ni steel deteriorate as the mass increases. Hardwick[9] records poor impact values at −196° C for a specimen taken from the centre of a 9 in. diameter forged billet double normalized at 900° and 790° C and tempered at 570° C. A Charpy V-impact value of only 5 ft-lb was obtained. After oil quenching from 900° and 790° C and tempering at 570° C the toughness was improved to 22 and 14 ft-lb. As previously stated, 9% Ni steel in common with many other steels yields far better properties at low temperatures when the cooling rate from both the austenitizing and the tempering temperatures is fast. Still better properties would no doubt have been achieved by water quenching. According to Marshall *et al.*[4] if the 9 in. diameter forged billet had been given a very prolonged tempering treatment a still further improvement in impact at −196° C would have resulted.

5% Nickel Steel

A low carbon steel containing 5% Ni has been used for many years for case-hardening applications and B.S. 970 EN 37 is an example. This steel possesses appreciable toughness—60/70 ft-lb Charpy V-notch at 0° C in the normalized condition.

For the purpose of low temperature applications which are not so severe as those for which 9% Ni is necessary, it has been found that 5% Ni steel in the quenched and tempered condition is a more economical material. It may be used, for example, for liquid ethylene containers (−103·8° C) and a German standard—Werkstoffblatt 680–60—stipulates the following composition and properties:

C %	Si %	Mn %	S %	P %	Ni %
0·20 max	0·15/0·35	0·3/0·5	0·035 max	0·035 max	4·5/5·5

Tensile strength 38·1/47·6 tons/in^2
Yield stress (min) 28·6 tons/in^2
Elongation % (min) 20   Gauge length $= 5d$
Red. of area % (min) 55

Min. impact values kgm/cm^2 (D.V.M. U-notch 3 mm)

°C	20	−50	−80	−120	−170
	16	14	12	10	5

The steel is water quenched from 800/830° C, tempered between 580/650° C, and air cooled. Lloyd's requirements for the containment of liquid ethylene are 40 ft-lb minimum Charpy V-notch at −104° C, while the U.S. Coastguard Authority stipulates 30 ft-lb minimum Charpy V-notch at −110° C.

Welding necessitates the use of austenitic electrodes of the 25 Cr–20 Ni or the 25 Cr–12 Ni stainless steel types or a high Cr–Ni alloy similar to those used for 9% Ni steel. There is no ferritic electrode available of matching composition and characteristics.

REFERENCES

1. *Properties of Ni-Alloy Steels at Sub-Zero Temperatures*. The Mond Nickel Co. Ltd, London.
2. G. Mayer and K. Balajiva. *Metallurgia*, **59** (1959), 221.
3. G. R. Brophy and A. J. Miller. *Trans. Am. Soc. Metals*, **41** (1949), 1185.
4. C. W. Marshall, R. F. Heheman and A. R. Troiano. *Trans. Am. Soc. Metals*, **55** (1962), 135.
5. W. Steven and K. Balajiva. *J. Iron Steel Inst.*, **193** (1959), 141.
6. T. N. Armstrong, J. H. Gross and R. E. Brien. *Weld. J.*, **38** (1959), 575-S (*Weld. Res. Suppl.*).
7. D. R. Thorneycroft and D. Heath. *Weld. Metal Fabric.* (Feb. 1963).
8. W. J. Jackson and E. J. Ridal. *B.S.C.R.A. Jl.*, no. 58 (Feb. 1961), p. 39.
9. D. Hardwick. B.I.S.R.A. Conference Paper MG/13/64 (Sheffield, 1964).

CHAPTER 15

METHODS OF TESTING FOR TOUGH-NESS AT AMBIENT AND LOW TEMPERATURES

Introduction

The standard tensile test carried out at atmospheric temperature to assess the ultimate tensile and yield strengths and the percentage elongation at fracture, does not, unfortunately, give a complete picture of the tendency to brittleness, particularly at low temperatures. The percentage elongation encountered in structural materials is far in excess of that required to render uniform any local stress concentrations which might exist in a structure. The measurement of this ability to deform plastically before fracture serves merely to eliminate materials which are essentially brittle at room temperature. White cast iron for instance fractures while undergoing true elastic deformation as distinct from plastic deformation—and therefore may be assessed as 'brittle'.

The ability of this test to discriminate between ductile and brittle materials, and their behaviour, particularly at low temperatures, is relatively crude. Failure of a normally ductile material by cleavage fracture can occur, and consequently more discriminating tests have been sought and developed to enable resistance to brittle fracture to be more accurately assessed—at least relatively, either with respect to different batches of like material or batches of different materials.

The aim of all these tests has been to produce a true brittle fracture in the material or failure by cleavage. While no test yet developed can be claimed as able to reproduce the conditions of actual failures in practice, many of them enable steels to be empirically classified in order of merit. These orders of merit, coupled with experience and a knowledge of operating conditions, have proved remarkably effective in (a) advancing the application of specific materials for certain service conditions, and (b) preventing failures in service which otherwise could undoubtedly have occurred. The introduction of steels of a higher degree of notch toughness than that of ordinary mild steel into

207

certain strakes in a ship has undoubtedly reduced the incidence of failures in recent years.

Requirements of a Suitable Test

To achieve a cleavage type of fracture in materials used for structural purposes and which are normally considered ductile at room temperature, we require a local stress concentration as distinct from a stress uniformly distributed over the whole cross-section. This is usually achieved by inserting a standard notch or notches in the specimen. The application of a force then results in a concentration of stress at the base of the notch. The magnitude of this stress differs from that of the remainder of the specimen. In addition, it is usual, in many forms of test for brittleness, to apply the total stress to the specimen in the form of an impact. Total fracture under these conditions shows different characteristics at various temperatures in that the fracture itself may be 'fibrous', that is, fine and silky—such as is usually obtained in static tensile testing, or it may be 'crystalline' indicating brittleness; or a mixture of both. In the case of a fibrous fracture considerable distortion of the cross-section may occur, suggestive in itself of a degree of resistance to fracture. On the other hand a bright crystalline fracture will not show any distortion of the cross-section. This cleavage fracture is indicative of the rupture of the metal along crystal planes over large areas of individual crystal grains. These two extreme types of fracture may be obtained in any one material by testing at two different temperatures, above room temperature and some temperature below. Tests at intermediate temperatures between the two may display mixed fractures, that is, there are areas of both fibrous and crystalline appearance in different proportions.

From such an impact test involving a stress concentration in the specimen, there are three quantities which may be evaluated, viz.

(1) The amount of energy (usually measured in 'ft-lb') required to fracture a specimen of a known and reproducible geometry at any specified temperature.

(2) The area of the 'crystalline' portion of the fracture expressed as a percentage of the original area fractured.

(3) The energy required to cause a fracture, which consists of arbitrary proportions of crystalline and fibrous material (e.g. 50% crystalline + 50% fibrous) at a chosen temperature. It is to be noted that this value can only be determined if a series of tests is conducted on the same material using specimens of identical geometry—each one being tested at successively lower temperatures. The results enable the well-known 'transition curves' to be drawn, in which 'energy absorbed' 'percent crystalline' (fibrous) are plotted against 'test temperature'.

PLATE 15

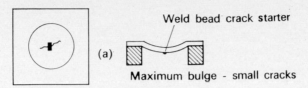

(a)

Weld bead crack starter

Maximum bulge - small cracks

Highest test temperature

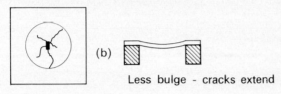

(b)

Less bulge - cracks extend

Lower temperature

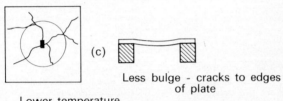

(c)

Less bulge - cracks to edges
of plate

Lower temperature

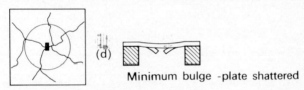

(d)

Minimum bulge -plate shattered

Lowest test temperature

Fracture appearance transition temperature
(b)above is that test temperature at which
cracks are confined to bulge

Diagrammatic representation of Pellini explosion bulge test.

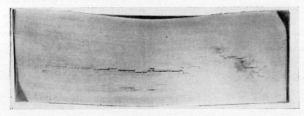

Charge weight, 3 oz.

PLATE 16

(a) Robertson crack arrest test specimen—$1\frac{1}{2}$ in. mild steel—stress 10 tons/in². A is a $\frac{3}{16}$ in. deep sawcut.

(b) Wide plate test (B.W.R.A.) showing supply of coolant to secure temperature gradient.

An additional criterion of the brittleness of a material can be ascertained in terms of temperature by determining that temperature at which a '100% crystalline fracture' first develops under reproducible testing conditions. This temperature may be without reference to the energy absorbed in effecting the fracture and is known as N.D.T.—the 'nil ductility temperature' for the material. For such a test the form of the specimen is not necessarily limited to that used for other types of test, but a number of determinations must be carried out at different temperatures on specimens of identical shape and size.

The most important requirement of a discriminating test for relative resistance to brittle fracture is that it shall be a practical test in the sense that it is easily, cheaply and speedily carried out. To place this latter requirement in true perspective, it is obvious that thoroughness of testing is primarily dependent on the number and frequency of tests in relation to either a unit weight of steel or the number of unit products. We may regard the former as being a 'cast' of the material which, because it is produced as a furnace charge, is of relatively uniform chemical composition. Moreover it is processed in sub-units (ingots), each being treated similarly. The physical units of the end product from this cast, for example, plates, billets, sections, or in the case of steel poured into castings, the actual castings themselves, require testing with some acceptable frequency of sampling. This may depend on various factors, for example, number of units, cost of testing, severity of the intended service. For common mild steel plate one test per 25 tons may be considered sufficient. In the case of plates intended to operate under severe service conditions—as in a boiler—each individual plate requires certification. Repetition castings may be treated 'one in ten' or 'one per ladle of liquid metal'. Large intricate castings are made with 'cast on' testpieces.

A modern plate mill may produce 7,000/10,000 tons of plates per week which may imply the production of a separate plate every $2\frac{1}{2}$ min throughout the week. To test every plate is therefore a sheer impossibility. While it would be possible to provide test material when cutting the plate to its finished size—the machining of test specimens for each plate would be prohibitive. In practice, therefore, the actual provision and identification of test coupons for inspection approval raises a formidable problem. It is essential therefore that in order to facilitate a suitable frequency of testing (or to increase it), both the testpiece and the type of test must be simple. This requirement automatically rules out many types of test which might in some circumstances be considered superior to those actually used. Additional or supplementary tests of a more involved nature may be used in some special cases, but if this involves the stoppage of material flow and stocking before final delivery the implication is obviously that such a procedure can only be applied to relatively small proportions of the total weekly output of a mill.

Certain mass-produced steels, the characteristics and properties of which

P

are well established, may be certified by the maker. For certain special grades the approval of a classification society (e.g. Lloyd's Register of Shipping) must be sought and obtained. Such approval is secured by submitting numerous test results obtained in the presence of the Society's inspector. These results must derive from several casts of steel rolled into the intended form. Provided such results show an agreed degree of consistency both from cast to cast and within each cast, and the specified composition limits are adhered to, then approval is given, subject to the manufacturer persisting in those methods of manufacture and processing which were used in the test casts. In such cases the daily routine testing of the product may be simplified, that is, it may involve the tensile test only, impact testing being waived. There is the proviso, however, that future random test samples may be called for by the authority and the results obtained are used to ensure that the initially established quality is still maintained. For extensive and detailed testing the test specimen must be economical—both with respect to the weight of product consumed and the speed and ease of machinability and handling.

Influence of Specimen Size

Specimens of different geometry do not give equivalent results with respect to the three quantities stated on page 208 when testing for the degree of resistance to brittleness at low temperatures. This is in sharp distinction to the tensile test. The use of specimens of different size and shapes (cross-sections) in this latter test yields identical strength results for the same material although the elongation values may differ in specimens of different forms and 'gauge lengths'. This is true irrespective of any testing temperature chosen, and strength expressed in 'tons force to fracture unit area' becomes an absolute value characteristic of the material. It is an essential value for design purposes.

The evaluation of brittleness, however, is less tangible. It occurs with little or no apparent plastic deformation, and moreover the response to testing depends very much on the geometry and mode of application of the fracturing stress. To produce evidence of the degree of brittleness, the fracturing stress is measured in units of energy absorbed, viz. ft-lb (or kgm). Such a value cannot be used in design as an absolute unit. It only serves to discriminate between classes or types of materials. For this reason the appearance of the fracture at any test temperature coupled with the energy absorbed is a more complete assessment of the brittleness of the material.

It may be stated that the determination of a 'transition' temperature by any accepted method, for example, the Charpy test, is valid only for comparison purposes with the transition temperatures of other materials if the same specimen geometry is used. For identical material, if the geometry is altered, the transition temperature ascertained by any chosen criteria will differ in each case. Large specimens yield a higher transition temperature than small ones. This effect arises from several causes including lack of complete correspondence of metallurgical features in the two specimens, that is, the degree of homogeneity in each, the increased rigidity of the larger specimen and the different elastic strain energy and different rate of straining.

These findings have been confirmed by Fearnehough[1] who used a falling weight to fracture V-notched specimens. His conclusions contradict those of Puzack and Babecki[2] who considered that if crack initiation conditions are made similar in each case (i.e. the base of the V-notch), then identical transition temperatures should be obtained for the same material. These authors, however, adjusted the maximum bend angle in the Pellini drop weight test (q.v.) in order to make the degree of strain at the notch the same for each size of specimen used. As a result they obtained similar 'nil ductility temperature' values over a wide range of specimen sizes.

Fearnehough, using specimen sizes of 14 in. $\times$ 2 in. $\times$ 1 in., 7 in. $\times$ 1 in. $\times$ 1 in., 14 in. $\times$ 1 in. $\times$ 1 in. and 7 in. $\times$ $\frac{1}{2}$ in. $\times$ $\frac{1}{2}$ in., did not obtain the same transition temperatures for each in spite of these adjustments. He did, however, find that by applying a longitudinal stress of 5–7 tons/in² to the small specimens during impact the same transition temperatures were obtained as for the large specimens. He concluded that this confirmed the role played by stored elastic strain energy on the initiation and propagation of cleavage cracks.

Influence of Different Forms of Notch

Impact test specimens usually employed may be of the same external dimensions but may vary with respect to the type of notch. Obviously both the depth of any notch and its acuity at the root exercise an influence on the results obtained. The sharper is the notch at the root, the greater is the local stress concentration at the root when energy is applied. If the notch occupies a greater proportion of the cross-section then the area to be fractured is smaller. Different combinations of these two factors yield different pictures of the relative brittleness of any one material. Fig. 24 shows some results obtained by the author for a commercial plate steel tested in a pendulum impact machine. Specimens were cut adjacent to each other, but carrying different standard notches. Since in some cases the depths of the notches were also different the results obtained are expressed in two ways: (1) as ft-lb required to fracture the actual specimen, and (2) as ft-lb/cm². Generally it is seen that V-notched specimens gave lower values than U-notched specimens. The highest energy absorption values were obtained from the Mesnager notch. The D.V.M. keyhole and 'ISO' notches show a similar level of values. At low testing temperatures differences in energy absorption for any type of notch (with the exception of the Mesnager notch) tend to diminish. The

D.V.M. and keyhole types of notch appear to give the most distinct indications of the transition temperature of this particular steel, as indicated by the steepness of the slope. Even so, the qualification is made that the above observations apply only to the particular steel tested. From Fig. 24 it is apparent that no conversion factors are derivable to enable results from one form of specimen to be translated to those obtained from others.

In this investigation the 'percent crystallinity' values in the fractures of all specimens were accurately assessed from magnified images projected on to a screen. The results reveal that temperature/crystallinity relationships also vary for different forms of specimen.

Various Types of Test

No attempt will be made to describe in detail all the numerous test methods developed by various workers for evaluating the degree of brittleness of a metal. Test methods have ranged from the use of a single specimen of simple geometry to a complex structure of built-up sections in simulation of some actual conditions under which failure may have occurred. Forms of test involving simple welded joints are necessary for obvious reasons and mention is made of one form which uses a weld bead as a means of locating the initiation of a crack in the test specimen.

Based on the requirements previously discussed, all the tests described involve the application of multi-axial stresses and the development of a local stress concentration by means of a notch (or weld bead). Coupled with the above it is essential to apply a series of decreasing temperatures for a number of specimens, or to develop a temperature gradient across a single specimen.

The application of a multi-axial stress may be conveniently considered under the following headings.

Bending in the Presence of a Notch or Weld Bead

This principle of testing may be subdivided into two types: (*a*) those involving slow bending, and (*b*) those in which the bending force is applied by impact as a result of a falling weight. It is the method (*b*) which is by far the most commonly used since it satisfies to the greatest extent the requirements of simplicity and speed which have already been emphasized as of prime importance to the producer.

(*a*) Slow Bend

Van der Veen Test. This test was devised for plate material. The specimen is shown in Fig. 48 and the bending force is applied above the notch which is pressed prior to testing into one edge of the full thickness of the plate by a sharp hardened tool. The load is therefore applied perpendicular to the edge

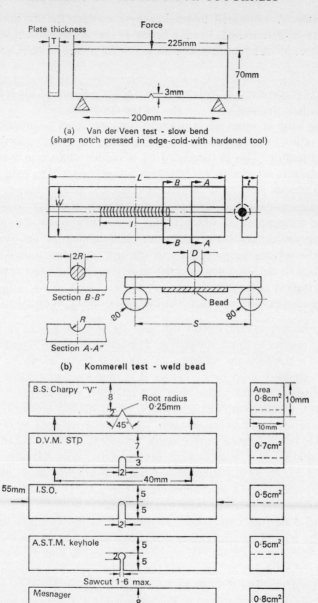

(a) Van der Veen test - slow bend
(sharp notch pressed in edge-cold-with hardened tool)

(b) Kommerell test - weld bead

(c) Forms of Charpy test specimens

FIG. 48. The Van der Veen, Kommerell and Charpy test specimens.

of the plate. A calibrated hydraulic press enables the maximum load to fracture to be determined. From a series of specimens broken with a slowly applied load at different temperatures, the following criteria can be determined.

(1) The temperature at which the crystalline portion of the fracture occupies half the depth, i.e. 35 mm of the specimen.
(2) The load at onset of crystalline fracture. This is observable as the cessation of the initial slow bending being followed by visible cracking and tearing. This is succeeded by a sudden change in speed of crack propagation indicating a final crystalline failure. The load at this sudden change may then be used in conjunction with results from other specimens (tested at different temperatures) to give:
(3) The temperature at which L_c/L_m is 0·7. Obviously the lower is this temperature, the better is the notch toughness of the steel. Because of the relative long duration of the test, a thermocouple must be attached to the specimen in order to determine the exact temperature at the instant of fracture.*
(4) The temperature at which the deflection at L_m is equal to 0·236 mm.

These arbitrary criteria enable different steels to be placed in an order of merit with respect to notch toughness. The test is, however, cumbersome and demands an appreciable quantity of material for a complete assessment over any extended temperature range. It is obviously unsuitable for routine rapid assessment in bulk production, but has been used in specific instances.

Benson[3], dealing with changes which occur during service life, refers to the deterioration in notch toughness of steel when irradiated by fast neutrons, vacant sites being formed in the lattice by atoms being knocked into interstitial positions. His results were obtained by slow bending large bars ($2\frac{3}{4}$ in. × 2 in. × 20 in.) containing Charpy V-notches. Both an irradiated and non-irradiated mild steel containing 0·13% C, 1·05% Mn grain-refined by aluminium were used for these experiments.

The load-deflection curves were ascertained at the different temperatures shown. The irradiated material is obviously more brittle, as shown by the transition zones in relation to the temperature scales, and the yield strengths are greater than those of the unirradiated material. The transition zone in both materials is defined as lying between 10% and 90% fibrous (or 90% and 10% crystalline respectively). By means of the slow bend test one could almost define the onset of the transition range, with respect to decreasing temperature, by ascertaining that temperature which did not permit a full deflection load curve to be obtained, that is, where suddenness of fracture

* L_c = load at onset of crystalline fracture; L_m = maximum load.

implied an instantaneous return to 'no load', this being the point at which deflection ceases.

(b) Fast Bend—Impact

This form of testing is by far the most prevalent by reason of its speed, economy and ease of testpiece preparation. A small bar (either round as in the Izod test or rectangular as in the Charpy test) is notched by careful milling with a standard cutter and broken by means of a striking weight in the form of a falling pendulum. The energy absorbed to fracture the specimen is measured by means of the angle through which the pendulum swings after passing bottom dead centre—the position in which the specimen is struck by a knife edge on the pendulum. This angle is a measure of the residual energy in the pendulum. The difference between this quantity and the initial striking energy is that absorbed by the specimen.

The Kommerell Test. This test is more recent and dates from 1938[4]. Unlike the Van der Veen test the specimen is bent in the principal plane of the plate. Instead of an impressed notch, a weld bead of a specified length is deposited along the centre line on one face of the plate in a machined groove. The testpiece dimensions vary with the thickness of the plate as shown in Table 31.

Table 31. *Dimensions of Kommerell testpieces for plate*

Plate thickness (mm)	L (mm)	W (mm)	R (mm)	I (mm)	D (mm)	S (mm)
19–25	358	150	3	125	75	240
26–30	380	150	3	150	90	260
31–35	410	150	3	175	105	290
36–40	440	200	4	190	120	320
41–45	470	200	4	220	135	350
46–50	400	200	4	250	150	380

NOTE. See Fig. 48(b) for details of dimensions.
The testpiece is bent as a beam with the weld bead (mm in length) equidistant from the two supports on the underside as in Fig. 48(b).

The weld bead is a single layer deposit. A series of specimens must obviously be cooled to different temperatures and the angles at which cracking occurs together with the appearance of the fractures are used to assess the comparative behaviour of the steel. The specimen may: (a) bend through 120° without cracking, (b) bend through 120° while showing small cracks in the weld and its vicinity but without complete fracture, or (c) it may bend through some smaller angle and show some degree of cracking and then finally fail in a brittle manner.

While this test is not used extensively in Britain, it is occasionally specified in inquiries received from abroad. The Austrian standard Önorm. No. 3052 gives details and requirements for the assessment of material from the results obtained.

Charpy and Izod Impact Tests. Both Izod and Charpy designed their tests early in the present century in order to study 'brittleness' and the problem of temper brittleness in steels. Initially their tests were carried out at room temperature and it was only subsequently that Charpy discovered the adverse effect of lower temperatures on toughness.

While both these workers used pendulum testing machines a difference existed in that the Izod testpiece was broken as a cantilever while the Charpy testpiece was broken as a beam. It is this difference that has caused preference for the latter, since the beam type specimen can be placed on the anvil of the machine in a correct position within a few seconds of its removal from a cooling bath maintained at the required test temperature. The cantilever specimen must be firmly gripped in a vice before striking. The time absorbed in this operation and locating the notch correctly is prejudicial to the precise temperature at which fracture should occur.

Curiously, however, the present-day Charpy specimen incorporates the same dimensioned V-notch of the earlier Izod specimens, although notches of other cross-sections may be specified. The original Charpy notch was shaped like a keyhole. Figs. 48(c) and 49 show the various forms of testpiece used and the notch dimensions.

Because the small size of the specimens, as well as other factors, adversely affect the reproducibility of the results, single tests are seldom permitted and it is customary to break three specimens to determine an average energy absorption. This value must exceed a specified minimum, and a specification may also stipulate additionally that the 'lowest' of the three must not fall below a certain value.

The smallness of the specimen also demands dimensional accuracies of a high order and these are detailed in B.S. 131–1962, Part 3, and in the I.S.O. Recommendations Nos. R148, Feb. 1960, and R83, Feb. 1959. (International Standards Organization.)

Rapid Preparatiom of Specimens. The original Izod specimens were of two forms, circular and rectangular as shown in Fig. 49. It was customary to cut on a round specimen three spaced notches in different positions round the circumference. This method had some virtue when testing bars, billets or rails which were equi-dimensional (or nearly so) about a central longitudinal axis. For plates, however, the notch is always located at right angles to the surface (i.e. 'through the thickness'). The round specimen is obviously inconvenient for this purpose since it would be relatively difficult to orientate the position of the notch with respect to the plate surface. The rectangular specimen is more accurately prepared in relation to the surface of a plate, and in testing thick plates the position of the specimen may be stipulated, for example, within $\frac{1}{8}$ in. of the original plate surface. Alternatively a depth below the surface equivalent to one-third of the plate thickness may be stipulated. This position is usually designated as T/3.

The rectangular specimens are usually prepared in multiples by rough sawing appropriate lengths from plate—either parallel or perpendicular to the direction of rolling. Several blanks may be gripped simultaneously in a jig and rough shaped or milled and then accurately ground on all four sides to the final 10 mm × 10 mm (or substandard size) section. Lengths are then usually

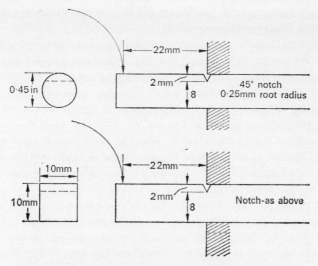

FIG. 49. Izod impact testpieces fractured as a cantilever.

cut into three specimens each 55 mm long and stamped for identification. Notches are accurately milled in a series of several specimens simultaneously by traversing the table of a milling machine carrying a special multi-tooth cutter of the correct notch profile. The specimens are conveniently held on a magnetic table. In the author's laboratory, using a circular saw, shaper, precision grinder and milling machine, three men have prepared up to 160 specimens in 8 hr.

It is important, to avoid a work-hardening effect, that several cuts be taken, these gradually decreasing in depth as the final depth of 2 mm is approached. It is also obvious that cutters must be carefully maintained and the profiles checked by standard gauges to ensure the correct notch shape and bottom radius. For this reason it is customary to return cutters for reprofiling by makers after 100 specimens of mild steel have been cut.

The accuracy of the notch profile is usually checked by special gauges before testing. The method described ensures a constantly reproducible standard of workmanship which gives consistent results, and it is known from various interchanges of both materials and specimens between different test laboratories that this is indeed so, when standard testing machines are used.

The importance of this standardized method of specimen preparation and the test results which accrue is emphasized by the emergence some years ago of remarkable Charpy values claimed for an ordinary steel from a foreign source. These values were so superior as to raise considerable doubts of their validity. It was found that the preparation of the testpieces involved the production of a mirror-polish at the base of the notch by 'finishing' the notch with a rapidly rotating taut piano wire (of the correct radius) in a lathe and feeding with a fine polishing medium!

A standard method of notch preparation is most important for such small specimens. While the ease of preparation is facilitated today by improved tools and special milling cutters it is interesting to note that Charpy's original 'keyhole' notch was designed specifically for reproducibility. This was most easily achieved at the time by 'drilling' a hole correctly located and then completing the keyhole by a fine saw cut.

The standard 'Charpy machine' is designed to deliver a blow of 30 kgm $\pm$ 1 kgm at bottom dead-centre of the arc of the pendulum. This is sufficient to fracture practically all steels having a cross-section of 8 mm $\times$ 10 mm below the notch. Some specimens of very high energy absorption value do not break completely into two pieces but the two halves are closed sufficiently to allow their passage through the width of the anvil shoulders on which the specimen is placed. There is obviously a slight error in such cases—the result being slightly higher due to the additional energy lost by increased friction between specimen and anvil. This, however, is relatively unimportant since it only occurs with completely fibrous fractures, which indicate a satisfactory degree of notch toughness.

It may also be noted that in Britain, the energy absorption value recorded is that obtained 'on the specimen', that is, on the fracture of the area below the notch, which is 0·8 cm² on the standard specimen. The value may be expressed in 'kgm' or in 'ft-lb'. On the Continent, however, values for the Mesnager and D.V.M. notches are expressed in kgm/cm². Some care is necessary therefore, in interpreting foreign specification values in terms of 'ft-lb Charpy' on the specimen.

Sub-standard Specimens. Strictly, since the standard specimen demands a minimum thickness of 10 mm, no plate below say 12 mm (or 0·5 in. approx.) to allow for a completely machined finish to all surfaces could be tested. This apparent limitation is overcome by permitting certain sub-standard sizes, viz. 7·5 mm $\times$ 10 mm, 5·0 mm $\times$ 10 mm, and in some cases 2·5 mm $\times$ 10 mm in which the 7·5, 5·0 and 2·5 mm become the lengths of the notches—the depth below the notch being constant. The areas below the notches are therefore 0·6, 0·4 and 0·2 cm² respectively. It is important to note that results are not necessarily proportionally less than those of the standard 10 mm × 10 mm specimen and in many specifications this is acknowledged in that the minimum energy value required for each sub-standard size is specified from predetermined arbitrary values. Examples from two different specifications are given below:

Table 32. *Examples of relationships between standard and sub-standard Charpy V-notch (longit.) impact requirements*

Size of specimen (mm)	Cross-section area under notch (cm²)	Quenched and tempered steel (min value in ft-lb −30° C)	9% Ni steel Code Case 1308 (min values at −196 °C ft-lb)
10 × 10	0·8	25	25
10 × 7·5	0·6	20	21
10 × 5·0	0·4	16	17
10 × 2·5	0·2	8	8

NOTE. The stipulated minimum values are those for sub-zero temperatures. At higher temperatures, including ambient, the values obtained for sub-standard testpieces tend to be in the same ratios as the areas under the notches. There is a tendency for energy curves for all specimen sizes to converge at the low end of the absorbed energy curve.

The Charpy impact test enables two criteria to be used in assessing relative brittleness, namely the energy absorbed to produce fracture at various temperatures and the amount of crystallinity in the fracture. These two values plotted against temperature give the complimentary curves illustrated in Fig. 37. Occasionally the degree of distortion of the cross-section at one edge of the fractured face can be measured and expressed as percentage lateral expansion. Reference is made to this later.

The Schnadt Test. Apart from modifications in notch form, the Charpy specimen has undergone no changes in principles since its inception early in the present century. In 1944, however, Schnadt attempted to introduce a new principle in impact testing. He inserted a hardened steel pin on the compression side of the 10 mm × 10 mm × 55 mm specimen and varied the acuity of the notch in different specimens (see Fig. 50(c)) and the rate of straining. By this an attempt was made to evolve diagrammatically a picture of the response of any steel to any combination of conditions. These combined the effect of temperature, strain rate and strain produced by various stresses. His work was complicated by the use of a new vocabulary and became so formidably involved thereby, that no extended use has been made of it. Obvious disadvantages of his method are (i) the more complicated testpiece preparation, and (ii) the great number of tests required to cover the multi-dimensional field.

Pellini Drop Weight Test. This form of impact test differs from the Charpy beam test in that the specimen is bent in the principal plane of the plate. The specimen is relatively large as in the case of the Van der Veen test and utilizes the whole thickness of the rolled plate (see Fig. 50(*a*)). A weight falling vertically is used and crack initiation is promoted by a short hard weld bead in which a notch is ground—this being located on the underside. Both the weight and its height of fall are adjusted so as to break the specimen in one blow within

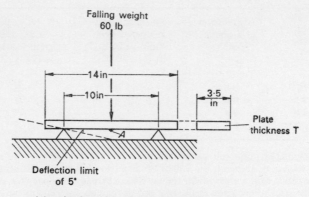

FIG. 50(*a*). The Pellini drop weight test. A 'go-no-go' type of test.

the amount of deflection possible, this being governed by the height of the specimen supports which are such as to permit a total deflection of 5° maximum between the 10 in. centres. Hence the test requires preliminary trials to determine the energy required to satisfy these conditions. These trials are carried out at room temperature and ensure that fracture takes place at any lower temperature under the prescribed deflection conditions.

This test is therefore not intended to measure the energy required to fracture—the principal criterion is the temperature at which the specimen fractures with one blow and in doing so undergoes very little plastic deformation (i.e. the amount permitted by the 5° deflection from the horizontal). The fracture appearance can be observed and also some idea can be obtained of the effect of welding on the material. A series of tests on one material at successively lower temperatures reveals one temperature at which the material is just completely brittle. This temperature is referred to as the 'Nil Ductility Temperature' (N.D.T.). On the usual transition curve determined by Charpy tests it lies therefore towards the bottom of the transition range slope.

The size and number of specimens required and the amount of coolant necessary, as well as the time involved, have prevented the adoption of the

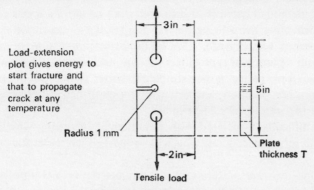

Load-extension plot gives energy to start fracture and that to propagate crack at any temperature

Radius 1 mm

FIG. 50(b). The Navy tear test.

Pellini test for routine purposes in steelworks. It would be impracticable to examine every plate in a cast of steel by this test as a means of routine approval.

The Pellini test was extensively used in the U.S.A. during early investigations of ship plate failures, and comparison of the results with those from Charpy V-notch tests on the same material indicated that the nil ductility temperature was higher than the temperature at which actual failure in service

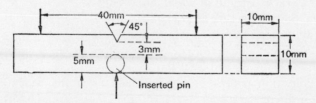

FIG. 50(c). The Schnadt test specimen V-notch as in Charpy specimen.

took place. This temperature corresponded to Charpy V-notch energy values less than 10 ft-lb, and because of this the early conclusion was reached that a minimum Charpy value of 15 ft-lb at an anticipated service temperature was a sufficiently safe level.

This view is discounted today and the following different interpretation is placed on requirements for a notch-tough steel.

If a steel specification demands a minimum Charpy value of 25 ft-lb at

$-30°$ C, then a better guarantee against failure in service is given if the N.D.T. is found to be for instance $10°$ C below the stipulated service temperature. Such a view tends to discount the importance of the level of energy absorption in fracture.

Relationship between the 'Nil Ductility Temperature' and the Charpy V-notch Transition Temperature. The general view adopted is that any reproducible test method is capable of differentiating between a series of different steels, thus enabling them to be placed in an order of merit with respect to toughness versus temperature. The quantitative conversion of the results obtained from a particular type of test for one steel in terms of those obtained from another form of test is not simple. In other terms, the order of merit may not coincide precisely, particularly if established differences between members of the series prove to be small.

This is a difficulty associated with any method of testing which does not determine an inherent concrete physical property such as tensile strength or density.

Gross[5] has, however, attempted to correlate the results obtained for the nil ductility transition temperature determined by the drop weight test with those obtained for various criteria emerging from Charpy V-notch tests on a series of steels. His steels, eleven in all, covered a range of tensile strengths from $23·5$ tons/in² to $84·8$ tons/in². By heat-treating these steels in different ways some sixty tests were possible, each of which enabled the following criteria to be determined.

(*a*) Drop weight test data:
    (i) N.D.T.
    (ii) Energy at N.D.T.
    (iii) Lateral expansion of specimen at N.D.T.
    (iv) % fibrous fracture at N.D.T.
(*b*) Charpy V-notch transition temperature data:
    (i) Transition temperature determined from curves, for energy absorptions of 10, 15 and 20 ft-lb.
    (ii) Transition temperature determined from the widening by distortion of the specimen at fracture to the extent of $0·010, 0·015$ and $0·020$ in.
    (iii) Transition temperatures ascertained from the curves corresponding to a 50% fibrous fracture.

The results enabled statistical correlations to be calculated and the conclusions arrived at were as follows:

There is a general linear correlation between the N.D.T. value and notch toughness, as indicated by the arbitrary transition temperature values for 10, 15 and 20 ft-lb. The relationship between the N.D.T. value and the arbitrary transition temperature corresponding to 50% fibrous fracture is also linear. The scatter of the results was of the same order as that encountered in all brittle fracture test data.

It was also found that the best correlation existed between the N.D.T. values and the Charpy V-notch transition temperatures, when the latter were determined by a lateral expansion of the specimen equivalent to 0·015 in. The results are shown in Fig. 51. Unfortunately the reliability of the correlation was reduced by the anomalous results for some quenched, unquenched and tempered steels which had been prestrained or prestrained and aged after the heat-treatment. These are shown in Fig. 51 towards the low-temperature

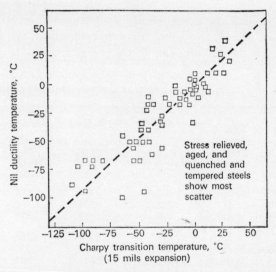

FIG. 51. Correlation between N.D.T. and Charpy V-notch (15 mils) results. (J. H. Gross[5].)

corner. The correlation coefficients of 0·94, 0·94 and 0·92 found for the 0·010, 0·015 and 0·020 in. distortion criteria respectively were higher than those for other criteria.

Wells[6], in discussing factors of safety in design, has indicated that a relationship exists between wide plate test results and Charpy results. This relationship is a function of the yield strength and the first power of the thickness of the wide plates used.

All such relationships are of interest, but their value is lessened by the fact that they are less precise than an absolute determination and they have been evolved from endeavours to interpret different sets of data on a common basis. They are of secondary importance in that they do not solve any problems of brittle fracture.

Combined Tension and Bend Test

The multi-axial stressing of a specimen can be achieved not only by simple bending in the presence of a notch or weld bead. It can also be achieved by the simultaneous application of both tension and bending. This constitutes the principle of the well-known Navy tear test. In this test the geometry of the specimen is less simple.

Navy Tear Test

The testpiece used is illustrated in Fig. 50(*b*). It is non-symmetrical with respect to the tensile load applied which exercises a tearing action. Sudden impact is not applied and consequently load-extension records are obtainable. From these records two values may be determined, viz. (1) the energy required to initiate the fracture, and (2) the energy required to propagate and

Table 33. *Navy tear test results for four steels (Lismer)*[7]

Steel	Test temperature (°C)	Max load (tons)	Corrected energy value (ft-lb)			Reduction of plate thickness ¼ in. from notch root (%)
			Initiation of crack	Propagation of crack	Total energy	
A	R.T.	10·5	202	474	676	24·5
C–Mn	−50	11·35	222	534	756	23·5
(N.D. IV)	−75	11·8	258	217	475	8·0
H	R.T.	28·75	377	1179	1556	18·0
Q and T	−50	30·75	350	—	350	11·0
	−75	34·0	597	—	597	4·0
K	R.T.	29·9	23,630	—	—	14·5
Q and T	−50	31·5	27,250	—	—	11·0
Boron	−75	32·6	32,020	—	—	11·0
M	R.T.	13·25	351	1216	1467	32·0
3·5% Ni	−50	13·25	317	267	584	21·0
	−75	14·1	297	—	297	9·0

Steel	Plate thickness (in.)	C%	Mn%	Si%	Ni%	Cr%	Mo%	Cu%	Others %
A	7/16	0·14	1·30	0·17	0·06	0·025	0·005	0·04	—
H	¾	0·11	1·01	0·15	1·58	0·29	0·28	—	0·11 V
K	0·84	0·13	0·76	0·23	0·92	0·51	0·42	0·28	0 04 V
									0·003 B
M	⅜	0·13	0·69	0·30	3·25	0·08	0·03	—	—

complete the fracture. The fracture appearance itself shows different percentages of fibre for different test temperatures and a sudden drop in energy to propagate occurs at the boundary between the fibrous and crystalline areas. Various steels differ considerably in their response to this test, some requiring high stresses to initiate fracture and low stresses to propagate it and vice versa.

Controversy exists, as in other types of test, as to whether a steel is superior if it has an extremely high resistance to the initiation of a crack at any temperature and a low resistance to propagation or vice versa. Such an argument can be applied to high v. low Charpy energy values coupled with the significance of the width of the transition range and its position on the temperature scale.

Some values for Navy tear tests indicating the order of differences obtainable for various steels are given in Table 33.

A variant of this test is the Bagsar cleavage tear test in which a sharp notch is pressed into the edge of the specimen (as in the Van der Veen test) to produce intense local work hardening. From Fig. 50(b) it may be seen that the tensile stress can be applied not through the centre of the 'keyhole' notch as in the Navy tear test but along a different axis and this may be varied in distance from the base of the V-notch to give differing degrees of eccentricity. The specimen may also be varied in size.

Neither of these tests is suitable for routine production inspection owing to the relatively complicated machining required and the time taken in completing a series of tests at different temperatures.

Explosion Tests

The application of shock energy resulting in multi-axial loading of a specimen can also be achieved by the use of explosives. Specimens of plate steels are particularly suitable for this and Pellini at the U.S. Naval Research Laboratories developed a 'bulge test' to measure the susceptibility of plate steels to brittle fracture.

A weld bead to start a crack is located at the centre of a 14 inch square plate. The plate is placed over a circular die (see Plate 15) and a disc of plastic sheet explosive is laid on top. The energy available from the explosion can be maintained constant in each test and its magnitude is known.

Detonation produces a compressive shock wave and the reflection of this wave from the bottom surface of the plate produces a tensile wave within the thickness of the plate (see Plate 15). The plate is suitably cooled and incorporates a thermocouple which gives the actual temperature at the instant of detonation. Depending on this temperature the plate bulges downwards to different degrees and shows varying lengths of cracks radiating outwards from the centre of the plate surface. As the temperature of successive specimens

Q

is lowered, the depth of the bulge decreases indicating a lower degree of ductility and cracks appear at the centre of the bulge. At some still lower test temperature, the plate will shatter in a completely brittle manner depending on the material. The transition temperature thus determined is a function of the fracture appearance. This temperature is that at which cracking is confined to the centre of the bulge only. A central width of 'shear lip' of 0·025 in. approx. is taken to indicate a limit above which fractures are unlikely to propagate in service.

The transition temperature of a material defined in the above manner is for many steels 20° to 30° C above the N.D.T. as ascertained by the Pellini drop weight test. These two tests, therefore, can be regarded as complementary in the sense that the explosion bulge test indicates a temperature above which a crack will not propagate in a material, while the Pellini drop weight test indicates the temperature below which the material is extremely susceptible to crack initiation.

Both these tests have been extensively used in detailed investigations on material such as ship plate but are not used for individual plate testing. They may be used, however, to 'approve' a particular type of steel. The explosion bulge test may be modified in detail to enable underwater explosion tests to be carried out. Shock waves from the explosion are obviously more effectively transmitted by water owing to its density, and the test is particularly pertinent to the examination and assessment of steels used for submarine hulls and naval vessels.

Tension Test in the Presence of a Notch or Weld Bead

Tipper Test

Stress concentration, as distinct from uniform stressing over a specific area, can be achieved in the usual plate tensile test specimen if it carries a notch. The use of the notched tensile testpiece is due to Tipper[8]. Provided the capacity of the testing machine is sufficiently large, the test specimen can be the full thickness of the material and its width should preferably be about twice its thickness.

Standard V-notches are machined through the thickness on each side, and located at the mid position of the gauge length (8 in.). In testing, the usual criteria of yield stress, stress at fracture, elongation and reduction of area are recorded and a series of specimens is broken at different temperatures. The most important information is the fracture appearance which changes from fibrous to completely crystalline as the temperature is lowered. Because the area of the fracture (i.e. that between the notches) is larger than that of the Charpy impact specimen the 'percentage crystallinity' is more easily and precisely determined.

From a series of tests the temperature at which the fracture shows 50% crystallinity can be determined. A plot of temperatures *v.* percent crystallinity in this test shows a sharper definition of the departure from 100% fibre (and 100% crystallinity) than does the Charpy test. If the transition temperature is however determined by a specific amount of crystallinity—this temperature tends to be higher than that similarly obtained from the Charpy impact test. The test has been extensively used in ship plate failure investigations and has occasionally been requested by classification societies as a form of assessment for newly introduced steels. It has never, however, seriously challenged the convenience, economy and rapidity of the Charpy test for production inspection purposes.

The Robertson Crack Arrest Test

Fractures in the Izod and Charpy notched-bar tests are preceded by a certain amount of yielding, initially at the base of the notch. In the Robertson[9] test the crack is started in a testpiece already stressed, the stress being perpendicular to the direction in which the crack will run. The objective sought is to arrest the crack at some distance from the point of its initiation by making it run in the direction of increasing toughness. This can be achieved by having a temperature gradient across the testpiece, the lowest temperature being at the point of crack initiation. Hence while the crack is initiated under conditions of brittleness (low temperature), if the temperature gradient from this point is suitable then the crack should cease at a distance where the temperature is higher and the material is sufficiently tough.

These objectives were achieved using a testpiece of the shape shown in Plate 16(*a*). The drilled hole is 1 in. diameter and a saw cut $\frac{3}{16}$ in. deep and 0·02 in. wide is made in the inside of the hole at *A*. The testpiece is welded to a suitably dimensioned plate on either side. The free ends of these plates are then connected to the two heads of a tensile testing machine. A known initial stress can then be imposed on the specimen itself.

In conducting the test, the drilled end of the testpiece is cooled by a suitable medium at the drilled hole, while the other end may be at room temperature (or even locally heated). A temperature gradient is thereby established across the specimen and the actual surface temperatures can be measured at $\frac{1}{2}$ in. intervals from the saw cut. Very fine thermocouples with thin flattened heads are used as surface pyrometers for this purpose. The intervals are marked on the specimen by light centre punch dots on lines 1 in. on either side of the centre line of the specimen and parallel to it.

Robertson considered the problem of the uniformity of stress distribution along the specimen in the presence of the temperature gradient. Obviously, under conditions of uniform temperature the imposed stress would be uniform but cooling one end and heating the other would upset this uniformity which is a requirement of the test. By means of strain gauges, however, he established that for a temperature gradient varying between 16° C/in. and 1° C/in. at the 'warm' end the maximum variation of stress did not exceed $0\cdot5$ tons/in². Normally where one end is cooled and the other heated the stress is substantially uniform over two-thirds of the 10 in. test length. Typical temperatures used for mild steel testing are $-70°$ C at the saw cut and $+60°$ C at the 'warm' end.

When the desired temperature gradient and the required stress are established, the rounded end of the testpiece is struck by a single high-speed blow applied by a 'bolt' gun. At the opposite end of the testpiece is a large reaction weight to damp the impact.

A crack running from the saw cut is thereby initiated and (if temperature gradient and the applied stress is suitable) the crack ceases at some distance along the length.

By cutting out the specimen proper from the auxiliary plates attached by welding the crack can be opened up by a drifting chisel and the end of the crack thereby exposed. This is easily distinguishable because the remainder of the specimen breaks by tearing and shows considerable yielding thus presenting a different appearance.

The crack itself ends in a curve, forming the 'thumbnail' marking shown in Plate 16(a), and the temperature which was measured at the peak of the 'thumbnail' just prior to fracture is used in the assessment of the results.

Robertson investigated the behaviour of some twenty-nine specimens covering four qualities of mild steel. For any one steel, a characteristic graph could be drawn by plotting the crack arrest temperatures against the different imposed stresses. From the form of this graph which is shown in Fig. 52 it is seen that the transverse stress may be varied over a wide range until a certain crack arrest temperature is reached. This temperature is known as the 'ductile arrest temperature'. Below this temperature there is a critical relationship between the transverse stress and temperature of arrest. At lower temperatures the 'thumbnail' curve limiting the end of the fracture tends to disappear owing to the absence of yielding of the metal in front of the advancing crack. This signifies complete brittleness.

This test, as related to the performance of mild steels in actual use, gives actual stress values at which catastrophic failure can take place. The arrest temperatures determined covered a range within which actual failures in practice have been encountered.

For ordinary mild steel in the 'as-rolled' condition the critical temperature may be as high as room temperature and the stress to produce fracture as low as 4–6 tons/in² for plates 1 in. thick. As plates decrease in thickness the critical temperature tends to become lower although the critical stress does not alter greatly. The conclusion reached is that the thickness effect may be due to the extra hot work imposed on the plate during rolling. The lower finishing temperature of thin plates is likely to give rise to a finer microstructure of the steel. Although this is entirely logical, there is an independent effect due to thickness only. This was proved by machining specimens of the thickest plate (1 in.) to 0·8 in. and 0·6 in. respectively. Separately conducted experiments on these different thicknesses (but having the same microstructure) did indeed prove that the specimen thickness exerted an independent effect, the thinnest plate showing the lowest ductile arrest temperature.

It has been mentioned earlier that while almost any test can place a series of different materials in approximately the same relative order of merit, this does not imply that different tests on the same material are likely to define

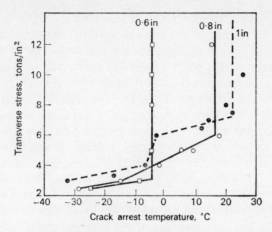

FIG. 52. Robertson arrests for three plates of different thicknesses machined from a 1 in. plate of a fine-grain mild steel.

the change from a ductile to a brittle type of fracture to the same extent. Robertson examined his steels also by three different notched bar tests and assessed the results on the fracture appearance (percentage crystallinity). He found that there was no systematic correlation between the arrest temperatures and any of the 'transition ranges' obtained from the notched bar tests. He concluded, therefore, that materials exhibiting good resistance to crack starting did not necessarily indicate that the crack-stopping properties would be good. This emphasizes the fact that one may have a high resistance to the initiation of fracture accompanied by a high energy absorption in a particular test, but a low energy level may be required to propagate the crack when once started (see Table 33).

The virtue of the Robertson test is that, for a particular steel, it gives an absolute figure which can be used for design, a feature not possessed by other forms of impact tests. It can hardly be described, however, as a suitable acceptance test. For use in a steelworks it would be impracticable, from the point of view of both cost and time.

Wide Plate Test

Wells[10] enlarged considerably the field of investigation of brittle fracture by using wide plates stressed in tension by means of hydraulic jacks. Welding, coupled with the introduction of a severe notch, resulted in fractures at very low stresses per unit area under certain temperature conditions. Individual tests are, however, time-consuming and expensive owing to the size of the 'testpiece' and the large total stresses required. This specimen is shown in Plate 11 and it will be noted that the 'notch' is introduced into the weld by saw cuts made with a jeweller's saw. These cuts are 0·006 in. wide in the V-shaped edges of the two plates prior to welding. Welding the two plates together then leaves a small imperfection (or 'notch') located at the centre and fracture is initiated at this point on cooling down and stressing. Measurements of stress at fracture and the deformation up to the point of fracture are made and related to crack length for different materials. The test is essentially best suited to the brittle temperature range of any material since the use of simple hydraulic jacks would not permit large pre-fracture extensions to be achieved as in the ordinary tensile testing machine. It will be noted that the plate ends have to be welded to the stressing heads of the machine and cutting out the testpiece after fracture as well as the welding necessary are costly operations. The type of test, however, has a considerable value because of the specimen size. This eliminates completely the objections to small specimens which may be far less representative of the material under test. In addition it has provided the ability to examine the characteristics of actual welds made with different electrodes, and the effect of stress-relieving.

Investigations by means of the wide plate test have led to important conclusions with respect to both materials and design criteria. The work of Woodley, Burdekin and Wells[11] investigating the effect of thickness on the brittle fracture of welded plates has been described in chapter 9.

REFERENCES

1. G. D. Fearnehough. *Br. Weld. J.*, **10** (1963), 607.
2. P. P. Puzack and A. J. Babecki. *Weld. J.*, **38** (1959), 209-S (*Weld. Res. Suppl.*).
3. L. E. Benson. *Jl. W. Scotl. Iron and Steel Inst.*, **72** (1964-5), 150.
4. O. Kommerell. *Stahlbau*, **11** (1938), 51.
5. J. H. Gross. *Weld. J.*, **39** (1960), 59-S (*Weld. Res. Suppl.*).
6. A. A. Wells. *Jl. W. Scotl. Iron Steel Inst.*, **72** (1964-5), 131.
7. R. E. Lismer. *Weld. Metal Fabric.* (Feb. 1962).

8. C. F. Tipper. *The Fracture of Mild Steel Plate*, Adm. Ship. Weld. Rep. R. 3 (H.M.S.O. 1948).
9. T. S. Robertson. *J. Iron Steel Inst.*, **175**, pt. 4 (1953), 361.
10. A. A. Wells. *Trans. Instn. nav. Archit.*, **98** (1956), 296.
11. C. C. Woodley, F. M. Burdekin and A. A. Wells. *Br. Weld. J.*, **11**, no. 3 (1964), 123.

APPENDIX

1. GENERAL REMARKS

No attempt has been made in the last chapter to describe all tests which have been used for the determination of temperature/brittleness relationships in ferrous alloys. Those listed may be classified under other headings or arranged in an 'order of merit' as to their relative suitability for routine inspection purposes. In such a classification, the simple Charpy test would undoubtedly be placed first because of its relative cheapness and speed. Because of this and its ability to place steels in relative series, the test now appears in nearly all British and foreign specifications covering steels intended for use at low temperatures. There does not yet appear any valid reason why this simple test should not continue to be satisfactory. Extensive usage has resulted in the association of specific values with fitness for the intended purpose.

R. Weck[1] has stated that for a low-stress brittle fracture to occur there must be three factors simultaneously operative.

(1) A crack-like defect must exist. Internal smooth-rounded holes arising from slight porosity do not constitute an undue risk.
(2) There must be high residual tensile stresses in the vicinity of the crack.
(3) The service temperature must be well below the Charpy V-notch transition temperature.

To eliminate any one of these factors permanently during service precludes the risk of brittle fracture. Since the third factor is the most controllable through a knowledge of the material used, the work summarized in this book is justified.

2. THE PROTECTION OF IRON AND STEEL

Apart from the 'stainless' iron and steel alloys which contain at least 14% Cr, all other ferrous alloys are subject to corrosion attack by industrial atmospheres, sea water and other agents. The degree of attack may vary with specific circumstances, and in themselves various structural steels may behave

232

differently. Rimming steel sheets and ordinary mild steel rust easily, whereas the low-alloy steels containing several different elements totalling 4–5% are somewhat more resistant. Small additions of copper (about 0·35%) to the simple structural steels improve their resistance to atmospheric weathering, without detriment to their mechanical properties. The formation of rust in all but the true stainless alloys can only be prevented or inhibited by an applied protective coating.

Severe corrosion may seriously shorten the useful life of a structure. A conveyor belt gantry in the corrosive environment of a chemical plant may even collapse if a section or multiple joint becomes sufficiently weakened by gross corrosion. The increasing local stress which occurs can lead to the development of a brittle fracture. Local corrosion may also be accelerated by the presence of stresses, so leading to stress-corrosion cracking which is usually intergranular in character.

Generally, steels in which the N_2 is interstitial are more susceptible to stress corrosion than those in which the N_2 is combined with aluminium (as in a grain-refined steel).

It is essential, therefore, that all iron and steel structures exposed to the atmosphere or sea water must be protected by a coating.

Plates for shipbuilding were at one time held in stock at builders' yards so that rusting which took place over several months assisted in removing mill scale. This was preferable to the presence of scale in patches, areas of which could be detached in working and assembly. The juxtaposition of scale and scale-free areas could lead to selective corrosion and pitting in spite of subsequent painting. These 'weathered' plates were then scratch-brushed prior to painting—usually with a red lead–oil mixture.

The modern method—which ensures a quicker use of material—is to grit-blast the plates, either at the steelworks, or the shipyard and immediately coat both sides by spraying with an anti-corrosive paint. Such paints may consist of an epoxy resin base and incorporate zinc or aluminium. The paints may be air hardening or coated plates may pass through an oven to assist in rapid setting. Thermosetting plastics have been used to coat ship plates—a margin being left round the edge to enable welding to be carried out. The resulting seam between two plates is then cleaned and coated with an air-setting compound. It has been found that plastic-coated plates permanently resist the adherence of marine growths on ship's bottoms, whereas the usual anti-fouling paints containing metallic poisons such as mercury or copper are only effective until the poison is leached out.

For exposed structures such as bridges the various members and sections are usually cleaned either by scratch-brushing or grit-blasting and coated in the fabrication shop. The red lead–oil coating is often used. As with ships, periodic cleaning and repainting is essential in service.

For special service conditions where periodic painting is difficult (e.g. high-voltage transmission towers) components of the structure may be galvanized before assembly by bolting. Angles and sections are pickled in acid to remove scale and rust and then immersed in a bath of molten zinc to give a coating which is alloyed with the steel surface. This is one of the most expensive methods.

Iron and steel castings may be grit-blasted and painted. Generally, grey iron castings are somewhat superior to steel in corrosion resistance, a feature associated with the presence of graphite.

Steel pipes may be coated internally with paint, and plastic linings can be applied by centrifugal spinning. Externally, they may be painted, sprayed or specially wrapped with fabrics impregnated with bituminous compounds especially when intended for immersion in sea water or for laying underground.

3. THE ACHIEVEMENT OF LOW TEMPERATURES FOR TEST PURPOSES

In Table 1 (p. 4) boiling points have been given for various liquefied gases. Of these, helium has the lowest boiling point, $-268 \cdot 9°$ C.

Many of these liquids cannot be used for cooling test specimens on account of toxicity or inflammability. Liquid N_2 is, however, safe to handle and is relatively easily available. Hence it is used for testing cryogenic steels at $-196°$ C, this temperature being an accepted standard.

The following list of refrigerants covers ranges of low temperatures. Specimen temperatures may be adjusted to any desired level by immersion in these mixtures; the proportions of the components being suitably varied.

Temperatures between

$+10°$ C and $-50°$ C	Methylalcohol + solid CO_2
$-50°$ C and $-75°$ C	Acetone + solid CO_2
$-78°$ C and $-129°$ C	Low boiling point petroleum ether + liquid N_2
$-129°$ C and $-159°$ C	Iso-pentane + liquid N_2
$-196°$ C	Liquid N_2

REFERENCE

1.   R. Weck. *Br. Weld. Res. Assoc. Bull.*, **7,** no. 4 (1966), 85.

AUTHOR INDEX

235

SUBJECT INDEX